ORDINARY DIFFERENTIAL EQUATIONS

ORDINARY DIFFERENTIAL EQUATIONS

WALTER LEIGHTON

Western Reserve University

WADSWORTH PUBLISHING COMPANY, INC.

Belmont, California

L.C. Cat. Card No.: 63–7564

Printed in the United States of America

PREFACE

The major aims of this book are to provide a text in the spirit of the current emphasis on quality mathematics for all students of the subject and to make available to the student those ideas which are fundamental to the understanding of ordinary differential equations.

The book is planned so that it may be used in different ways, depending on the preparation of the class. Experience in teaching the material indicates that students who have completed a sound course in elementary calculus will be able to understand the statements of all theorems and that they will find the solutions of all but a few exercises attainable. Numerous worked examples are provided. Teachers of this subject are aware that the proofs of some of the central theorems necessarily require a working knowledge of advanced calculus. Accordingly, if it is desired to include in the course all proofs provided by the book, the student should have had such a course, or at least be taking one concurrently.

A word or two about the arrangement of the book may be helpful. The first two chapters deal with the usual elementary methods of solving first-order differential equations and linear differential equations with constant coefficients. The methods are largely formal. Simple applications appear in Chapter 3. The study of the nature of solutions starts in Chapter 4, which begins, as it must, with a careful definition of a solution—a definition that simply formalizes what the student has already learned. The existence theorem is stated, and simple applications are made in this chapter and again in the study of properties of solutions of linear differential equations in Chapters 5 and 7. Its proof appears in Chapter 9. (Here, and at many points, the book follows the time-tested "first how, then why" approach to learning mathematics.) The book contains material on the Laplace transform (Chapter 2, Sections 6, 7, and 8), an additional chapter on applications (Chapter 6), and the ideas involved in Liapunov's "direct method"—ideas that have become of such great importance in recent times in studying the stability of differential systems (Chapter 7, Sections 4, 5, and 6). A special effort has been made to present these results in such a way that they will be usable by the student even though the proofs of the relevant theorems are rather sophisticated. A reasonably adequate account of power-series solutions appears in Chapter 8. The methods of this chapter are, of course, necessarily rather formal. The book concludes with Chapters 10 and 11 on the fundamentals of oscillation theory and the related theory of characteristic functions.

The text is accordingly so arranged that classes unfamiliar with differential equations may begin with Chapter 1. Other classes already acquainted with elementary methods of solving differential equations may review the first three chapters quickly before beginning their study of Chapter 4. And some classes, those for whom the ideas of Chapter 1–3 are quite familiar, may well choose to begin their course of study with Chapter 4. Chapters 3 and 6, the chapters on physical applications, may be omitted by classes interested only in the mathematical theory without interrupting the continuity of the text.

My thanks are owed to many. Helpful ideas have come from many teachers and students who used my earlier book on the same subject. Special thanks are due Professors R. H. Bruck and R. C. MacCamy for their valued comments. I wish to acknowledge helpful and stimulating conversations I have had with Professors S. Lefschetz, Jack Hale, Joseph LaSalle, and their colleagues at RIAS. Finally, I wish to express my gratitude to The McGraw-Hill Book Company for permitting use of material from my earlier book and to the present publishers for their unfailing courtesy and helpfulness to me in the publication of the present book.

WALTER LEIGHTON

CONTENTS

1

Elementary Methods

1 Introduction

Differential equations are equations that involve derivatives. For example, the equations

$$
\begin{aligned}
&y' = f(x), \\
&y'' + y = 0, \\
(1.1) \qquad &y'' = (1 + y'^2)^{1/2}, \\
&\frac{\partial^2 u}{\partial x^2} + \frac{\partial^2 u}{\partial y^2} = 0
\end{aligned}
$$

are differential equations. The first three of these equations are called ordinary differential equations because they involve the ordinary derivatives of the unknown y. The last equation is an example of a partial differential equation. We shall be concerned with ordinary differential equations and their solutions.

To solve an algebraic equation, such as

$$
x^2 - 3x + 2 = 0, \tag{1.2}
$$

we seek a number with the property that when the unknown x is replaced by this number the left-hand member of the equation reduces to zero. In equation (1.2) either the number 1 or the number 2 has this property. We say that this equation has the two solutions 1 and 2. To solve a differential equation we seek to determine not an unknown number but an unknown function. For example, in the equation

$$y'' + y = 0, \tag{1.3}$$

y is regarded as the unknown. To find a solution we attempt to determine *a function defined on an interval* with the property that when y is replaced by this function, the equation reduces to an identity on this interval. It is clear that $\sin x$ is a solution of (1.3) for all values of x, for,

$$(\sin x)'' + \sin x \equiv 0 \qquad (-\infty < x < \infty).$$

Similarly, it is easy to verify that $\cos x$ is also a solution of the differential equation (1.3).

Differential equations play a fundamental role in almost every branch of science and of engineering. They are of central importance in mathematical analysis. A differential equation describes the flow of current in a conductor; another describes the flow of heat in a slab. Other differential equations describe the motion of an intercontinental missile; still another describes the behavior of a chemical mixture. Sometimes it is important to find a particular solution of a given differential equation. Often we are more interested in the existence and behavior of solutions of a given differential equation than we are in finding its solutions.

In this chapter we shall begin our study by solving certain simple and important types of differential equations.

The order of a differential equation is the order of the highest derivative that appears in the equation. Accordingly, the first equation in (1.1) is of first order, and the next two equations are of second order. Similarly, the differential equation

$$y''' + y^4 = e^x$$

is of the third order, and the equation

$$(y'''')^2 + yy' = 3$$

is of fourth order. The differential equation

(1.4) $$M(x,y) + N(x,y)y' = 0$$

is of first order. It is frequently useful to rewrite this equation in the form

(1.4)′ $$M(x,y)\,dx + N(x,y)\,dy = 0.$$

Thus,

$$(x^2 + y^2)\,dx + 2x\,dy = 0,$$
$$xe^y\,dx + (1 + y)\,dy = 0$$

are differential equations of the first order written in the form (1.4)′.

EXERCISES

1. Verify that if c_1 and c_2 are constants, $c_1 \sin x + c_2 \cos x$ is a solution of the differential equation $y'' + y = 0$.

2. Find by inspection a solution of each of the following differential equations:

(a) $y' - y = 0$;
(b) $y' + 2y = 0$;
(c) $y' = \sin x$.

3. Verify that the function $c_1e^x + c_2e^{2x}$ (c_1, c_2 constants) is a solution of the differential equation $y'' - 3y' + 2y = 0$.

4. Determine $r(x)$ such that the function $\sin \log x$ ($x > 0$) is a solution of the differential equation $[r(x)y']' + \dfrac{y}{x} = 0$.

5. Verify that $\sin x$ is a solution of the differential equation $y'^2 + y^2 = 1$.

6. Verify that if c_1 and c_2 are constants and $x > 0$, the function $c_1 \sin \dfrac{1}{x} + c_2 \cos \dfrac{1}{x}$ is a solution of the differential equation $(x^2y')' + x^{-2}y = 0$.

ANSWERS

2. (a) e^x.

4. x.

2 Exact Differential Equations of First Order

A particularly important class of differential equations are the so-called *exact* differential equations. A differential equation

$$M(x,y)\,dx + N(x,y)\,dy = 0 \tag{2.1}$$

is said to be exact if there exists a function $g(x,y)$ such that

$$d[g(x,y)] = M(x,y)\,dx + N(x,y)\,dy;$$

that is to say, if there exists a function $g(x,y)$ such that

$$g_x(x,y) = M(x,y) \quad \text{and} \quad g_y(x,y) = N(x,y).$$

Thus, the equation

$$(4x - y)\,dx + (2y - x)\,dy = 0 \tag{2.2}$$

is exact, since its left-hand member is the differential of the function,

$$g(x,y) = 2x^2 - xy + y^2,$$

for

$$d(2x^2 - xy + y^2) = (4x - y)\,dx + (2y - x)\,dy.$$

Clearly, we might equally well have chosen $g(x,y) = 2x^2 - xy + y^2 + 3$, or $g(x,y) = 2x^2 - xy + y^2 + c$, where c is any constant.

When $g(x,y)$ is a differentiable function such that

$$d[g(x,y)] = M(x,y)\,dx + N(x,y)\,dy,$$

any function $g(x,y) - c$, where c is a constant, is called an *integral* of the corresponding differential equation (2.1). Curves defined by the equations

$$g(x,y) = c \qquad (c \text{ constant})$$

are called *integral curves* of the differential equation. Accordingly, the function $2x^2 - xy + y^2$ is an integral of equation (2.2). Integral curves of equation (2.2) are given by the equation

$$2x^2 - xy + y^2 = c. \tag{2.3}$$

When $c > 0$ the curves given by (2.3) are readily seen to be ellipses.

It is natural to inquire how we may identify those differential equations (2.1) that are exact, and how, when they are exact, corresponding integrals $g(x,y)$ may be determined. The following theorem is fundamental.

Theorem 2.1. *If the functions $M(x,y)$, $N(x,y)$ and the partial derivatives $M_y(x,y)$, $N_x(x,y)$ are continuous in a square region R, a necessary and sufficient condition that the differential equation*

$$M(x,y)\,dx + N(x,y)\,dy = 0$$

be exact is that

$$\frac{\partial M}{\partial y} \equiv \frac{\partial N}{\partial x}. \tag{2.4}$$

The proof of the necessity of the condition is immediate. We suppose the differential equation is exact; that is, there exists a function $g(x,y)$ with the property that

$$g_x(x,y) = M(x,y), \qquad g_y(x,y) = N(x,y).$$

Since $g_{xy} = g_{yx}$ it follows at once that

$$\frac{\partial M}{\partial y} = \frac{\partial N}{\partial x}$$

The proof of the necessity is complete.

In proving the sufficiency we exhibit a function $g(x,y)$ whose partial derivatives satisfy the condition

$$g_x(x,y) = M(x,y) \qquad g_y(x,y) = N(x,y).$$

Such a function is*

$$g(x,y) = \int_{x_0}^{x} M(x,y_0)\,dx + \int_{y_0}^{y} N(x,y)\,dy, \tag{2.5}$$

* The student who is familiar with line integrals will recognize the integral in (2.5) as the line integral $\int M\,dx + N\,dy$ taken over an "elbow path" from the point (x_0, y_0) to (x,y). Condition (2.4) will be seen to be precisely the condition that the line integral be independent of the path in R.

where (x_0, y_0) is a fixed point and (x, y) is an arbitrary point of the region R. For,

$$\begin{aligned} g_x &= M(x, y_0) + \int_{y_0}^{y} N_x(x, y)\, dy \\ &= M(x, y_0) + \int_{y_0}^{y} M_y(x, y)\, dy \\ &= M(x, y_0) + [M(x, y) - M(x, y_0)] \\ &= M(x, y); \end{aligned}$$

while

$$g_y = N(x, y).$$

The proof of the theorem is complete.

Example. In the differential equation

$$(3x^2 + y^2)\, dx + 2xy\, dy = 0 \tag{2.6}$$

we see that $M(x,y) = 3x^2 + y^2$, $N(x,y) = 2xy$, and $M_y = 2y$, $N_x = 2y$. Thus, the differential equation is exact. To find an integral $g(x,y)$ we choose the point (x_0, y_0) to be the origin, and we have

$$g(x, y) = \int_0^x (3x^2 + 0^2)\, dx + \int_0^y 2xy\, dy$$

$$= x^3 + xy^2. \tag{2.7}$$

It is easily seen that the differential of (2.7) is given by the left-hand member of (2.6). Integral curves are given by the equation

$$x^3 + xy^2 = c, \tag{2.8}$$

where c is a constant.

By finding (2.8) we have solved equation (2.6) in the sense that if we solve equation (2.8) for y and obtain a differentiable function of x, then that function is a solution of the differential equation. Specifically, we find that

$$y = \pm\sqrt{\frac{1}{x}(c - x^3)}.$$

It is easy to verify that both $\sqrt{\frac{1}{x}(c - x^3)}$ and $-\sqrt{\frac{1}{x}(c - x^3)}$ are indeed solutions of (2.6) over a suitable interval of the x-axis.

This is the general situation, as will be seen from the following theorem.

Theorem 2.2. *If $g(x,y)$ is an integral of the exact differential equation $M(x,y)\,dx + N(x,y)\,dy = 0$, any differentiable solution $y(x)$ of the equation $g(x,y) = c$ is a solution of the differential equation.*

To prove the theorem note that because $g(x,y)$ is an integral of the differential equation it follows that

$$g_x(x,y) \equiv M(x,y), \qquad g_y(x,y) \equiv N(x,y).$$

Thus,

$$g_x[x,y(x)] \equiv M[x,y(x)], \qquad g_y[x,y(x)] \equiv N[x,y(x)].$$

Further, since $y(x)$ is a solution of the equation $g(x,y) = c$, we have

$$g[x,y(x)] \equiv c \qquad (c \text{ constant}).$$

It follows that

$$g_x[x,y(x)] + g_y[x,y(x)]y'(x) \equiv 0$$

and, hence, that

$$M[x,y(x)] + N[x,y(x)]y'(x) \equiv 0;$$

that is to say, $y(x)$ is a solution of the given differential equation.

Alternate method. The line integral (2.5) provides a simple and direct method of solving an exact differential equation. An alternate method, the validity of which may be established by the preceding analysis, will be illustrated by an example.

We have observed that the differential equation

$$(3x^2 + y^2)\,dx + 2xy\,dy = 0 \qquad (2.9)$$

is exact. To find an integral we first integrate the term $2xy\,dy$ formally with respect to y, obtaining

$$xy^2.$$

Next, we determine a function $f(x)$, of x alone, such that

$$d[xy^2 + f(x)]$$

is given by the left-hand member of (2.9). That is, we wish to find a function $f(x)$ such that

$$2xy\,dy + y^2\,dx + f'(x)\,dx = (3x^2 + y^2)\,dx + 2xy\,dy.$$

This is equivalent to the equation

$$f'(x) = 3x^2.$$

It follows that

$$f(x) = x^3 + c,$$

and that integrals of (2.9) are given by

$$xy^2 + x^3 + c.$$

We might equally well have commenced by integrating formally the term $(3x^2 + y^2)\,dx$, obtaining $x^3 + xy^2$. Then we seek to determine a function $g(y)$, of y alone, such that $d[x^3 + xy^2 + g(y)]$ is given by the left-hand member of (2.9).

An advantage of the alternate method may be observed in the first treatment of equation (2.9). Clearly, if we can determine the function $f(x)$, the equation is necessarily solved. It is desirable, however, to demonstrate that under the conditions of Theorem 2.1, such a function $f(x)$ can always be determined. This can be seen as follows. Consider the differential equation

$$M(x,y)\,dx + N(x,y)\,dy = 0,$$

and suppose that the conditions of Theorem 2.1 are satisfied. By "formal integration" of the term $N(x,y)\,dy$ is meant determining a function

$$H(x,y) = k + \int_{y_0}^{y} N(x,y)\,dy \qquad (k \text{ constant}),$$

where the points (x, y_0) and (x, y) lie in R. We note that

$$H_y(x,y) = N(x,y),$$

$$(2.10) \qquad H_x(x,y) = \int_{y_0}^{y} N_x(x,y)\,dy = \int_{y_0}^{y} M_y(x,y)\,dy$$

$$= M(x,y)\Big|_{y=y_0}^{y=y} = M(x,y) - M(x,y_0).$$

To complete the demonstration we show that there exists a function $f(x)$, of x alone, such that

$$(2.11) \qquad d[H(x,y) + f(x)] = M(x,y)\,dx + N(x,y)\,dy.$$

This is equivalent to demonstrating that there exists a function $f(x)$ such that

$$H_x(x,y)\,dx + H_y(x,y)\,dy + f'(x)\,dx = M(x,y)\,dx + N(x,y)\,dy,$$

or, by (2.10), such that

$$f'(x) = M(x,y_0).$$

It is clear that $f(x)$ may be taken as

$$f(x) = \int_{x_0}^{x} M(x,y_0)\,dx,$$

if (x_0, y_0) lies in R.

Remark. It is frequently desirable in differential equation theory to note a distinction between solving a differential equation and finding a solution of a differential equation. Recall that a *solution* is always a function of x defined on an interval which satisfies the differential equation. On the other hand, it is customary to regard a first-order differential equation as *solved* when we can write equations of its integral curves. Theorem 2.2, of course, justifies this seeming ambiguity.

EXERCISES

Show that the following differential equations are exact, and solve them. In the first five exercises sketch several integral curves.

1. $3x^2y\,dx + x^3\,dy = 0.$

2. $3(x - 1)^2\,dx - 2y\,dy = 0.$

3. $(2x - y)\,dx + (2y - x)\,dy = 0.$

4. $(2x - y)\,dx - x\,dy = 0.$

5. $(x - 2y)\,dx + (4y - 2x)\,dy = 0.$

6. $\cos x \sec y\,dx + \sin x \sin y \sec^2 y\,dy = 0.$

7. $\left(x + \dfrac{y}{x^2 + y^2}\right) dx + \left(y - \dfrac{x}{x^2 + y^2}\right) dy = 0.$

8. $(y^2 + 6x^2y)\,dx + (2xy + 2x^3)\,dy = 0.$

9. $(2xy + e^y)\,dx + (x^2 + xe^y)\,dy = 0.$

10. $(2x \cos y - e^x)\,dx - x^2 \sin y\,dy = 0.$

Find the solutions $y(x)$ of the following three differential equations that satisfy the given condition.

11. $(x^2 + y^2)\,dx + 2xy\,dy = 0,\ y(1) = 1.$

12. $\dfrac{y\,dx}{x^2 + y^2} - \dfrac{x\,dy}{x^2 + y^2} = 0,\ y(2) = 2.$

13. $(x - y)\,dx + (2y - x)\,dy = 0,\ y(0) = 1.$

14. Solve the differential equation (2.6) by evaluating the line integral $\int M\,dx + N\,dy$ along a straight line joining the points (0,0) and (x,y).

15. Do the same as Exercise 14 for the general differential equation of Theorem 2.1.

ANSWERS

1. $x^3y = c.$

3. $x^2 - xy + y^2 = c^2.$

5. $x - 2y = c.$

9. $x^2y + xe^y = c$.

11. $[(4 - x^3)/3x]^{1/2}$.

13. $\frac{1}{2}(x + \sqrt{4 - x^2})$.

3 Integrating Factors

In the last section we learned how to treat an exact differential equation of the form

$$M(x,y)\,dx + N(x,y)\,dy = 0. \tag{3.1}$$

When an equation of the form (3.1) is not exact we may try to find an *integrating factor*; that is, a function $I(x,y)$ with the property that the equation

$$I(x,y)[M(x,y)\,dx + N(x,y)\,dy] = 0 \tag{3.1$'$}$$

is exact. In general, such a function exists* but, except in certain special cases, it is likely to be difficult to determine.

Variables separable. When a differential equation has the form

$$a(x)k(y)\,dx + b(x)h(y)\,dy = 0, \tag{3.2}$$

the variables are said to be *separable*. It is easy to see that

$$\frac{1}{b(x)k(y)}$$

is an integrating factor in regions of the xy-plane in which $b(x)k(y) \neq 0$. The differential equation (3.2) becomes

$$\frac{a(x)}{b(x)}\,dx + \frac{h(y)}{k(y)}\,dy = 0,$$

which is evidently exact. Integral curves are given by

$$\int_{x_0}^{x} \frac{a(x)}{b(x)}\,dx + \int_{y_0}^{y} \frac{h(y)}{k(y)}\,dy = C.$$

* See, for example, the author's *An Introduction to the Theory of Differential Equations*, Appendix 3, McGraw-Hill, New York (1952).

Example. Consider the differential equation

$$x\,dy - y\,dx = 0. \tag{3.3}$$

It is easy to verify that any of the following functions are integrating factors:

$$\frac{1}{xy},\quad \frac{1}{x^2},\quad \frac{1}{y^2},\quad \frac{1}{x^2 + y^2}, \tag{3.4}$$

except for values of x and y for which these fractions are meaningless. If we choose the first integrating factor, we have

$$\frac{dy}{y} - \frac{dx}{x} = 0,$$

and integral curves are given by

$$\log|y| - \log|x| = \log|C|, \tag{3.5}$$

or,

$$\log\left|\frac{y}{x}\right| = \log|C|,$$

where C is a constant. The latter is equivalent to

$$y = Cx.$$

The method we employed breaks down when $xy = 0$; that is, along the coordinate axes. A reference to equation (3.3) shows that both $x = 0$ and $y = 0$ are also integral curves. We chose the constant in (3.5) in the form $\log|C|$ for convenience.

If we had chosen the integrating factor $\frac{1}{x^2}$, we would have been led to the equation

$$\frac{x\,dy - y\,dx}{x^2} = 0 \qquad (x \neq 0).$$

This may be rewritten as

$$d\left(\frac{y}{x}\right) = 0.$$

Integral curves are then readily seen to be given by the equation

$$\frac{y}{x} = C.$$

We must examine the curve $x = 0$ separately by reference to the original equation (3.3).

We conclude this section by presenting a few problems where an integrating factor can be found by trial and error. One device which is occasionally useful may be understood from the following example. Usually, however, we must depend on ingenuity in rearranging a differential equation to put it into exact form in those cases when it is possible.

Example. Consider the differential equation

$$(2y^2 - 6xy)\,dx + (3xy - 4x^2)\,dy = 0. \tag{3.6}$$

Here,

$$M(x,y) = 2y^2 - 6xy, \qquad N(x,y) = 3xy - 4x^2,$$

and

$$M_y = 4y - 6x, \qquad N_x = 3y - 8x.$$

Thus, equation (3.6) is not exact. We shall try to determine constants m and n so that

$$x^m y^n$$

may be an integrating factor. Multiplying both members of equation (3.6) by this function we have

$$(2x^m y^{n+2} - 6x^{m+1}y^{n+1})\,dx + (3x^{m+1}y^{n+1} - 4x^{m+2}y^n)\,dy = 0.$$

This equation will be exact if

$$2(n + 2)x^m y^{n+1} - 6(n + 1)x^{m+1}y^n = 3(m + 1)x^m y^{n+1} - 4(m + 2)x^{m+1}y^n,$$

or if

$$2(n + 2)y - 6(n + 1)x = 3(m + 1)y - 4(m + 2)x,$$

identically in x and y. This will be true if

$$2(n + 2) = 3(m + 1),$$
$$6(n + 1) = 4(m + 2);$$

that is, if $n = 1$ and $m = 1$. Accordingly, xy is an integrating factor of (3.6).

EXERCISES

The first six exercises below are thinly disguised review problems in formal integration. It is recommended that the student not employ integral tables in finding equations of the integral curves for these differential equations.

1. $\sqrt{a^2 - y^2}\,dx + (b^2 + x^2)\,dy = 0.$

2. $(2x - 1)(y - 1)^2\,dx + (x - x^2)(1 + y)\,dy = 0.$

3. $x \sin y\,dx + ye^{-x}\,dy = 0.$

4. $\sin y\,dx + (1 - \cos x)\,dy = 0.$

5. $y \log x\,dx + (1 + 2y)\,dy = 0.$

6. $(2x - 1)\cos^4 y\,dx + (x^2 - 2x + 2)\,dy = 0.$

7. $y' = e^{x-y}.$

8. $e^{x+y}y' = e^{2x-y}.$

9. $e^{x^2-y^2}yy' = x + 2x^3.$

Put the following differential equations in equivalent exact forms, and solve.

10. $x\,dy - y\,dx = (x^2 + y^2)\,dx.$

11. $x\,dy + y\,dx + x^4y^4(x\,dx + y\,dy) = 0.$

12. $3xy\,dx + 2x^2\,dy = 6y^3\,dx + 12xy^2\,dy.$

13. $3y(y\,dx + 3x\,dy) = 2x^2(3y\,dx + 2x\,dy).$

14. $x\,dy - y\,dx + x^2y^4(x\,dy + y\,dx) = 0.$

15. $x^2(x\,dx + y\,dy) + \sqrt{x^2 + y^2}(x\,dy - y\,dx) = 0.$

ANSWERS

10. $y = x \tan (x + c)$.

12. $x^3y^2 - 3x^2y^4 = c$.

14. $x^3y^4 - 3x = 3cy$.

4 Linear Differential Equations of First Order

A linear differential equation of first order is an equation which can be put in the form

$$k(x)y' + m(x)y = s(x). \tag{4.1}$$

On intervals on which $k(x) \neq 0$ both members of this equation may be divided by $k(x)$, and the resulting equation has the form

$$y' + a(x)y = b(x). \tag{4.2}$$

We shall suppose that $a(x)$ and $b(x)$ are continuous on some interval $a \leq x \leq b$.

There are two commonly employed elementary methods for solving an equation of the form (4.2).

Method 1. It is readily verified that*

$$e^{\int a(x)\,dx} \tag{4.3}$$

is an integrating factor for (4.2). For the equation

$$e^{\int a(x)\,dx}[y' + a(x)y] = e^{\int a(x)\,dx}b(x)$$

can be rewritten as

$$[e^{\int a(x)\,dx}y]' = b(x)e^{\int a(x)\,dx}. \tag{4.4}$$

To solve (4.4) for y we have

$$e^{\int a(x)\,dx}\,y = c + \int b(x)e^{\int a(x)\,dx}\,dx \qquad (c \text{ constant}),$$

and, finally,

$$y = e^{-\int a(x)\,dx}\left[c + \int b(x)e^{\int a(x)\,dx}\,dx\right]. \tag{4.5}$$

* By the symbol $\int a(x)\,dx$ is meant any function $A(x)$ such that $A'(x) = a(x)$ $(a \leq x \leq b)$.

The student is advised to use the method described for solving an equation (4.2) rather than formula (4.5).

Example. Solve the differential equation

$$x^2y' + xy = 2 + x^2 \qquad (x > 0). \tag{4.1)'$$

We first put this equation in the form (4.2) by dividing it through by x^2:

$$y' + \frac{1}{x}y = \frac{2}{x^2} + 1. \tag{4.2)'$$

Here $a(x) = \dfrac{1}{x}$ and $b(x) = 1 + \dfrac{2}{x^2}\cdot$ An integrating factor is

$$e^{\int \frac{dx}{x}} = e^{\log x} = x. \tag{4.3)'$$

If both members of (4.2)′ are multiplied by x, we have

$$(xy)' = \frac{2}{x} + x. \tag{4.4)'$$

From (4.4)′ we have successively

$$xy' = 2\log x + \frac{x^2}{2} + c,$$

and

$$y = \frac{2}{x}\log x + \frac{x}{2} + \frac{c}{x} \qquad (x > 0). \tag{4.5)'$$

Method 2. This method is of theoretical importance, and it is a method that generalizes to linear differential equations of higher order.

Consider the differential equation (4.2)

$$y' + a(x)y = b(x)$$

and the associated *homogeneous** equation

$$y' + a(x)y = 0.$$

* We shall follow the custom of *italicizing* words and phrases that are being defined either explicitly or implicitly in the text.

It is easy to see by substitution that a solution of the latter equation is

$$e^{-\int a(x)\,dx}$$

To complete the solution of (4.2) we introduce a new variable v in (4.2) by means of the substitution

$$y = e^{-\int a(x)\,dx}v, \tag{4.6}$$

$$y' = e^{-\int a(x)\,dx}[v' - a(x)v].$$

Equation (4.2) becomes

$$e^{-\int a(x)\,dx}v' = b(x),$$

and so

$$v' = b(x)e^{\int a(x)\,dx}.$$

The last equation yields

$$v = c + \int b(x)e^{\int a(x)\,dx}\,dx.$$

Using (4.6) we then have

$$y = e^{-\int a(x)\,dx}\left[c + \int b(x)e^{\int a(x)\,dx}\,dx\right],$$

which agrees with equation (4.5).

It will be instructive to apply the second method to the equation

$$x^2y' + xy = 2 + x^2 \qquad (x > 0) \tag{4.1$'$}$$

of the preceding example. The associated homogeneous equation

$$y' + \frac{1}{x}y = 0$$

has the solution

$$e^{-\int a(x)\,dx} = e^{-\int \frac{dx}{x}} = \frac{1}{x}.$$

We accordingly substitute

$$y = \frac{1}{x} v$$

in (4.1)′, obtaining

$$x^2\left(\frac{1}{x} v' - \frac{1}{x^2} v\right) + x\left(\frac{1}{x} v\right) = 2 + x^2 \qquad (x > 0),$$

or

$$v' = \frac{2}{x} + x.$$

Thus,

$$v = 2 \log x + \frac{x^2}{2} + c,$$

and

$$y = \frac{2}{x} \log x + \frac{x}{2} + \frac{c}{x} \qquad (x > 0),$$

which is (4.5)′.

The homogeneous linear equation. In practice, to solve the linear homogeneous equation

$$k(x)y' + m(x)y = 0$$

we note that the variables are separable and write

$$\frac{dy}{y} + \frac{m(x)}{k(x)} dx = 0,$$

when $k(x) \neq 0$. The integration of the last equation is immediate.

EXERCISES

Solve each of the following differential equations by two methods.

1. $y' + y = 3.$

2. $y' - 2y = x.$

3. $xy' + y = 2x + e^x$.

4. $x^2y' - xy = x^3 + 4$.

5. $y' + ay = b$ (a, b constants).

6. $y' + \frac{1}{x}y = e^{x^2}$.

7. $y'' + y' = 2$. (*Hint.* Set $p = y'$.)

8. $xy'' + y' = x - 2$.

9. $y^2\,dx + (y^2x + 2xy - 1)\,dy = 0$. (*Hint.* Reverse the roles of x and y.)

10. $y + (x - y^3 - 2)y' = 0$.

In the next four exercises find solutions $y(x)$ of the given differential equations which satisfy the given *side* conditions.

11. $y' - y = 1$, $y(0) = 0$.

12. $xy' + y = 2x$, $y(1) = 1$.

13. $e^{-x}y' + 2e^xy = e^x$, $y(0) = \frac{1}{2} + \frac{1}{e}$.

14. $(\sin x)y' + (\cos x)y = \cos 2x$, $y\left(\frac{\pi}{2}\right) = \frac{1}{2}$.

15. Show that the substitution

$$u = y^{1-n}$$

reduces the so-called *Bernoulli* equation

$$y' + p(x)y = q(x)y^n \qquad (n \neq 1)$$

to the linear equation

$$\frac{1}{1-n}u' + p(x)u = q(x).$$

16. Solve the equation

$$y' - y = xy^{1/2}.$$

17. Solve the equation

$$\frac{dx}{dy} + x = x^2.$$

18. Show that if $y_0(x)$ is a solution of the equation

$$y' + a(x)y = b(x),$$

then

$$y_0(x) + ce^{-\int a(x)\,dx} \qquad (c \text{ constant})$$

is also a solution of this equation for each value of the constant c.

ANSWERS

1. $y = 3 + ce^{-x}$.

3. $y = x + \dfrac{1}{x}e^x + \dfrac{c}{x}$.

5. $y = \dfrac{b}{a} + ce^{-ax}$.

7. $y = 2x + c_1e^{-x} + c_2$.

9. $x = y^{-2}[1 + ce^{-y}]$.

11. $e^x - 1$.

13. $e^{-e^{2x}} + \frac{1}{2}$.

17. $x = (1 + ce^y)^{-1}$

5 Homogeneous Differential Equations of First Order

If the coefficients $M(x,y)$ and $N(x,y)$ of the differential equation

$$M(x,y)\,dx + N(x,y)\,dy = 0 \qquad [N(x,y) \not\equiv 0] \tag{5.1}$$

have the property that

$$\frac{M(ax,ay)}{N(ax,ay)} \equiv \frac{M(x,y)}{N(x,y)}, \tag{5.2}$$

where a is an arbitrary number not equal to zero, the equation (5.1) is said to have *homogeneous* coefficients. When this is true, either the substitution

$$y = vx, \qquad dy = v\,dx + x\,dv \tag{5.3}$$

or

$$x = wy, \qquad dx = w\,dy + y\,dw \tag{5.3$'$}$$

will reduce (5.1) to an equation in which the variables are separable.

We shall verify this statement for the substitution (5.3). In that case (5.1) becomes

$$M(x,vx)\,dx + N(x,vx)(x\,dv + v\,dx) = 0.$$

This equation may be written

$$\frac{M(x,vx)}{N(x,vx)}\,dx + v\,dx + x\,dv = 0. \tag{5.4}$$

Since equation (5.2) is an identity in the three variables a, x, and y, we may write

$$\frac{M(x,vx)}{N(x,vx)} \equiv \frac{M(1,v)}{N(1,v)}.$$

Accordingly, equation (5.4) may be rewritten in the form

$$[M(1,v) + vN(1,v)]\,dx + xN(1,v)\,dv = 0,$$

and the variables x and v are separable.

Example. The differential equation

$$(x^2 + y^2)\,dx + 3xy\,dy = 0 \tag{5.1$'$}$$

has homogeneous coefficients since

$$\frac{(ax)^2 + (ay)^2}{3(ax)(ay)} \equiv \frac{x^2 + y^2}{3xy} \qquad (axy \neq 0).$$

We may employ either substitution (5.3) or (5.3)′. If the former is used, equation (5.1)′ becomes

$$(x^2 + v^2x^2)\,dx + 3x(vx)(v\,dx + x\,dv) = 0,$$

or

$$\frac{dx}{x} + \frac{3v\,dv}{1 + 4v^2} = 0.$$

The formal integration is easily managed, and we have

$$\log|x| + \tfrac{3}{8}\log(1 + 4v^2) = \tfrac{3}{8}\log c.$$

Setting $v = \frac{y}{x}$ we obtain

$$x^2(x^2 + 4y^2)^3 = c.$$

The substitution $x = wy$ would have led to a similar result.

An integrating factor. When the equation

$$M(x,y)\,dx + N(x,y)\,dy = 0 \tag{5.5}$$

has homogeneous coefficients, an integrating factor is

$$\frac{1}{xM + yN}.$$

To verify this we require the following result, which is due to Euler.

Lemma. If the coefficients $M(x,y)$ and $N(x,y)$ of (5.5) are homogeneous and possess continuous partial derivatives in some region R of the xy-plane,

$$\frac{xM_x + yM_y}{xN_x + yN_y} \equiv \frac{M}{N}. \tag{5.6}$$

To prove the lemma we differentiate both sides of the identity (5.2) partially with respect to a obtaining

$$\begin{aligned} N(ax,ay)[xM_x(ax,ay) + yM_y(ax,ay)] \\ - M(ax,ay)[xN_x(ax,ay) + yN_y(ax,ay)] \equiv 0. \end{aligned} \tag{5.7}$$

If we set $a = 1$ in (5.7), (5.6) follows at once.

The proof that $\frac{1}{xM + yN}$ is an integrating factor is now readily accomplished and will be left to the student as an exercise. Let us, however, apply this integrating factor to the last example. We have then

$$\frac{1}{xM + yN} = \frac{1}{x^3 + 4xy^2}$$

as an integrating factor for equation (5.1)′; that is, the equation

$$\frac{x^2 + y^2}{x^3 + 4xy^2}\,dx + \frac{3xy}{x^3 + 4xy^2}\,dy = 0 \tag{5.8}$$

is exact. We may use the *alternate* method of Section 2 and integrate formally the second term of (5.8), obtaining

$$\tfrac{3}{8}\log|x^3 + 4xy^2|.$$

Next, we seek a function $f(x)$, of x alone, such that

$$d(f(x) + \tfrac{3}{8}\log|x^3 + 4xy^2|)$$

is the left-hand member of (5.8). We see at once that

$$f'(x) = -\frac{1}{8x};$$

hence, $f(x)$ may be taken as $-\frac{1}{8}\log|x|$, and it follows that

$$x^2(x^2 + 4y^2)^3 = c.$$

EXERCISES

Solve the following differential equations.

1. $(x - y)\,dx + x\,dy = 0$. (Use both methods of this section; also solve as a linear equation.)

2. $(x - 2y)\,dx + x\,dy = 0$. (Use both methods of this section.)

3. $(x^2 - y^2)\,dx + 2xy\,dy = 0$.

4. $\sqrt{x^2 + y^2}\,dx = x\,dy - y\,dx$.

5. $(x^2y + 2xy^2 - y^3)\,dx - (2y^3 - xy^2 + x^3)\,dy = 0$.

6. $\left(x\sin\frac{y}{x} - y\cos\frac{y}{x}\right)dx + x\cos\frac{y}{x}\,dy = 0$.

7. $(x^3 + 2xy^2)\,dx + (y^3 + 2x^2y)\,dy = 0$.

8. $(4x^4 - x^3y + y^4)\,dx + x^4\,dy = 0$.

9. $\left(x^2 \sin \dfrac{y^2}{x^2} - 2y^2 \cos \dfrac{y^2}{x^2}\right) dx + 2xy \cos \dfrac{y^2}{x^2}\,dy = 0$.

10. $(x^2e^{-y^2/x^2} - y^2)\,dx + xy\,dy = 0$.

11. $(2x + y - 2)\,dx + (2y - x + 1)\,dy = 0$. (*Hint*. Reduce to an equation with homogeneous coefficients by the substitution $x = u + h$, $y = v + k$, where h and k are suitably chosen constants.)

12. $(x - 3y)\,dx + (x + y + 4)\,dy = 0$.

13. $(x - y)\,dx + (x - y + 2)\,dy = 0$. (*Hint*. Set $u = x - y$.)

14. $(x + 2y + 1)\,dx + (2x + 4y + 3)\,dy = 0$.

15. Prove that $(xM + yN)^{-1}$ is an integrating factor for equation (5.5) when the equation has homogeneous coefficients.

16. Prove that if $f(ax,ay) \equiv a^nf(x,y)$ (n constant), then

$$xf_x(x,y) + yf_y(x,y) \equiv nf(x,y).$$

17. When (5.2) holds show that the substitution (5.3)′ reduces the differential equation (5.1) to a differential equation whose variables are separable.

ANSWERS

1. $xe^{y/x} = c$.

3. $x^2 + y^2 = 2ax$.

5. $(x^2 - y^2)e^{x/y} = c$.

7. $x^4 + 4x^2y^2 + y^4 = c$.

9. $x \sin (y^2/x^2) = c$.

11. $\log [(x - 1)^2 + y^2] - \arctan [y/(x - 1)] = c$.

13. $x + y - \log |x - y + 1| = c$.

6 Orthogonal Trajectories

The equation

$$(6.1) \qquad x^2 + y^2 = C \qquad (C > 0 \text{ constant})$$

represents a circle with center at the origin and radius $\sqrt{C}$. If C is regarded as a parameter, (6.1) may be interpreted as the equation of a family of circles with centers at the origin and of variable radius $\sqrt{C}$. If both members of (6.1) are differentiated with respect to x, the constant C is eliminated, and we have the differential equation

$$(6.2) \qquad x + yy' = 0,$$

or

$$(6.2)' \qquad x\,dx + y\,dy = 0.$$

It is readily seen, conversely, that equation (6.1) represents integral curves of this differential equation. The family (6.1) is frequently called a *one-parameter* family since it depends on a single parameter C.

Similarly, we may verify by substitution that the *two-parameter* family of curves

$$(6.3) \qquad y = c_1 \sin x + c_2 \cos x \qquad (c_1, c_2 \text{ constants})$$

satisfies the differential equation

$$(6.4) \qquad y'' + y = 0.$$

More precisely, the right-hand member of (6.3) provides a solution of (6.4) for all choices of the constants c_1 and c_2. We note that equation (6.4) may be derived from (6.3) by eliminating the constants c_1 and c_2 through differentiation, for,

$$(6.5) \qquad y' = c_1 \cos x - c_2 \sin x,$$

$$(6.6) \qquad y'' = -c_1 \sin x - c_2 \cos x.$$

If the equations (6.3) and (6.6) are added, equation (6.4) results.

Let us return to the family of circles (6.1) (see Fig. 1.1). Note that there is one and only one member of the family which passes

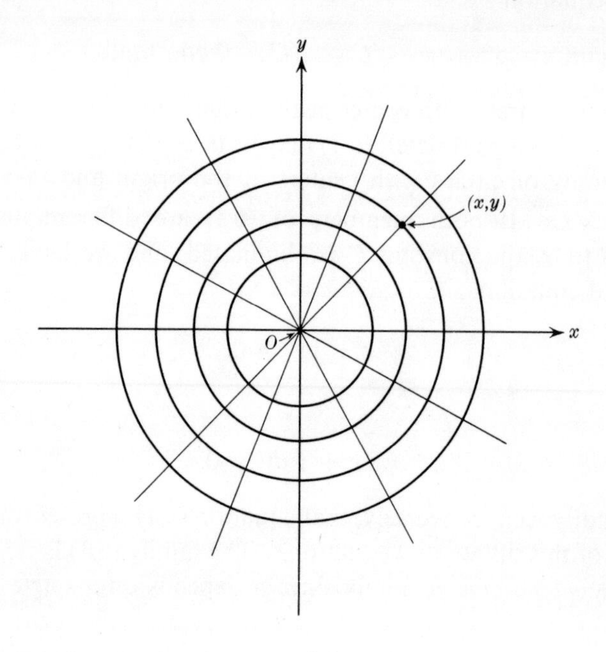

FIG. 1.1

through each point of the plane except the origin. For example, the circle through the point $(-3,4)$ has the equation

$$x^2 + y^2 = 25;$$

that is, $C = 25$. In general, if the circle passes through the point (x_0, y_0), then $C = x_0^2 + y_0^2$, and the circle of the family through this point has the equation

$$x^2 + y^2 = C \qquad (C = x_0^2 + y_0^2).$$

At the point (x, y) the slope of the circle passing through this point is given by equation (6.2):

$$y' = -\frac{x}{y} \qquad (y \neq 0). \tag{6.7}$$

Suppose we wish to find a second family of curves with the property that each member of the second family intersects each member of the first family at right angles, or *orthogonally*. When this occurs each family of curves is called *orthogonal trajectories* of the other. Because the slope of each circle of the given family at the point (x,y) is given by $-\frac{x}{y}$, the slope of an orthogonal trajectory to the circle at this point must be the negative reciprocal of this number, or $\frac{y}{x}$. That is, in the family of curves which cut the circles orthogonally we must have

$$y' = \frac{y}{x} \qquad (x \neq 0),$$

or

$$x\,dy - y\,dx = 0. \tag{6.8}$$

The variables are separable in equation (6.8). We see at once then that among the integral curves associated with (6.8) are the straight lines

$$y = Cx \qquad (C \neq 0). \tag{6.9}$$

This is a family of straight lines passing through the origin. To avoid dividing by zero we required both $x \neq 0$ and $y \neq 0$ in the preceding analysis. It is clear from the geometry (see Fig. 1.1), however, that the orthogonal trajectories of the family of circles (6.1) are the family (6.9) plus the lines $x = 0$ and $y = 0$.

This suggests a general method. Suppose the equation

$$f(x,y) = C \tag{6.10}$$

represents a one-parameter family F_1 of curves. If $f(x,y)$ is differentiable, the curves (6.10) are integral curves of the differential equation

$$f_x(x,y)\,dx + f_y(x,y)\,dy = 0.$$

The orthogonal trajectories of the family (6.10) are then integral curves F_2 of the differential equation (see Fig. 1.2)

$$f_y(x,y)\,dx - f_x(x,y)\,dy = 0.$$

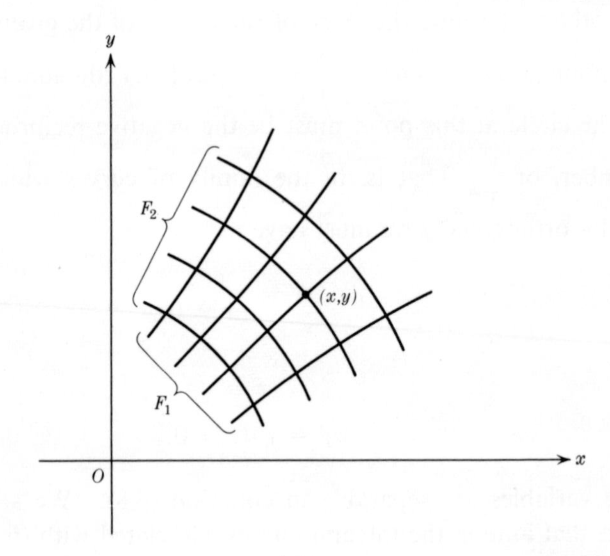

FIG. 1.2

EXERCISES

1. Find a first-order differential equation possessing the given family of integral curves:

(a) $y = cx$; (c) $x^2 + y^2 - 2ax = 0$;
(b) $y^2 = 2ax$; (d) $xy = c$.

2. Find a second-order differential equation possessing the given two-parameter family of solutions:

(a) $y = c_1x + c_2x^2$; (c) $y = c_1 \sin 2x + c_2 \cos 2x$;
(b) $y = c_1e^x + c_2e^{2x}$; (d) $y = c_1e^{-x} + c_2xe^{-x}$.

3. Find the orthogonal trajectories of the one-parameter family of curves given below. Sketch a few members of each family.

(a) $y = cx$; (d) $xy = c$;
(b) $y^2 = 2ax$; (e) $y = ce^x$;
(c) $x^2 + y^2 - 2ax = 0$; (f) $x^2 - 2y^2 = c$.

ANSWERS

1. (a) $x\,dy - y\,dx = 0$; (c) $(x^2 - y^2)\,dx + 2xy\,dy = 0$.

2. (a) $x^2y'' - 2xy' + 2y = 0$; (c) $y'' + 4y = 0$.

3. (a) $x^2 + y^2 = a^2$; (c) $x^2 + y^2 - 2cy = 0$; (e) $y^2 + 2x = c$.

7 Equations Reducible to Differential Equations of First Order

Consider the differential equation

$$y'' - y' = 0. \tag{7.1}$$

This equation is of first order in the variable y'. This observation may be exploited by the use of the substitution

$$p = y'. \tag{7.2}$$

Equation (7.1) then becomes the first-order differential equation

$$p' - p = 0, \tag{7.1$'$}$$

the solution of which is

$$p = c_1 e^x \qquad (c_1 \text{ constant}).$$

Thus, we set

$$y' = c_1 e^x,$$

and an integration yields

$$y = c_1 e^x + c_2 \qquad (c_2 \text{ constant}).$$

The substitution (7.2) will ordinarily be effective when the letter y is not present in the given differential equation. When the letter x is not present, a helpful substitution frequently is

$$\begin{aligned} y' &= p, \\ y'' &= \frac{dp}{dx} = \frac{dp}{dy}\frac{dy}{dx} = p\frac{dp}{dy}. \end{aligned} \tag{7.3}$$

Example. It has been noted that the solution of the differential equation

$$y'' + y = 0 \tag{7.4}$$

is $c_1 \sin x + c_2 \cos x$, where c_1 and c_2 are constants.

We observe that the variable x is not present formally in the equation and we apply the substitution (7.3). We have

$$p \frac{dp}{dy} + y = 0.$$

The variables are separable, and we write

$$p\,dp + y\,dy = 0;$$

hence

$$\frac{p^2}{2} + \frac{y^2}{2} = \frac{a_1^2}{2} \qquad (a_1 \text{ constant}, \neq 0).$$

Accordingly, we have

$$y'^2 + y^2 = a_1^2, \tag{7.5}$$

and consequently,

$$\frac{dy}{dx} = \pm\sqrt{a_1^2 - y^2}.$$

Again the variables are separable, and we may write

$$\frac{dy}{\sqrt{a_1^2 - y^2}} = \pm\,dx.$$

An integration yields

$$\text{arc sin}\,\frac{y}{a_1} = \pm x + a_2,$$

or

$$y = a_1 \sin(\pm x + a_2). \tag{7.6}$$

The equations (7.6) are readily seen to be equivalent to

$$y = k_1 \sin(x - k_2), \tag{7.7}$$

where k_1 and k_2 are new constants. The solution of (7.4) provided by the right-hand member of (7.7) may, if it is desired, be put in the form $c_1 \sin x + c_2 \cos x$ since

$$\begin{aligned} k_1 \sin (x - k_2) &= k_1 (\sin x \cos k_2 - \cos x \sin k_2) \\ &= k_1 \cos k_2 \sin x - k_1 \sin k_2 \cos x. \end{aligned}$$

We set

$$c_1 = k_1 \cos k_2, \qquad c_2 = -k_1 \sin k_2.$$

It will be observed that the above method of treating equation (7.4) is equivalent to multiplying both members of the equation by $2y'$:

$$2y'y'' + 2yy' = 0.$$

We then have

$$y'^2 + y^2 = a_1^2,$$

which is equation (7.5).

EXERCISES

Solve the following differential equations.

1. $y'' - 2y' = 0$ (two methods).

2. $y'' + y' = 0$ (two methods).

3. $xy'' - y' = 0$.

4. $xy'' + 3y' = 0$.

5. $y''' + y' = 0$.

6. $y''' - y' = 0$.

7. $y'' + a^2y = 0$.

8. $y'' = (1 + y'^2)^{3/2}$.

9. $2yy'' = 1 + y'^2$.

10. Show that integrals of the differential equation

$$(1 - x^2 - y^2)y'' + 2(1 + y'^2)(xy' - y) = 0$$

are provided by the family of circles

$$x^2 + y^2 - 2ax - 2by + 1 = 0.$$

Describe this family geometrically.

ANSWERS

1. $y = c_1 + c_2e^{2x}$.

3. $y = c_1 + c_2x^2$.

5. $y = c_1 + c_2 \sin x + c_3 \cos x$.

7. $y = c_1 \sin ax + c_2 \cos ax$.

9. $4k(y - k) = (x - h)^2$.

8 Some Applications

In this section we consider some typical applications of linear differential equations of first order. The equations we shall consider are of the form

$$\frac{dx}{dt} = b + f(t)x,$$

where b is a constant, possibly zero, and $f(t)$ is either always positive or always negative. In the former case $[f(t) > 0]$, the quantity x increases with the time t, and in the latter case $[f(t) < 0]$, x decreases with time. In both cases the change in x is roughly proportional to the amount x present at time t [when $b = 0$ and $f(t)$ is constant, it will be observed from the differential equation that the change in x is precisely proportional to the amount x present at time t].

Mixtures. We are now in a position to solve a typical problem concerning mixtures. A large tank contains 100 gal. of brine in which 50 lb. of salt is dissolved. Brine containing 2 lb. of salt to the gallon runs into the tank at the rate of 6 gal./min. The mixture, kept uniform by stirring, runs out of the tank at the rate of 4 gal./min. Find the amount of salt in solution in the tank at the end of t min.

Let x be the number of pounds of salt in solution after t min., and note that the tank will contain $100 + (6 - 4)t$ gal. of brine at this time. The concentration will then be

$$\frac{x}{100 + 2t} \text{ lb./gal.}$$

Thus,

$$\frac{dx}{dt} = 2(6) - \frac{x}{100 + 2t} \cdot 4; \tag{8.1}$$

that is, the rate at which the amount of salt in solution is changing at time t is the amount per minute entering into solution minus the rate at which the salt leaves the tank. Equation (8.1) is linear, and we seek the solution with the property that $x = 50$ when $t = 0$. This solution may be obtained using the methods of Section 4. It is seen to be

$$x = 2(100 + 2t) - \frac{15(10^5)}{(100 + 2t)^2}.$$

After 50 min., for example, there will be 362.5 lb. of salt in solution in the tank.

Decompositions. Suppose that a quantity of a radioactive substance originally weighing x_0 grams decomposes at a rate proportional to the amount present and that half the original quantity is left after a years. To find the amount x of the substance remaining after t years, note that we may solve the differential equation

$$\frac{dx}{dt} = -kx, \tag{8.2}$$

subject to the condition that $x = x_0$ when $t = 0$. This equation is linear, and the solution which satisfies the given condition is

$$x = x_0 e^{-kt}. \tag{8.3}$$

The constant of proportionality k is then determined by the equation

$$\frac{x_0}{2} = x_0 e^{-ak},$$

or $ak = \log 2$. Thus, equation (8.3) becomes

$$x = x_0 2^{-t/a}, \tag{8.4}$$

and we note that the number x of grams of the substance remaining undecomposed decreases exponentially. From equation (8.4) the student can readily determine, for example, the number of years which would be required for the substance to be reduced to one-tenth the original amount, or the amount of the substance which will be undecomposed after, say, 500 years.

Compound interest. Here is a problem very similar to the foregoing. Suppose that a sum of money A_0 is invested at the rate of $k\%$ per year compounded *continuously*. To find the value A of the investment after t years, we are led to consider the differential equation

$$\frac{dA}{dt} = \frac{k}{100} A. \tag{8.5}$$

This may best be seen as follows. If interest is earned at the rate of $k\%$ per year compounded n times a year, the amount A_n of interest plus principal at the end of t years is defined to be

$$A_n = A_0\left(1 + \frac{k}{n}\frac{1}{100}\right)^{nt} = A_0\left[\left(1 + \frac{k}{n}\frac{1}{100}\right)^n\right]^t.$$

To *define* the amount A at continuous compound interest, we would quite naturally use

$$A = \lim_{n \to \infty} A_n = \lim_{n \to \infty} A_0\left[\left(1 + \frac{k}{n}\frac{1}{100}\right)^n\right]^t.$$

Since,

$$\lim_{n \to \infty}\left(1 + \frac{k}{n}\frac{1}{100}\right)^n = e^{k/100},$$

we have as the amount A, which an original principal of A_0 will realize after t years, when interest is compounded continuously at the rate of $k\%$ per year,

$$A = A_0 e^{kt/100}. \tag{8.6}$$

Since (8.5) and (8.6) may be regarded as equivalent statements, we see *ex post facto* that it is appropriate to regard interest compounded continuously at the rate of $k\%$ per year as being equivalent to the idea that the rate of change of the amount is proportional to the amount present at time t, where the constant of proportionality is $\frac{k}{100}$.

Example. The sum of \$100 is invested at the rate of 4% per year compounded continuously. When will the amount be \$200?

The differential equation to be solved is

$$\frac{dA}{dt} = 0.04A, \tag{8.5$'$}$$

and its solution is

$$A = 100e^{0.04t}. \tag{8.6$'$}$$

Setting $A = 200$, we have $0.04t = \log 2$, or $t = 25 \log 2 = 17.3$ years.

EXERCISES

1. A tank contains 100 gal. of brine in which 50 lb. of salt is dissolved. Brine containing 2 lb. of salt to the gallon runs into the tank at the rate of 3 gal./min. The mixture, kept uniform by stirring, flows out at the same rate. How much salt is in solution in the tank at the end of 20 min.?

2. A tank contains 50 gal. of brine in which 20 lb. of salt is dissolved. Pure salt is fed into the tank at the rate of 1 lb./min. The mixture is kept uniform and flows out of the tank at the rate of 2 gal./min. How much salt is in solution in the tank at the end of 10 min.? What is the concentration at that time?

3. A tank contains 100 gal. of brine in which 50 lb. of salt is dissolved. Brine containing 2 lb. of salt to the gallon enters the tank at the rate of 3 gal./min. The mixture, kept uniform, flows out at the rate of 1 gal./min. How much salt is in solution in the tank at the end of 100 min.? What is its concentration?

4. A tank contains a gal. of brine in which b lb. of salt is dissolved. Brine containing h lb. of salt to the gallon runs into the tank at the rate of g gal./min. The mixture, kept uniform by stirring, flows out of the tank at the rate of k gal./min. How much salt is in the tank at the end of t min.? What is its concentration? Prove that the answer you obtain in which you assume that $g \neq 0$ and $g \neq k$ yields correct results as you allow g to tend to zero and also as $g \to k$. Check the formula you obtain for the case $g = k$ by allowing t to become infinite.

5. A tank contains 50 gal. of a mixture containing equal parts of alcohol and water. A mixture containing 2 parts of water to 1 part of alcohol flows into the tank at the rate of 3 gal./min. The fluid in the tank, kept uniform by stirring, flows out of the tank at the rate of 2 gal./min. How much alcohol will there be in the solution after half an hour?

6. A radioactive substance decomposes at a rate proportional to the amount present, and half the original quantity is left after 1,500 years. In how many years would the original amount be reduced by three-fourths? How much of the substance will be left after 2,000 years?

7. Show that

$$\lim_{n \to \infty} \left(1 + \frac{a}{n}\right)^n = e^a.$$

8. Find the value at the end of 20 years of an investment of \$100 which earns interest at the rate of 5% compounded continuously.

9. At what nominal rate of interest per year compounded continuously must \$1 be invested to double its value in 10 years?

10. A large tank (A) contains initially 60 gal. of water and 40 gal. of alcohol. Water flows into the tank at the rate of 3 gal./min., while alcohol flows into the tank at the rate of 1 gal./min. The mixture, kept thoroughly agitated, flows into a second tank (B) at the rate of 3 gal./min. Tank B initially contained 100 gal. of water. The mixture in tank B is kept stirred and flows out of it at the rate of 2 gal./min. How much alcohol is in each tank at the end of 50 min.? Which tank eventually contains the larger quantity of alcohol?

ANSWERS

1. 117.5 lb.

2. 19.7 lb.; 0.66 lb./gal.

3. 513.5 lb.; 1.7 lb./gal.

5. 29.9 gal.

6. 3,000 years; $0.4A_0$.

8. $271.83.

9. 6.93%.

10. Tank A: 42 gal.; tank B: 33 gal.

REFERENCES

It is hoped that the student will wish to seek additional information about differential equations from other sources as he proceeds through this book. The literature on the subject is vast, but the following selected list of references should prove useful.

1. R. P. Agnew, *Differential Equations*, second edition, McGraw-Hill, New York (1960). A book characterized by an unusual combination of high mathematical quality and charm of style.
2. E. A. Coddington and N. Levinson, *Theory of Ordinary Differential Equations*, McGraw-Hill, New York (1955). A very useful book, rather tersely written.
3. R. Courant and D. Hilbert, *Methods of Mathematical Physics*, Vol. 1, Interscience, New York (1953). A classic.
4. E. L. Ince, *Ordinary Differential Equations*, Longmans, Green, London (1927). This book contains a large amount of material, and although somewhat dated today, it is still one of the basic reference books in the field.

5. J. LaSalle and S. Lefschetz, *Stability by Liapunov's Direct Method with Applications*, Academic Press, New York (1961). A most valuable introduction to the modern theory of control.

6. M. R. Spiegel, *Applied Differential Equations*, Prentice-Hall, Englewood Cliffs, N.J. (1958). This book contains an especially good collection of elementary applications of differential equations.

2

Linear Differential Equations with Constant Coefficients

The simplest linear differential equations are those in the form

$$(1) \qquad a_0 y^{(n)} + a_1 y^{(n-1)} + \cdots + a_{n-1} y' + a_n y = f(x),$$

where $a_0, a_1, \ldots, a_n$ are real constants. The *associated homogeneous equation* is

$$(2) \qquad a_0 y^{(n)} + a_1 y^{(n-1)} + \cdots + a_{n-1} y' + a_n y = 0.$$

When $a_0 \neq 0$, these differential equations are of order n. It is the latter equation to which we shall first devote our attention.

The general method of attack on (2) is to try for a solution of the form $y = e^{mx}$, where m is a constant. If we substitute in (2), we obtain

$$(3) \qquad e^{mx}(a_0 m^n + a_1 m^{n-1} + \cdots + a_{n-1} m + a_n) = 0.$$

It is clear that if m_1 is any root of the ordinary polynomial equation (called the *auxiliary* or *indicial* equation)

$$(4) \qquad a_0 m^n + a_1 m^{n-1} + \cdots + a_{n-1} m + a_n = 0,$$

then $e^{m_1 x}$ is a solution of (2). The treatment varies according as roots of (4) are real or imaginary and also according as equation (4) possesses or fails to possess multiple roots.

In order to understand this chapter we shall need the following result concerning the more general linear homogeneous differential equation:

$$(5) \qquad a_0(x)y^{(n)} + a_1(x)y^{(n-1)} + \cdots + a_{n-1}(x)y' + a_n(x)y = 0,$$

where $a_0(x), a_1(x), \ldots, a_n(x)$ are continuous, and $a_0(x) \neq 0$ on an interval (a,b).

Theorem. There exist n solutions

$$(6) \qquad y_1(x), y_2(x), \ldots, y_n(x)$$

of (5) *on the interval* (a,b) *with the property that the determinant*

$$(7) \qquad \begin{vmatrix} y_1(x) & y_2(x) & \cdots & y_n(x) \\ y_1'(x) & y_2'(x) & \cdots & y_n'(x) \\ \cdot & \cdot & \cdot & \cdot \\ y_1^{(n-1)}(x) & y_2^{(n-1)}(x) & \cdots & y_n^{(n-1)}(x) \end{vmatrix} \not\equiv 0.$$

Further, if $y_1(x), y_2(x), \ldots, y_n(x)$ *are any n solutions of* (5) *for which* (7) *holds, every solution of* (5) *can be written in the form*

$$(8) \qquad c_1y_1(x) + c_2y_2(x) + \cdots + c_ny_n(x),$$

where $c_1, c_2, \ldots, c_n$ *are constants.*

The function (8) is properly called the *general solution* of (5) since every solution can be written in this form, and every such linear combination of solutions is a solution of (5). The determinant (7) is called the *wronskian* of the n solutions (6).

The theorem is proved in Chapter 5.

If there is a value of x for which one or more of the functions $a_0(x), a_1(x), \ldots, a_n(x)$ fails to be continuous or for which $a_0(x)$ vanishes, it will be called a *singular* point of equation (5).

1 Distinct Real Roots*

If the roots of (4) are the n real, distinct numbers

$$m_1, m_2, \ldots, m_n,$$

* In this chapter we shall give, usually without proof, methods of solving linear differential equations with constant coefficients. Substitution in the differential equation of the solutions so obtained will always provide a proof when one is required.

the functions

$$e^{m_1 x}, e^{m_2 x}, \ldots, e^{m_n x} \tag{1.1}$$

are a set of n solutions which satisfy (7), and the general solution of (2) is

$$c_1 e^{m_1 x} + c_2 e^{m_2 x} + \cdots + c_n e^{m_n x}. \tag{1.2}$$

The proof that the solutions (1.1) satisfy (7) is suggested by Exercise 16 of Section 3.

Example. Find the general solution of

$$y'' + y' - 2y = 0. \tag{1.3}$$

The auxiliary equation

$$m^2 + m - 2 = 0 \tag{1.4}$$

has the roots 1, -2, which are real and distinct. The general solution of (1.3) is then

$$y = c_1 e^x + c_2 e^{-2x}.$$

2 Repeated Real Roots

Consider the differential equation

$$y'' - 2y' + y = 0. \tag{2.1}$$

The auxiliary equation

$$m^2 - 2m + 1 = 0 \tag{2.2}$$

has the roots 1, 1. It is clear that e^x is then a solution of (2.1), but a second linearly independent solution needs to be found. In this case we substitute $y = e^x v$ in (2.1) obtaining

$$e^x v'' = 0. \tag{2.3}$$

The solution $v = x$ of (2.3) leads then to the solution xe^x of (2.1). Thus, the general solution of (2.1) is

$$y = c_1e^x + c_2xe^x. \tag{2.4}$$

We anticipate the following generalization. If, for example, the differential equation is of third order and leads to an auxiliary equation having 2, 2, 2 as roots, the general solution of the differential equation is

$$y = c_1e^{2x} + c_2xe^{2x} + c_3x^2e^{2x},$$

and so on. The student can easily construct the differential equation which would have led to this solution.

Finally, if the roots of the auxiliary equation were the set

$$2,\ 2,\ 2,\ -3,\ -3,\ -\tfrac{1}{2},$$

the general solution of the corresponding differential equation would be

$$y = c_1e^{2x} + c_2xe^{2x} + c_3x^2e^{2x} + c_4e^{-3x} + c_5xe^{-3x} + c_6e^{-x/2}.$$

3 Imaginary Roots

If the auxiliary equation has the imaginary root $a + ib$ (a,b real, $b \neq 0$), it also has the *conjugate* root $a - ib$. Corresponding linearly independent solutions of the differential equation are $e^{ax}\cos bx$ and $e^{ax}\sin bx$.

In order to understand how these solutions arise we borrow from the theory of functions of a complex variable. First, it is shown there that

$$\frac{d}{dx}e^{cx} = ce^{cx},$$

even when c is an imaginary number. Accordingly, if $c = a + ib$ is a root of the auxiliary algebraic equation, the function e^{cx} formally satisfies the differential equation, and so does $e^{\bar{c}x}$, where

$\bar{c} = a - ib$. Also, the sum and difference of these functions satisfy the differential equation; that is,

$$e^{cx} + e^{\bar{c}x} \quad \text{and} \quad e^{cx} - e^{\bar{c}x}$$

formally satisfy the differential equation.

Next, we borrow the Euler identity which states that

$$e^{(a+ib)x} = e^{ax}e^{ibx} = e^{ax}(\cos bx + i \sin bx),$$
$$e^{(a-ib)x} = e^{ax}e^{-ibx} = e^{ax}(\cos bx - i \sin bx),$$

for all values of x. We have then that the functions

$$e^{cx} + e^{\bar{c}x} = 2e^{ax} \cos bx,$$
$$e^{cx} - e^{\bar{c}x} = 2ie^{ax} \sin bx,$$

formally satisfy the differential equation, and hence that the functions

$$e^{ax} \cos bx \quad \text{and} \quad e^{ax} \sin bx$$

satisfy the differential equation.

Example. Consider the differential equation

$$y'' - 4y' + 13y = 0. \tag{3.1}$$

The corresponding auxiliary equation has roots $c = 2 + 3i$ and $\bar{c} = 2 - 3i$. According to our theory, the functions

$$e^{2x} \sin 3x \quad \text{and} \quad e^{2x} \cos 3x$$

should be solutions of (3.1). Let us verify that the former function is indeed a solution. We have

$$y = e^{2x} \sin 3x,$$
$$y' = e^{2x}(3 \cos 3x + 2 \sin 3x),$$
$$y'' = e^{2x}(12 \cos 3x - 5 \sin 3x).$$

It is readily seen that $e^{2x} \sin 3x$ is a solution of (3.1). A similar computation will show that $e^{2x} \cos 3x$ is also a solution.

If the auxiliary equation has the repeated imaginary roots

$$a + ib, \quad a + ib, \quad a - ib, \quad a - ib,$$

it can be verified that the corresponding solution of the differential equation is

$$c_1 e^{ax} \cos bx + c_2 e^{ax} \sin bx + c_3 x e^{ax} \cos bx + c_4 x e^{ax} \sin bx.$$

Example. Consider the differential equation

$$y'''' - 8y''' + 42y'' - 104y' + 169y = 0. \tag{3.2}$$

Its auxiliary equation

$$m^4 - 8m^3 + 42m^2 - 104m + 169 = 0$$

has the roots $2 + 3i$, $2 + 3i$, $2 - 3i$, $2 - 3i$. The general solution of (3.2) is then

$$c_1 e^{2x} \cos 3x + c_2 e^{2x} \sin 3x + c_3 x e^{2x} \cos 3x + c_4 x e^{2x} \sin 3x.$$

EXERCISES

Find the general solutions of the following differential equations.*

1. $y'' - 3y' + 2y = 0.$

2. $y'' + 2y' + 2y = 0.$

3. $y'' + 4y' + 4y = 0.$

4. $y'' + 4y' + 8y = 0.$

5. $y'' + 6y' + 9y = 0.$

6. $y'' - 4y' + 3y = 0.$

7. $8y'' + 4y' + y = 0.$

8. $4y'' + 4y' + y = 0.$

9. $y''' - 3y'' + 4y' - 2y = 0.$

* Exercises 11 and 12 require some ingenuity in solving the associated auxiliary equation.

10. $y''' - y'' - y' + y = 0.$

11. $y'''' + 4y = 0.$

12. $y'''' - 6y''' + 19y'' - 26y' + 18y = 0.$

13. A homogeneous linear differential equation with constant coefficients has

$$2,\ 2,\ 2,\ 3 - 4i,\ 3 + 4i,\ 3 - 4i,\ 3 + 4i,\ 3,\ 3$$

as roots of its auxiliary equation. What is its general solution?

14. Do the same as Exercise 13 when the roots are

$$2,\ 2,\ 3 - 4i,\ 3 + 4i,\ 3 - 4i,\ 3 + 4i,\ 3 - 4i,\ 3 + 4i,\ 7.$$

15. Show that the wronskian of $e^{ax} \cos bx$ and $e^{ax} \sin bx$ $(b \neq 0)$ is be^{ax} (or $-be^{ax}$).

16. Prove that the wronskian of the functions

$$e^{m_1 x},\quad e^{m_2 x},\quad e^{m_3 x}$$

is equal to $(m_1 - m_2)(m_2 - m_3)(m_3 - m_1)e^{(m_1 + m_2 + m_3)x}$. From this result guess the value of the wronskian of the n functions (1.1).

ANSWERS

1. $c_1 e^x + c_2 e^{2x}$.

2. $e^{-x}(c_1 \cos x + c_2 \sin x)$.

3. $c_1 e^{-2x} + c_2 x e^{-2x}$.

4. $e^{-2x}(c_1 \cos 2x + c_2 \sin 2x)$.

5. $c_1 e^{-3x} + c_2 x e^{-3x}$.

6. $c_1 e^x + c_2 e^{3x}$.

7. $e^{-x/4}(c_1 \cos \frac{1}{4}x + c_2 \sin \frac{1}{4}x)$.

8. $c_1 e^{-x/2} + c_2 x e^{-x/2}$.

9. $e^x(c_1 + c_2 \cos x + c_3 \sin x)$.

10. $c_1 e^{-x} + c_2 e^x + c_3 x e^x$.

11. $e^x(c_1 \cos x + c_2 \sin x) + e^{-x}(c_3 \cos x + c_4 \sin x)$.

12. $e^x(c_1 \cos x + c_2 \sin x) + e^{2x}[c_3 \cos (x\sqrt{5}) + c_4 \sin (x\sqrt{5})]$.

4 The Nonhomogeneous Case

Consider the differential equation

$$y'' - 3y' + 2y = 4. \tag{4.1}$$

With (4.1) we associate the homogeneous equation

$$y'' - 3y' + 2y = 0. \tag{4.2}$$

The general solution of (4.2) is

$$c_1e^x + c_2e^{2x}.$$

We wish to find the general solution of (4.1). To obtain it we make use of the following result, which is proved in Chapter 5.

Theorem 4.1. *If* $c_1y_1(x) + c_2y_2(x)$ *is the general solution of*

$$a(x)y'' + b(x)y' + c(x)y = 0,$$

and if $y_0(x)$ *is any particular solution of the nonhomogeneous differential equation*

$$a(x)y'' + b(x)y' + c(x)y = f(x), \tag{4.3}$$

the general solution of (4.3) *is*

$$y_0(x) + c_1y_1(x) + c_2y_2(x).$$

Theorem 4.1 is stated for second-order linear differential equations. A similar statement is valid for linear differential equations of order n ($n = 1, 2, \ldots$).

We return to equation (4.1). By inspection, we see that a particular solution of (4.1) is $y = 2$. Accordingly, the general solution of (4.1) is

$$2 + c_1e^x + c_2e^{2x}.$$

When a particular solution of a nonhomogeneous differential equation cannot be found by inspection, other methods are available. A general method, called variation of parameters, is discussed in Chapter 5. In the present chapter we confine our attention to certain special devices that are sometimes useful.

Roughly speaking, we can apply these devices when the right-hand member of the equation is composed of the sum of terms each of which possesses a finite number of essentially different derivatives. For example, the right-hand member of the nonhomogeneous differential equation

$$y'' - y' + 2y = 2e^x - 4\cos x \tag{4.4}$$

contains the terms e^x and $\cos x$ (except for constant multipliers). Except for constant factors, these terms and their possible derivatives are e^x, $\sin x$, $\cos x$. The plan is to try to determine constants a, b, and c so that the function

$$ae^x + b\sin x + c\cos x$$

is a solution of (4.4). If this function is substituted for y in (4.4), we have

$$2ae^x + (b + c)\sin x + (c - b)\cos x = 2e^x - 4\cos x.$$

We then have the equations*

$$\begin{aligned} 2a &= 2, \\ b + c &= 0, \\ b - c &= 4, \end{aligned}$$

to determine a, b, and c. It follows that $a = 1$, $b = 2$, $c = -2$, and a solution of (4.4) is

$$e^x + 2\sin x - 2\cos x.$$

Since the general solution of the corresponding homogeneous equation

$$y'' - y' + 2y = 0$$

is

$$c_1e^{-x} + c_2e^{2x},$$

* Although it is true that the following equations must hold if the preceding equation is to be an identity, we need not be concerned with this. The problem is clearly solved if any constants a, b, and c can be found such that $ae^x + b\sin x + c\cos x$ is a solution of (4.4).

the general solution of (4.4) is

$$e^x + 2\sin x - 2\cos x + c_1 e^{-x} + c_2 e^{2x}.$$

Example. Solve the differential equation

$$y'' + y = 3. \tag{4.5}$$

The general solution of the corresponding homogeneous equation

$$y'' + y = 0$$

is $c_1 \sin x + c_2 \cos x$. By inspection we see that a particular solution of (4.5) is 3; thus, the general solution of (4.5) is

$$3 + c_1 \sin x + c_2 \cos x.$$

Example. Solve the differential equation

$$y'' + 4y = -4x^2 + 2. \tag{4.6}$$

The general solution of the corresponding homogeneous equation is seen to be $c_1 \sin 2x + c_2 \cos 2x$. We try for a solution of (4.6) of the form $y = ax^2 + bx + c$. We have

$$4ax^2 + 4bx + (2a + 4c) = -4x^2 + 2.$$

Thus, we try to determine constants a, b, and c such that

$$4a = -4,$$

$$4b = 0,$$

$$2a + 4c = 2.$$

It follows that we may set $a = -1$, $b = 0$, $c = 1$, and a particular solution of (4.6) is then $-x^2 + 1$. Its general solution is

$$-x^2 + 1 + c_1 \sin 2x + c_2 \cos 2x.$$

Consider the differential equation

$$y'' - y = 2e^x. \tag{4.7}$$

The general solution of the corresponding homogeneous equation

$$y'' - y = 0 \tag{4.8}$$

is

$$c_1e^x + c_2e^{-x}.$$

We try to determine the constant $a \neq 0$ so that $y = ae^x$ is a solution of (4.7). Upon substitution in (4.7) we have the equation

$$0 = 2e^x$$

for the determination of the constant a. This is not possible, and another method of solution must be attempted.

The method we have been employing failed for equation (4.7) because the term e^x in the right-hand member is also a solution of the homogeneous equation (4.8). The difficulty can be circumvented by the device of determining a constant $a \neq 0$ such that $y = axe^x$ is a solution of (4.7). We have then

$$2ae^x = 2e^x.$$

It follows that $a = 1$ and that a particular solution of (4.7) is xe^x. Its general solution is, then,

$$xe^x + c_1e^x + c_2e^{-x}.$$

Example. Solve the differential equation

$$y'' + y = 2e^x + 4 \sin x. \tag{4.9}$$

The general solution of the corresponding homogeneous equation is $c_1 \sin x + c_2 \cos x$. We observe that the term $4 \sin x$ in the right-hand member of (4.9) is a solution of the corresponding homogeneous equation. This suggests that we try for a particular solution of (4.9) of the form

$$y = ae^x + bx \sin x + cx \cos x, \tag{4.10}$$

where a, b, and c are constants. Upon substituting (4.10) in (4.9) we have

$$2ae^x + 2b \cos x - 2c \sin x = 2e^x + 4 \sin x,$$

and we may take

$$a = 1, \qquad b = 0, \qquad c = -2.$$

The general solution of (4.9) is, accordingly,

$$e^x - 2x \cos x + c_1 \sin x + c_2 \cos x.$$

If the given equation were

$$y'' + 4y = x \sin x + 2e^{2x},$$

we should try for a particular solution of the form

$$y = c_1 e^{2x} + c_2 x \sin x + c_3 x \cos x + c_4 \sin x + c_5 \cos x,$$

since this is a combination of the functions $x \sin x$, e^{2x} and their various derivative forms.

The method above would fail, for example, if the equation were

$$y'' + y = \tan x,$$

since $\tan x$ does not have only a finite number of essentially different forms for its derivatives.

Addition of Solutions. To find a particular solution of the differential equation

$$y'' + 4y = e^x - 2 \sin x + x, \tag{4.11}$$

we may determine constants c_1, c_2, c_3, c_4, c_5 such that the function

$$c_1 e^x + c_2 \sin x + c_3 \cos x + c_4 x + c_5$$

will be a solution of (4.11). We may also find particular solutions of each of the following differential equations:

$$y'' + 4y = e^x,$$

$$y'' + 4y = -2 \sin x,$$

$$y'' + 4y = x.$$

The sum of these three particular solutions will be seen to be a solution of (4.11). The validity of this method is readily established. The proof for the case of a second-order linear differential equation is left to the student as an exercise (Exercise 13).

EXERCISES

Find the general solutions of the following differential equations.

1. $y'' - 3y' + 2y = \sin x$.

2. $y'' + 2y' + 2y = 1 + x^2$.

3. $y'' + 4y' + 4y = x - 2e^{2x}$.

4. $y'' + 4y' + 8y = x - e^x$.

5. $y'' - 6y' + 9y = e^x \sin x$.

6. $y'' - 4y' + 3y = x^3$.

7. $8y'' + 4y' + y = \sin x - 2 \cos x$.

8. $4y'' + 4y' + y = e^x - 2 \cos 2x$.

9. $y'' + y = 3 \cos x$.

10. $y'' + y = e^x + 3 \cos x$.

11. $y'' - 3y' + 2y = 2 + e^x$.

12. $y'' - 3y' + 2y = e^x - 2e^{2x} + \sin x$.

13. Establish the validity of the method of addition of solutions for the equation

$$y'' + a(x)y' + b(x)y = f_1(x) + f_2(x).$$

14. Find the general solution of

$$y'' - 2y' + y = 4e^x.$$

15. Find a particular solution of the differential equation (4.7) by means of the substitution $y = e^x v$.

16. Use Exercise 13 and the method of Exercise 15 to solve the differential equation (4.9).

ANSWERS

1. $\frac{1}{10} \sin x + \frac{3}{10} \cos x + c_1 e^x + c_2 e^{2x}$.

2. $1 - x + \frac{1}{2}x^2 + e^{-x}(c_1 \cos x + c_2 \sin x)$.

3. $-\frac{1}{4} + \frac{x}{4} - \frac{1}{8} e^{2x} + c_1 e^{-2x} + c_2 x e^{-2x}$.

4. $-\dfrac{1}{16} + \dfrac{x}{8} - \dfrac{1}{13}e^x + e^{-2x}(c_1 \cos 2x + c_2 \sin 2x)$.

5. $e^x(\frac{3}{25}\sin x + \frac{4}{25}\cos x) + c_1e^{3x} + c_2xe^{3x}$.

6. $\frac{80}{27} + \frac{26}{9}x + \frac{4}{3}x^2 + \frac{1}{3}x^3 + c_1e^x + c_2e^{3x}$.

7. $\frac{2}{13}\cos x - \frac{3}{13}\sin x + e^{-x/4}\left(c_1 \cos\dfrac{x}{4} + c_2 \sin\dfrac{x}{4}\right)$.

8. $\frac{1}{9}e^x + \frac{30}{289}\cos 2x - \frac{16}{289}\sin 2x + c_1e^{-x/2} + c_2xe^{-x/2}$.

9. $\frac{3}{2}x \sin x + c_1 \cos x + c_2 \sin x$.

10. $\frac{1}{2}e^x + \frac{3}{2}x \sin x + c_1 \cos x + c_2 \sin x$.

11. $1 - xe^x + c_1e^x + c_2e^{2x}$.

12. $\frac{1}{10}\sin x + \frac{3}{10}\cos x + xe^x - 2xe^{2x} + c_1e^x + c_2e^{2x}$.

14. $2x^2e^x + c_1e^x + c_2xe^x$.

5 Euler-type Equations

An equation of the form

$$a_0x^ny^{(n)} + a_1x^{n-1}y^{(n-1)} + a_2x^{n-2}y^{(n-2)} + \cdots + a_{n-1}xy' + a_ny = 0, \qquad (a_0 \neq 0), \tag{5.1}$$

where $a_0, a_1, \ldots, a_n$ are constants, is an *Euler-type* equation. The transformation $x = e^t$ reduces (5.1) to a linear equation with constant coefficients.

Example. Find the general solution of the differential equation

$$x^2y'' - 2xy' + 2y = 0. \tag{5.2}$$

Under the transformation $x = e^t$ we have

$$\begin{aligned} y' &= \frac{dy}{dx} = \frac{dy}{dt}\Big/\frac{dx}{dt} = \frac{1}{x}\frac{dy}{dt}, \\ y'' &= \frac{d}{dx}\left(\frac{dy}{dx}\right) = \frac{d}{dt}\left(\frac{dy}{dx}\right)\Big/\frac{dx}{dt} = \frac{1}{x^2}\left(\frac{d^2y}{dt^2} - \frac{dy}{dt}\right). \end{aligned} \tag{5.3}$$

Equation (5.2) becomes

$$\frac{d^2y}{dt^2} - 3\frac{dy}{dt} + 2y = 0.$$

Its general solution is

$$y = c_1e^t + c_2e^{2t}.$$

Thus, the general solution of (5.2) is, accordingly,

$$y = c_1x + c_2x^2. \tag{5.4}$$

Critique. The student will note that the point $x = 0$ is singular for Euler equation (5.1). Solutions will be defined then, in general, only on intervals not containing the origin. Further, the substitution $x = e^t$ presupposes that $x > 0$. For negative values of x, the substitution $-x = e^t$ is appropriate. Equations (5.3) remain unchanged. These two substitutions may be combined into $|x| = e^t$, for which equations (5.3) remain valid. The resulting solutions will then be correct both on intervals on which $x > 0$ and on those where $x < 0$ (see Exercise 10).

An alternate method. The form of the solution (5.4) of the equation (5.2) suggests an alternate method for solving Euler-type equations. We may substitute $y = x^m$ directly in the original equation and try to determine constants m such that x^m is a solution. For example, if we set $y = x^m$ in (5.2), we are led at once to the equation

$$x^2(m^2 - 3m + 2) = 0.$$

It is clear that m may be taken as 1 or 2. That is,

$$x \text{ and } x^2$$

are solutions of (5.2), and the general solution of (5.2) is, then,

$$c_1x + c_2x^2.$$

If the substitution $y = x^m$ is made in the general equation (5.1), we are led to an equation

$$x^n(b_0m^n + b_1m^{n-1} + \cdots + b_{n-1}m + b_n) = 0 \qquad (b_0 = a_0 \neq 0),$$

where $b_0, b_1, b_2, \ldots, b_n$ are constants, for the determination of the exponents m. When the n roots of the equation

$$b_0 m^n + b_1 m^{n-1} + \cdots + b_{n-1} m + b_n = 0 \tag{5.5}$$

are real and distinct, the alternate method is the simpler of the two. While this alternate method is quite as general as the earlier one, it is recommended that the first method be employed whenever equation (5.5) has either repeated real roots or imaginary roots.

Example. Solve the differential equation

$$x^2 y'' + xy' + y = \log x \qquad (x > 0). \tag{5.6}$$

The corresponding homogeneous equation is

$$x^2 y'' + xy' + y = 0.$$

If we set $y = x^m$, we are led to the equation

$$m^2 + 1 = 0.$$

This leads to the solution

$$c_1 x^i + c_2 x^{-i}$$

from which we could deduce a general solution in real form. We elect, however, to transform (5.6) by means of the substitution $x = e^t$. Using equations (5.3) we have

$$\frac{d^2 y}{dt^2} + y = t. \tag{5.7}$$

The corresponding homogeneous equation has the general solution

$$c_1 \sin t + c_2 \cos t.$$

We next try for a particular solution of (5.7) by attempting to determine constants a and b so that $at + b$ is a solution. A substitution in (5.7) leads to the conditions $a = 1, b = 0$, so that t is seen to be the particular solution we seek (this is clear by inspection).

Accordingly, the general solution of (5.7) is

$$t + c_1 \sin t + c_2 \cos t,$$

and, consequently, the general solution of (5.6) is

$$\log x + c_1 \sin \log x + c_2 \cos \log x.$$

EXERCISES

Find the general solution of the following differential equations.

1. $x^2y'' - 3xy' + 3y = 0.$

2. $x^2y'' - xy' + 2y = 0.$

3. $x^2y'' + 3xy' + 2y = 0.$

4. $x^2y'' - 2y = 0.$

5. $x^2y'' + 5xy' + 8y = 0.$

6. $x^2y'' - 3xy' + 3y = \log |x|.$

7. $x^2y'' - xy' + 2y = 1 + \log^2 |x|.$

8. $x^2y'' - 2xy' + 2y = \sin \log |x|.$

9. $x^3y''' - 3x^2y'' + 6xy' - 6y = 0.$

10. $4x^2y'' - 4xy' + 3y = 0.$

11. $4x^2y'' - 4xy' + 3y = \sin \log(-x) \qquad (x < 0).$

12. Show that the wronskian of the functions

$$x^a, \; x^b, \; x^c \qquad (x > 0)$$

is equal to $(a - b)(b - c)(c - a)x^{a+b+c-3}$. (Hence, the wronskian is never zero when the numbers a, b, and c are distinct.)

ANSWERS

1. $c_1x + c_2x^3.$

2. $x(c_1 \cos \log |x| + c_2 \sin \log |x|).$

3. $x^{-1}(c_1 \cos \log |x| + c_2 \sin \log |x|).$

4. $c_1x^{-1} + c_2x^2$.

5. $x^{-2}(c_1 \cos \log x^2 + c_2 \sin \log x^2)$.

6. $\frac{4}{9} + \frac{1}{3} \log |x| + c_1x + c_2x^3$.

7. $1 - \log |x| + \frac{1}{2} \log^2 |x| + x(c_1 \cos \log |x| + c_2 \sin \log |x|)$.

8. $\frac{1}{10} \sin \log |x| + \frac{3}{10} \cos \log |x| + c_1x + c_2x^2$.

9. $c_1x + c_2x^2 + c_3x^3$.

10. $c_1|x|^{1/2} + c_2|x|^{3/2}$.

11. $\frac{1}{65} \sin \log (-x) - \frac{8}{65} \cos \log (-x) + c_1(-x)^{1/2} + c_2(-x)^{3/2}$.

6 The Laplace Transform

In recent years the use of the Laplace transform in solving special types of differential equations has come into vogue. The Laplace transform is of considerable interest in itself to mathematicians,* and it can be useful in solving certain differential equations, as we shall see. It is, however, of limited importance in the *theory* of differential equations.

The Laplace transform $L[f(x)]$ of a function $f(x)$ is defined by the equation

$$L[f(x)] = \int_0^\infty e^{-px} f(x)\, dx. \tag{6.1}$$

It is clear that $L[f(x)]$ will exist only if $f(x)$ is a function such that the improper integral in (6.1) exists. When it exists, the Laplace transform is a function $F(p)$.

Let us compute a few transform $L[f]$ of simple functions $f(x)$:

$$f(x) = 1, \qquad L[f] = \int_0^\infty e^{-px} 1\, dx = \frac{1}{p} \qquad (p > 0);$$

$$f(x) = x, \qquad L[f] = \int_0^\infty e^{-px} x\, dx = \frac{1}{p^2} \qquad (p > 0);$$

* See, for example, D. V. Widder, *The Laplace Transform*, Princeton University Press, Princeton (1941).

$$f(x) = \sin ax, \qquad L[f] = \int_0^\infty e^{-px} \sin ax \, dx = \frac{a}{p^2 + a^2} \qquad (p > 0);$$

$$f(x) = \cos ax, \qquad L[f] = \int_0^\infty e^{-px} \cos ax \, dx = \frac{p}{p^2 + a^2} \qquad (p > 0);$$

$$f(x) = e^{ax}, \qquad L[f] = \int_0^\infty e^{-px} e^{ax} \, dx = \frac{1}{p - a} \qquad (p > a).$$

The foregoing results are readily obtained; the first and last are immediate, and the others may be calculated using integration by parts.

Next, we compute $L[x^n]$, where n is a positive integer. We have

$$\begin{aligned} L[x^n] &= -\left.\frac{x^n e^{-px}}{p}\right|_0^\infty + \frac{n}{p}\int_0^\infty e^{-px} x^{n-1} \, dx \\ &= \frac{n}{p} L[x^{n-1}]. \end{aligned}$$

If $n > 1$, it follows that

$$L[x^n] = \frac{n(n-1)}{p^2} L[x^{n-2}],$$

and, accordingly, that

$$\begin{aligned} L[x^n] &= \frac{n!}{p^n} L[1] \\ &= \frac{n!}{p^{n+1}} \qquad (p > 0). \end{aligned} \tag{6.2}$$

It follows from the definition of the Laplace transform that if c_1 and c_2 are constants, and if $L[f_1]$ and $L[f_2]$ exist, then

$$L[c_1 f_1(x) + c_2 f_2(x)] = c_1 L[f_1(x)] + c_2 L[f_2(x)];$$

that is to say, the Laplace transform is a *linear operator*. Thus, if k is any constant,

$$L[k] = kL[1] = \frac{k}{p} \qquad (p > 0),$$

and

$$L[kx^n] = kL[x^n] = \frac{kn!}{p^{n+1}} \qquad (p > 0, n \text{ a positive integer}).$$

Similarly,

$$L[3x + 2] = 3L[x] + 2L[1]$$

$$= \frac{3}{p^2} + \frac{2}{p} \qquad (p > 0).$$

EXERCISES

1. Use the formulas derived in the text to compute the following Laplace transforms:

(a) $L[3]$;

(b) $L[\pi]$;

(c) $L[2x - 1]$;

(d) $L[ax^2 + bx + c]$, a, b, and c constants;

(e) $L[x - \sin x]$;

(f) $L[3e^x + \cos 2x]$.

2. Find functions whose Laplace transforms are the following:

(a) $\frac{7}{p^2}$;

(b) $\frac{60}{p^5}$;

(c) $\frac{1}{p^8}$;

(d) $\frac{1}{p^3} + \frac{1}{p^2 + 1}$;

(e) $\frac{1}{p(p^2 + 1)}$;

(f) $\frac{2}{p(p - 1)}$.

ANSWERS

1. (a) $\frac{3}{p} \quad (p > 0)$; (d) $\frac{2a}{p^3} + \frac{b}{p^2} + \frac{c}{p} \quad (p > 0)$;

(e) $\frac{1}{p^2} - \frac{1}{p^2 + 1} \quad (p > 0)$.

2. (a) $7x$; (c) $\frac{x^7}{7!}$; (e) $x - \cos x$.

7 Some Supporting Theory

Before using the Laplace transform to solve types of linear differential equations, we shall note conditions sufficient for the existence of this transform.

Theorem 7.1. *If for x sufficiently large*

$$|f(x)| < Me^{ax}, \tag{7.1}$$

where M and a are constants, $f(x)$ has a Laplace transform; that is, the integral

$$\int_0^\infty e^{-px} f(x)\, dx \tag{7.2}$$

exists if p is sufficiently large.

To prove the theorem we borrow a result from the theory of improper integrals which the student will recognize as an analogue of a theorem in the theory of infinite series. First, we require a definition.

If the integrals

$$\int_0^\infty f(x)\, dx, \tag{7.3}$$

and

$$\int_0^\infty |f(x)|\, dx$$

exist, the integral (7.3) is said to *converge absolutely.*

Lemma. If there exists a positive function $g(x)$ such that $|f(x)| \leq g(x)$ and if $\int_0^\infty g(x)\, dx$ converges, the integral $\int_0^\infty f(x)\, dx$ converges absolutely (hence converges).

Theorem 7.1 is now readily proved. We have

$$|e^{-px} f(x)| = e^{-px} |f(x)| < Me^{-(p-a)x}.$$

Since, for $p > a$, the integral

$$\int_0^\infty Me^{-(p-a)x}\,dx$$

converges, the integral (7.2) converges absolutely for $p > a$.

The proof is complete.

A function $f(x)$ which satisfies (7.1) is said to be of *exponential order*.

The functions x^n, e^{3x}, and $\sin 10x$ are examples of functions of exponential order. They possess Laplace transforms. The function

$$e^{x^2},$$

however, is an example of a function which increases too rapidly to possess a Laplace transform. It is not of exponential order.

We note the following result.

Theorem 7.2. *If*

$$\int_0^\infty e^{-px}f(x)\,dx$$

converges absolutely for $p = p_0$, *it converges absolutely for each* $p > p_0$.

It is given that

$$\int_0^\infty e^{-p_0x}|f(x)|\,dx$$

converges. Since

$$|e^{-px}f(x)| < e^{-p_0x}|f(x)| \qquad (p > p_0),$$

Theorem 7.2 follows from the lemma.

We state the following theorem.

Theorem 7.3. *If $f(x)$ and $g(x)$ are of exponential order and if*

$$L[f(x)] = L[g(x)],$$

then

$$f(x) = g(x)$$

at each point where both functions are continuous.

The proof of this theorem is omitted.

As an example of the application of the last theorem recall that

$$L[x] = \frac{1}{p^2};$$

accordingly, if it is given that the transform of a function $f(x)$ is $\frac{1}{p^2}$, then $f(x)$ must be the function x, at least if $f(x)$ is continuous and of exponential order. Similarly, if it is assumed that $f(x)$ is continuous and of exponential order, and if

$$L[f(x)] = \frac{p}{p^2 + 1},$$

then $f(x) = \cos x$.

Not every function $f(p)$ can be a Laplace transform, for it follows from (6.1) that if $f(x)$ is of exponential order,

$$\lim_{p \to \infty} F(p) = 0.$$

EXERCISE

Compute $L[f(x)]$, where $f(x)$ is the largest integer $\leq x$ $(0 \leq x < \infty)$. Graph the function.

Answer. $1/[p(e^p - 1)]$.

8 Applying the Transform

In order to apply the Laplace transform we shall need formulas for the transform of a derivative. Proceeding formally we have

$$L[y'] = \int_0^\infty e^{-px} y' \, dx,$$

and, after an integration by parts,

$$L[y'] = ye^{-px}\Big|_0^\infty + p \int_0^\infty e^{-px} y \, dx$$

$$= ye^{-px}\Big|_0^\infty + pL[y].$$

If y is of exponential type, $ye^{-px} \to 0$, as $x \to \infty$, and

$$L[y'] = pL[y] - y(0).$$

Similarly,

$$L[y''] = y'e^{-px}\Big|_0^\infty + pL[y'],$$

and if $y'e^{-px} \to 0$, as $x \to \infty$,

$$\begin{aligned} L[y''] &= -y'(0) + p\{-y(0) + pL[y]\} \\ &= p^2L[y] - [y'(0) + py(0)]. \end{aligned}$$

An induction leads to the formula

(8.1)

$$L[y^{(n)}] = p^nL[y] - [y^{(n-1)}(0) + py^{(n-2)}(0) + \cdots + p^{n-1}y(0)].$$

It can be shown that formula (8.1) is valid for solutions of differential equations of the form

$$a_0y^{(n)} + a_1y^{(n-1)} + \cdots + a_{n-1}y' + a_ny = f(x),$$

where $a_0, a_1, \ldots, a_n$ are constants and $f(x)$ is of exponential order.

Consider now the differential system

$$\begin{aligned} &y'' + y = x, \\ &y(0) = 0, \qquad y'(0) = 2. \end{aligned} \tag{8.2}$$

Suppose there is a solution $y(x)$ to which the foregoing analysis applies. Then

$$y''(x) + y(x) \equiv x,$$

and the Laplace transforms of each side of this identity must be equal; that is,

$$L[y''] + L[y] = L[x].$$

We have

$$\{p^2L[y] - py(0) - y'(0)\} + L[y] = \frac{1}{p^2} \qquad (p > 0),$$

or

$$(p^2 + 1)L[y] = 2 + \frac{1}{p^2}.$$

Thus,

$$L[y] = \frac{2p^2 + 1}{p^2(p^2 + 1)}. \tag{8.3}$$

Our problem will be solved (according to Theorem 7.3) if we can determine a function $y(x)$ the Laplace transform of which is given by the right-hand member of (8.3). How shall such a function be found? A table of Laplace transforms is a necessity* but, as is the case with integral tables, one cannot expect to find *every* function listed. That in (8.3), in particular, is not likely to be found in such a table. However, writing the right-hand member of (8.3) in terms of partial fractions will be helpful. We have

$$L[y] = \frac{1}{p^2} + \frac{1}{p^2 + 1}.$$

A reference to the transforms in Section 6 indicates that

$$\begin{aligned} L[y] &= L[x] + L[\sin x], \\ &= L[x + \sin x], \end{aligned}$$

and, by Theorem 7.3,

$$y = x + \sin x$$

—the solution we seek.

The student will observe that this result is correct, since the general solution of (8.2) is quickly seen to be

$$y = x + c_1 \sin x + c_2 \cos x.$$

The conditions $y(0) = 0$, $y'(0) = 2$ imply at once that $c_1 = 1$, $c_2 = 0$.

EXERCISES

Use the method of Laplace transforms to solve the following

* There are tables of Laplace transforms to which the student may refer. See, for example, *Standard Mathematical Tables*, Chemical Rubber Publishing Co., Cleveland (1957).

differential systems. Check your answer in each case by solving the problem by the earlier methods of this chapter.

1. $y'' - y = 1 + x,$
$y(0) = 3,$
$y'(0) = 0.$

2. $y'' + y = 2,$
$y(0) = 1,$
$y'(0) = 0.$

3. $y'' - y' - 2y = \sin x,$
$y(0) = 4,$
$y'(0) = 1.$

4. $y'' - 3y' + 2y = 2 \cos x,$
$y(0) = 1,$
$y'(0) = 1.$

5. $y''' + 4y'' + 3y' = 8e^x,$
$y(0) = 4,$
$y'(0) = -3,$
$y''(0) = 11.$

6. Find the Laplace transforms of the following functions:

(a) xe^x, x^2, x^2e^x;
(b) $e^x \sin x$, $e^x \cos x$.

7. Verify formally that if

$$L[f(x)] = F(p) = \int_0^\infty e^{-px} f(x)\, dx,$$

then

$$F^{(n)}(p) = (-1)^n \int_0^\infty e^{-px} x^n f(x)\, dx = (-1)^n L[x^n f(x)].$$

ANSWERS

6. (a) $1/(p-1)^2 \quad (p > 1)$, $2/p^3 \quad (p > 0)$, $2/(p-1)^3 \quad (p > 1)$;
(b) $1/(p^2 - 2p + 2)$, $(p-1)/(p^2 - 2p + 2)$.

3

Applications to Mechanics

1 Newton's Laws of Motion

Differential equations had their beginnings in mechanics, and some of the most interesting applications of the theory of differential equations are still to be found in this area of applied mathematics. In this chapter we shall examine simpler, general mechanical situations that can be described by differential equations and whose behavior can be better understood by analyzing the solutions of these differential equations.

We begin with a statement of Newton's laws of motion:

1. *A particle at rest remains at rest, and a particle in motion moves in a straight line with constant velocity unless acted upon by some external force.*

2. *The time rate of change of momentum of a particle is proportional to the resultant of the external forces acting upon the particle.*

3. *Action and reaction are two forces which are equal in magnitude and opposite in sense along the same line of action.*

The second law of motion leads immediately to a differential equation. The momentum of a particle is defined as the product mv, where m is its mass and v its velocity. If f denotes the resultant force acting on the particle, Newton's second law states that

$$\frac{d}{dt}(mv) = gf, \tag{1.1}$$

where g is a constant of proportionality. If the mass is constant, this equation becomes

$$(1.2) \qquad m\frac{dv}{dt} = gf.$$

The quantity $\frac{dv}{dt}$ is, of course, the acceleration of the particle. Thus, if the mass of the particle remains constant, the second law states that the product of mass by acceleration is proportional to the applied force.

The value of the constant g depends upon the units employed. In this chapter we shall, in general, use *English* units (mass in pounds, time in seconds, distance in feet, and force in pounds), and g will have the value of approximately 32.

Example. A particle of mass m is projected with initial velocity v_0 down a frictionless inclined plane whose angle with the horizontal is θ $\left(0 < \theta < \frac{\pi}{2}\right)$ (Fig. 3.1). Study the motion of the particle.

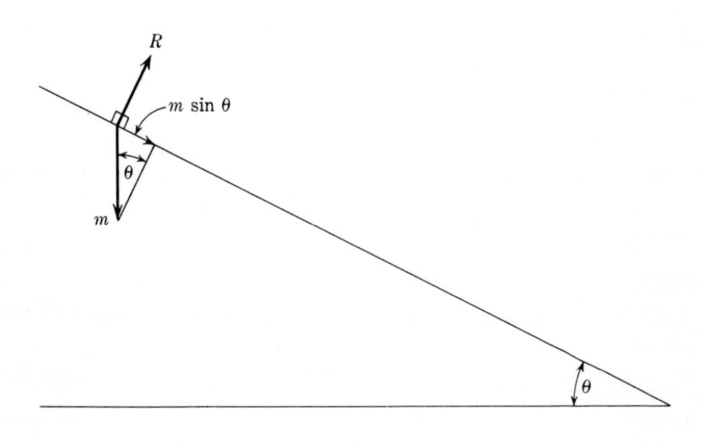

FIG. 3.1

We shall suppose that the only forces acting upon the body are the force of gravity acting vertically (that is, the weight of the particle) and the reaction R of the plane (the line of action of which is perpendicular to the plane). The weight is numerically equal to the mass, so the vertical force is m pounds. The component of this force along the plane is $m \sin \theta$. Since the component of R parallel to the plane is zero, by Newton's second law we have

$$m \frac{dv}{dt} = gm \sin \theta,$$

or

$$\frac{dv}{dt} = g \sin \theta. \tag{1.3}$$

Since $g \sin \theta$ is constant, it follows that

$$v = (g \sin \theta)t + c_1,$$

where c_1 is a constant which may be determined from the condition that $v = v_0$ when $t = 0$ (since the initial velocity was given as v_0). Thus, if s is the distance of the particle at time t measured from its initial position down the inclined plane,

$$v = \frac{ds}{dt} = (g \sin \theta)t + v_0, \tag{1.4}$$

and

$$s = \tfrac{1}{2}(g \sin \theta)t^2 + v_0 t + c_2.$$

Since we have supposed that $s = 0$ when $t = 0$, it follows that the constant of integration c_2 has the value zero.

The motion of the particle is then completely described by the equation

$$s = \tfrac{1}{2}(g \sin \theta)t^2 + v_0 t. \tag{1.5}$$

Note that equation (1.4) is immediately obtainable from (1.5) by differentiation.

If, for example, $\theta = \frac{\pi}{6}$ and $v_0 = 10$ ft./sec., then $g = 32$, and

$$s = 8t^2 + 10t.$$

After, say, 3 sec. the particle has moved down the plane a distance of 102 ft. from its starting point, and its velocity at this instant is 58 ft./sec.

If the particle were sliding with a coefficient of friction μ, the differential equation of motion would become

$$m\frac{dv}{dt} = g(m \sin\theta - \mu m \cos\theta), \tag{1.6}$$

since the resultant force acting upon the particle along its path would be $m \sin\theta$ (the component of its weight along its path) minus $\mu m \cos\theta$ (by definition, the force of friction acting to retard the motion of the particle along its path). The conditions the solution of (1.6) must satisfy would again be

$$(1.6)' \qquad \begin{aligned} t &= 0, \quad s = 0, \\ t &= 0, \quad v = v_0. \end{aligned}$$

Conditions such as (1.6)′ which must be satisfied by a solution of a differential equation are commonly called *boundary* or *side* conditions. When the differential equation is combined with its side conditions, the result is frequently called a *differential system.* Thus, equations (1.6) and (1.6)′ lead to the differential system

$$(1.7) \qquad \begin{aligned} &\frac{dv}{dt} = g(\sin\theta - \mu\cos\theta), \\ &t = 0, \quad s = 0, \\ &t = 0, \quad v = v_0. \end{aligned}$$

We readily obtain

$$s = \tfrac{1}{2}g(\sin\theta - \mu\cos\theta)t^2 + v_0 t \tag{1.8}$$

as the solution of (1.7). Equation (1.8) together with

$$v = \frac{ds}{dt} = g(\sin\theta - \mu\cos\theta)t + v_0$$

enable us to describe the position and the velocity of the particle at time t.

Critique. More precisely, when $\mu \neq 0$, two cases arise in the preceding example: (1) $\mu \leq \tan\theta$, and (2) $\mu > \tan\theta$. In case (1) the solution as given applies without modification. In case (2) it is clear that unless the particle is given an initial velocity there will be no motion.

Example. At a point 96 ft. above the ground a ball of mass m is thrown upward with an initial speed of 16 ft./sec. Assuming that the only force acting is that of gravity, find how long it will take the ball to reach the ground and the velocity with which it strikes the ground.

Let us suppose the motion of the ball is along an axis y, distance being measured in a positive sense from the ground to the ball (see Fig. 3.2). Then velocity in an upward direction will have

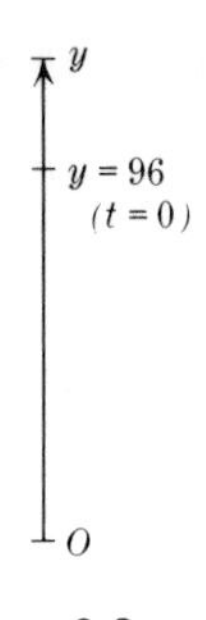

FIG. 3.2

positive values and velocity toward the ground will have negative values.

Since the only force acting upon the ball is the weight m pounds, we have as the differential equation of motion

$$m\frac{dv}{dt} = -gm, \tag{1.9}$$

or

$$\frac{dv}{dt} = -32. \tag{1.9$'$}$$

Note the minus sign in (1.9) and in (1.9)′. This appears because the force is acting downward, and hence tends to decrease v algebraically.

We must solve the differential system

$$\frac{dv}{dt} = -32,$$

$$t = 0, \quad \frac{dy}{dt} = 16,$$

$$t = 0, \quad y = 96.$$

It is readily seen that

$$v = -32t + 16, \tag{1.10}$$

and

$$y = -16t^2 + 16t + 96.$$

The ball will strike the ground when $y = 0$; that is, when

$$-16t^2 + 16t + 96 = 0,$$

or when $t = 3$ or $t = -2$. Since the value $t = -2$ has no meaning in this problem, we conclude that the ball hits the ground in 3 sec. Substituting this value in (1.10) we see that the corresponding velocity is -80 ft./sec. The answer states that the ball is traveling at a speed of 80 ft./sec., when $t = 3$ sec., and the minus sign indicates that its direction of motion at that instant is downward.

If in this example the ball had been thrown *downward* initially at a speed of 16 ft./sec., the differential system to be solved would have been

$$\frac{dv}{dt} = -32,$$

$$t = 0, \quad \frac{dy}{dt} = -16,$$

$$t = 0, \quad y = 96.$$

Example. A particle of mass m leaves the earth with initial velocity v_0 in a direction that makes an angle α with the horizontal.

Study the particle's motion, neglecting all forces except that of gravity.

It is convenient to apply Newton's second law to the components of motion as follows. The only force acting is that of gravity, which acts in a vertical direction; consequently, we have (see Fig. 3.3)

$$m\frac{d^2y}{dt^2} = -gm, \qquad m\frac{d^2x}{dt^2} = g\cdot 0,$$

$$t = 0, \quad \frac{dy}{dt} = v_0 \sin\alpha, \qquad t = 0, \quad \frac{dx}{dt} = v_0 \cos\alpha,$$

$$t = 0, \quad y = 0; \qquad t = 0, \quad x = 0.$$

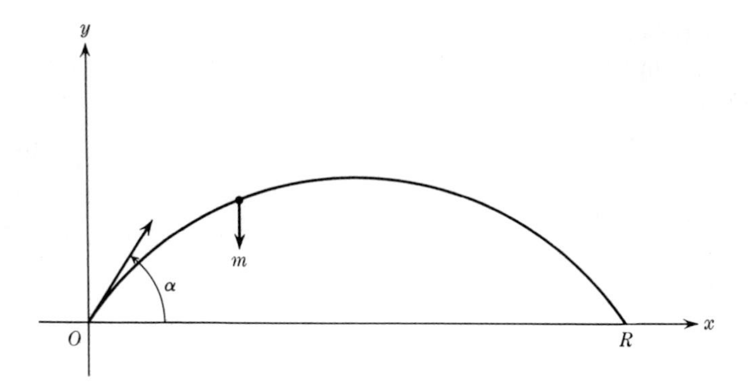

FIG. 3.3

It is easy to see, successively, that

$$\frac{dy}{dt} = -gt + v_0 \sin\alpha, \qquad \frac{dx}{dt} = v_0 \cos\alpha, \tag{1.11}$$

and

$$y = -\tfrac{1}{2}gt^2 + (v_0 \sin\alpha)t, \qquad x = (v_0 \cos\alpha)t. \tag{1.12}$$

Thus, equations (1.12) furnish the position of the particle at time t, and equations (1.11) provide components of its velocity at that instant.

EXERCISES

In the first six exercises set up the differential equations of motion of the given particles. Solve these equations, determining the constants of integration by use of suitable boundary conditions.

1. A ball is thrown downward from a balloon 960 ft. above the earth. The initial speed of the ball is 256 ft./sec. When and with what velocity will the ball strike the earth? (Neglect all forces except that of gravity.)

2. Answer the same question and assume the same conditions given in Exercise 1, except that the ball is thrown upward with an initial speed of 256 ft./sec.

3. A ball leaves the earth at an angle of $\frac{\pi}{6}$ and an initial speed of 30 ft./sec. When will it strike the ground? What will be its speed in its path at the instant of impact? How far will it then be from its starting point?

4. The coefficient of friction of a plane making an angle of $\frac{\pi}{4}$ with the horizontal is $\mu = 0.15$. A block is projected down the plane with an initial speed of 20 ft./sec. How far will the block have moved from its starting point after 4 sec.? At what velocity will it be traveling?

5. A block is initially projected up the plane of Exercise 4, at a speed of 30 ft./sec. Where will it be at the end of 1 sec.? What will be its velocity? Where will it be at the end of 3 sec.? What will its velocity be then? (Assume that the coefficient of "starting" friction is also $\mu = 0.15$.)

6. A particle initially of mass m_0 is projected upward from the surface of the earth with an initial speed of 32 ft./sec. It loses mass at the rate of $\frac{1}{2}m$ lb./sec., where m is the mass at time t. When and with what velocity will the particle strike the earth? (Assume that the only force acting is that of gravity and that Newton's second law of motion applies as stated.)

Note. It will be helpful to employ some sort of approximate method in solving for the time of impact.

7. Show that the path of the particle in the last example in the text (page 70) is a parabola. Find the range OR. What value of α makes the range a maximum?

8. In the same example suppose same the sun is directly overhead. Discuss the motion of the shadow of the particle on the ground.

9. Suppose the motion in the same example is projected onto the y-axis, the projection being parallel to the x-axis. Discuss the motion of the projected particle along the y-axis.

10. A sled has an initial velocity of 30 mi./hr. on a level ice field. It comes to rest in 20 min. What is the coefficient of friction between the sled and the ice?

11. A body slides down an inclined plane without friction. Just as it starts to slide, a particle is dislodged from the plane and falls freely to the earth. Show that on reaching the earth both objects have attained the same speed.

12. Study the motion of a particle on a plane which makes an angle of $\pi/6$ with the horizontal when $\mu = 0.6$ and the initial speed is (a) 10 ft./sec. up the plane and (b) 10 ft./sec. down the plane.

ANSWERS

1. 3.14 sec.; -356.5 ft./sec.

2. 19.14 sec.; -356.5 ft./sec.

3. 0.94 sec.; 30 ft./sec.; 24.42 ft.

4. -233.84 ft.; -96.92 ft./sec.

5. 17.0 ft.; 4 ft./sec.; -15.6 ft.; -35.6 ft./sec.

6. 2.51 sec.; -48.32 ft./sec.

7. $(v_0^2 \sin 2\alpha)/g$; $\pi/4$.

10. 0.0011.

2 Gravitational Attraction

Newton's celebrated law of gravitation asserts that *every particle of matter in the universe attracts every other particle, with a force whose direction is that of the line joining the two, and whose* *magnitude is directly as the product of their masses, and inversely as the square of their distance from each other.**

Example. Study the motion of a particle falling to the earth from a great distance. Neglect all forces except the gravitational force between the two bodies.

Let the mass of the particle be m and that of the earth (assumed to be a homogeneous sphere) be M. Then the force acting upon the particle is given by

$$f = \frac{kmM}{r^2},$$

where r is the distance of the particle from the center of the earth† and k is a constant of proportionality. When $r = R$, the radius of the earth, f is the weight m of the particle at the earth's surface. Thus, $k = \frac{R^2}{M}$, and

$$f = \frac{mR^2}{r^2} \text{ lb.}$$

Newton's second law of motion may now be invoked, and we have as the differential equation of motion of the particle

$$m\frac{d^2r}{dt^2} = -gm\frac{R^2}{r^2},$$

or

$$\frac{d^2r}{dt^2} = -g\frac{R^2}{r^2}. \tag{2.1}$$

We multiply both members of equation (2.1) by $2\frac{dr}{dt}$, and a quadrature yields at once

$$\left(\frac{dr}{dt}\right)^2 = \frac{2gR^2}{r} + c_1. \tag{2.2}$$

* This statement of the law is taken from O. D. Kellogg, *Foundations of Potential Theory*, Springer-Verlag (1929). Kellogg credits Thomson and Tait, *A Treatise on Natural Philosophy*, Cambridge University Press, New York (1912), with this formulation.

† It may be shown that it is a correct extension of the law of gravitation in this situation to treat the mass of the earth as though it were concentrated at the center (see Kellogg, *op. cit.*).

Let us set $r = r_0$ and $\frac{dr}{dt} = 0$ when $t = 0$. Then

$$c_1 = -\frac{2gR^2}{r_0},$$

and (2.2) becomes

$$\left(\frac{dr}{dt}\right)^2 = 2gR^2\left(\frac{1}{r} - \frac{1}{r_0}\right). \tag{2.3}$$

Thus, the velocity v_R of the particle at the earth's surface is given by

$$v_R^2 = 2gR^2\left(\frac{1}{R} - \frac{1}{r_0}\right). \tag{2.4}$$

If r_0 is very large, v_R is approximately $\sqrt{2gR}$, which is about 7 mi./sec.

Equation (2.3) leads at once to

$$\frac{dr}{dt} = -\sqrt{\frac{2gR^2}{r_0}}\,\frac{\sqrt{r_0 r - r^2}}{r}. \tag{2.5}$$

The minus sign is employed since r decreases as t increases. The variables are separable in equation (2.5), and we have at once

$$\frac{r\,dr}{\sqrt{r_0 r - r^2}} + \sqrt{\frac{2gR^2}{r_0}}\,dt = 0 \qquad (0 < r < r_0). \tag{2.6}$$

An integration yields

$$t = \sqrt{\frac{r_0}{2gR^2}}\left(\sqrt{r_0 r - r^2} - \frac{r_0}{2}\sin^{-1}\frac{2r - r_0}{r_0}\right) + c_1.$$

Since, as $r \to r_0$, $t \to 0$, we must have $c_1 = \sqrt{\frac{r_0}{2gR^2}}\,\frac{\pi r_0}{4}$, and finally

$$t = \sqrt{\frac{r_0}{2gR^2}}\left(\sqrt{r_0 r - r^2} - \frac{r_0}{2}\sin^{-1}\frac{2r - r_0}{r_0} + \frac{\pi r_0}{4}\right).$$

The time required for the particle to fall to the earth's surface is

$$t = \sqrt{\frac{r_0}{2gR^2}}\left(\sqrt{r_0 R - R^2} - \frac{r_0}{2}\sin^{-1}\frac{2R - r_0}{r_0} + \frac{\pi r_0}{4}\right).$$

The student will recall that if t is measured in seconds and r and r_0 in feet, then $g = 32$.

EXERCISES

1. Show that the velocity of escape from the earth's gravitational field is $\sqrt{2gR}$, or about 7 mi./sec. (This result neglects air resistance.)

2. It can be shown that if a hole is bored through the center of the earth, the attraction on a particle in the resulting tunnel is proportional to the distance of the particle from the center of the earth. (Air resistance is neglected.) A stone is dropped into the tunnel. Discuss its motion.

3. Two solid homogeneous lead spheres of diameter 1 ft. are placed with their surfaces $\frac{1}{2}$ in. apart. Neglecting all forces except their mutual gravitational attraction, find how long it will take for their surfaces to come together. Assume that the spheres attract each other as though their masses were concentrated at their centers (assume average density of the earth to be half that of lead).

4. Show that the differential equation of motion of a simple pendulum bob is $\dfrac{md^2s}{dt^2} = -mg \sin \theta$. Note that $s = l\theta$, and thus obtain the

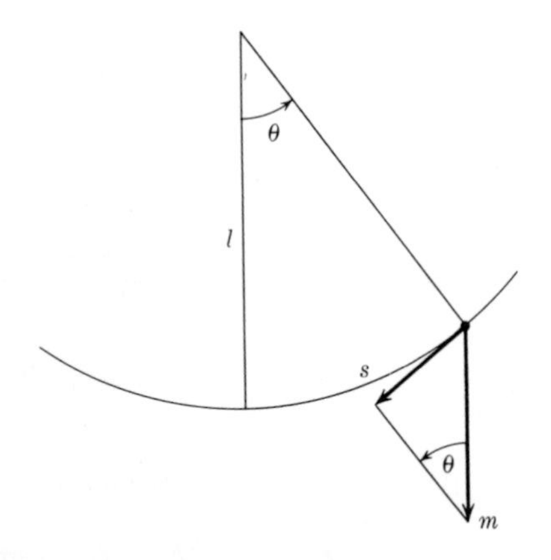

FIG. 3.4

differential equation

$$\frac{d^2\theta}{dt^2} + \frac{g}{l} \sin \theta = 0.$$

Discuss the motion when $\sin \theta$ above is supplied by θ (a good approximation when $|\theta|$ is small).

ANSWER

3. $5\frac{1}{2}$ min.

3 Simple Harmonic Motion

If a particle moves along the x-axis according to the law

$$m \frac{d^2x}{dt^2} = -kx, \tag{3.1}$$

where k is a positive constant, it is said to be in *simple harmonic motion* in its path. Equation (3.1) may be written in the form

$$\frac{d^2x}{dt^2} + a^2x = 0 \qquad (a^2 > 0). \tag{3.2}$$

The general solution of (3.2) is seen to be

$$x = c_1 \sin at + c_2 \cos at,$$

the *period* of which is

$$T = \frac{2\pi}{a},$$

and the *amplitude* of which is $\sqrt{c_1^2 + c_2^2}$.

EXERCISES

1. A particle moves along the x-axis in simple harmonic motion, and it is known that at $t = 0$, $x = 0$ and $\frac{dx}{dt} = 1$. Given that the particle's period is 2π, discuss its motion.

2. Show that the particle in Exercise 2, Section 2 is in simple harmonic motion.

3. A point moves on the circumference of a circle at constant angular speed. Show that the vertical projection of the point on the x-axis is in simple harmonic motion.

4 The Vibrating Spring

In this section we study the motion of a body B which is fastened to the lower end of a vertical coiled spring, the upper end of which is rigidly secured (see Fig. 3.5). Let B be lowered carefully to the

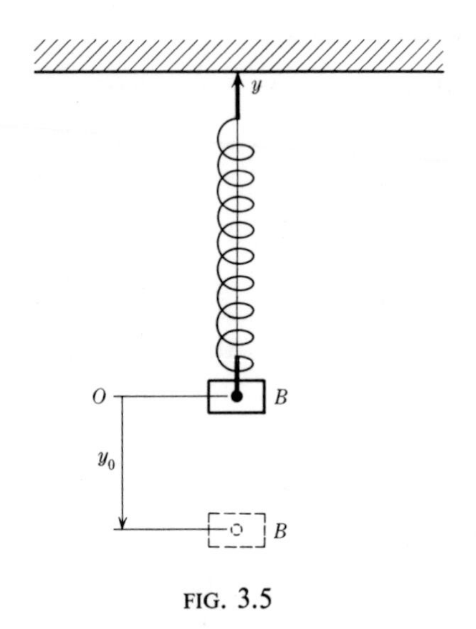

FIG. 3.5

point O of equilibrium, that is, the point at which it will remain at rest. Suppose B is given a small vertical displacement of y_0 ft. and released with an initial vertical velocity v_0. We shall suppose that the force exerted by the spring on B has the following properties:

1. It acts along a vertical line through the center of gravity of B and is directed from the position of B toward O, its point of equilibrium.

2. Its magnitude at any instant t is proportional to the difference $l - l_0$, where l is the length of the spring at time t and l_0 is its length when B is at the point of equilibrium.

The constant of proportionality in property 2 is known as the *spring constant*.

It is clear that if we neglect any other forces acting on B (such as air resistance) we may analyze the motion of B as follows. Since the motion of B occurs along a vertical line, we suppose that it takes place along a y-axis oriented as usual with its origin at O. Velocities and accelerations directed upward will be regarded as being of positive sign and those directed downward as being negative. As usual, we shall measure force in pounds, mass in pounds, distance in feet, and time in seconds. We then have as the differential system expressing the motion of B:

$$\text{(4.1)} \qquad m\frac{d^2y}{dt^2} = -g(ky),$$

$$t = 0, \qquad y = y_0, \qquad \frac{dy}{dt} = v_0,$$

where k is the spring constant and g is approximately 32.

Example. A spring is stretched 4 in. by a 6-lb. weight. Let a 16-lb. weight B be attached to the spring and released 3 in. below the point of equilibrium with an initial velocity of 2 ft./sec. directed downward. Describe the motion of B.

The first sentence in the statement of the problem enables us to determine the spring constant k. We have

$$f = k(l - l_0),$$

or

$$6 = k(\tfrac{1}{3}).$$

Thus, $k = 18$, and equations (4.1) become

$$\text{(4.1)}' \qquad \frac{d^2y}{dt^2} + 36y = 0,$$

$$t = 0, \qquad y = -\tfrac{1}{4}, \qquad \frac{dy}{dt} = -2.$$

It is readily seen that the solution of this system is

$$y = -\tfrac{1}{3}\sin 6t - \tfrac{1}{4}\cos 6t.$$

The amplitude of this motion is

$$\sqrt{\tfrac{1}{9} + \tfrac{1}{16}} = \tfrac{5}{12},$$

and its period is

$$T = \frac{2\pi}{6} = \frac{\pi}{3}.$$

EXERCISES

1. A spring is stretched 3 in. by an 8-lb. weight. Suppose a 4-lb. weight B is attached to the spring and released 6 in. below the point of equilibrium with an initial velocity of 3 ft./sec. directed downward. Study the motion of B.

2. Assume the same conditions given in Exercise 1, but with the point of release 4 in. above the point of equilibrium and an initial velocity of 2 ft./sec. directed downward. Study the motion of B.

3. Assume the same conditions given in Exercise 1, but with the point of release 6 in. above the point of equilibrium and an initial velocity of 0 ft./sec. Study the motion of B.

4. A spring is such that it would be stretched a ft. by a weight of b lb. Suppose a weight of c lb. is attached to the spring and released at a point h ft. above the point of equilibrium with an initial velocity of v_0 ft./sec. Describe the motion.

ANSWERS

1. $-\frac{1}{2}\cos 16t - \frac{3}{16}\sin 16t$.

2. $\frac{1}{3}\cos 16t - \frac{1}{8}\sin 16t$.

3. $\frac{1}{2}\cos 16t$.

4. $h\cos pt + (v_0/p)\sin pt,\ p = \sqrt{gb/ac}$.

5 Damped Vibrations

If account is taken of the fact that the vibration of the weight B on the spring discussed in the previous section usually occurs in a fluid, such as air or water or oil or molasses, it is realistic to recognize that the resistance of the fluid retards the motion of B.

In many instances it has been found that the retarding or *damping* forces may be approximated by a quantity proportional to the velocity and oppositely directed. The differential equation of motion then becomes

$$m\frac{d^2y}{dt^2} = g\left(-ky - c\frac{dy}{dt}\right), \tag{5.1}$$

where the positive constant c is an empirical constant determined by experiment.

Equation (5.1) may be written in the form

$$\frac{d^2y}{dt^2} + 2\alpha\frac{dy}{dt} + \beta^2 y = 0, \tag{5.1$'$}$$

where

$$2\alpha = \frac{cg}{m} > 0, \qquad \beta^2 = \frac{gk}{m}.$$

The indicial equation associated with equation (5.1)′ is

$$m^2 + 2\alpha m + \beta^2 = 0,$$

the roots of which are

$$m = -\alpha \pm \sqrt{\alpha^2 - \beta^2}.$$

We note that the solutions of (5.1)′ are oscillatory if and only if

$$\beta^2 > \alpha^2.$$

When $\beta^2 = \alpha^2$, the system is said to be *critically* damped.

EXERCISE

Find the value of c which would cause the motion of the spring of the example in Section 4 to be critically damped. Graph y as a function of t for this value of c. Draw the graphs also when c has half this value and when it has twice this value. *Ans.* $c = 6$.

6 Forced Vibrations

Frequently, in addition to the forces already considered in our study of the vibration of a spring, we may also have to deal with an *impressed* force acting vertically upon the weight B, such as might be induced by the vibration of the "rigid" support to which the spring is attached. If we suppose that such a force is a function of the time t, the differential equation of motion may be given the form

$$\frac{d^2y}{dt^2} + 2\alpha \frac{dy}{dt} + \beta^2 y = f(t). \tag{6.1}$$

The situation in which $f(t) = c_1 \sin \omega t + c_2 \cos \omega t$, where c_1, c_2, and ω are given constants, is of especial importance in practical applications.

EXERCISES

Solve the following differential systems. In each case sketch y as a function of t.

1. $\dfrac{d^2y}{dt^2} + 2\dfrac{dy}{dt} + y = \sin t, \qquad t = 0,\ y = 1,\ \dfrac{dy}{dt} = 2.$

2. $\dfrac{d^2y}{dt^2} + 2\dfrac{dy}{dt} + 2y = \cos t, \qquad t = 0,\ y = -1,\ \dfrac{dy}{dt} = -2.$

3. $\dfrac{d^2y}{dt^2} + 4y = -2 \sin 2t, \qquad t = 0,\ y = 0,\ \dfrac{dy}{dt} = 1.$

(The behavior of the amplitudes in the vibration characterized by this differential system is termed *resonance*.)

4

The Existence and Nature of Solutions

1 Preliminary Remarks

In preceding chapters we were able to find solutions of certain special differential equations. The methods employed were tailored to take advantage of the peculiarities of form exhibited by the differential equation being studied. We cannot go very far nor can we acquire more than superficial understanding simply by treating special cases. For example, the differential equation

$$(2x + y^2)\,dx + 2xy\,dy = 0$$

is readily seen to be exact, and it may be solved by methods familiar to us. A slight change in the coefficients yields the equation

$$(2x + y^2)\,dx + 3xy\,dy = 0, \tag{1.1}$$

which is no longer exact, and a different method must be sought. Perhaps we might be fortunate and find a simple integrating factor —and perhaps not.

We may ask, indeed, if there exists a solution of (1.1), and, if so, under what conditions. Are there general methods for finding it which do not involve special devices geared to the special peculiarities of form the equation possesses? Can we tell something about the behavior of a solution without solving the differential equation? In this chapter we begin our study of such questions.

Recall that there are algebraic equations which do not possess solutions. For example, the equation

$$\sqrt{x} = -1$$

has no real solution x, since the radical is by definition never negative. Similarly, it is easy to construct examples of differential equations which have no solution. There is no *real* function that satisfies the differential equation

$$y'^2 + y^2 + 1 = 0.$$

And other less obvious examples can be constructed.

Before we can discuss the existence of solutions of differential equations we shall need to define a solution with some care.

Definition. A solution of the n th-order differential equation

$$y^{(n)} = f[x, y, y', \ldots, y^{(n-1)}] \tag{1.2}$$

is a function $y(x)$ defined on an interval of the x-axis which satisfies the differential equation identically on the interval.

This definition implies that a solution is of at least class C^{n-1} on this interval.* Note that a solution is a function of x defined on an interval.

To illustrate the definition consider the first-order differential equation

$$y' = 2x + 1.$$

The function $x^2 + x$ is clearly a solution of this equation over every interval on the x-axis. So is the function $x^2 + x + c$, where c is any constant.

Again, the second-order differential equation

$$y'' + y = 0 \tag{1.3}$$

has the solution $\sin x$ on every interval of the x-axis. Another solution of this differential equation is $\cos x$. Indeed, every

* A function $f(x)$ which together with its first k derivatives is continuous on an interval is said to be of class C^k ($k = 0, 1, 2, \ldots$) on the interval.

function $c_1 \sin x + c_2 \cos x$, where c_1 and c_2 are constants, is a solution of this differential equation.

Finally, observe that the differential equation

$$y' = 2x + 1 \qquad (0 \leq x < 1)$$

has the solution $x^2 + x + c$ on the interval $0 \leq x < 1$. Note that the differential equation has been assigned no meaning outside this interval.

Close scrutiny of the following examples will enrich the student's knowledge of the nature of a solution. To understand what is *not* a solution is quite as important as understanding what *is* a solution.

Example. The differential equation

$$y' = 1 \tag{1.4}$$

has the solution $y = x - 1$ over every interval. It also has the solution $y = x + 1$. The function $y(x)$ defined on the interval $-1 \leq x \leq 1$ by the equations

$$\begin{aligned} y(x) &= x - 1 \qquad (-1 \leq x \leq 0), \\ &= x + 1 \qquad (0 < x \leq 1), \end{aligned}$$

however, is not a solution of (1.4) on the interval $(-1,1)$.

Example. Consider the differential equation

$$y'' = 0. \tag{1.5}$$

A solution on every interval is clearly the function $-x$. So, also, is $+x$. The function $y(x)$ defined on the interval $-1 \leq x \leq 1$ by the equations

$$\begin{aligned} y(x) &= -x \qquad (-1 \leq x < 0). \\ &= x \qquad (0 \leq x \leq 1), \end{aligned} \tag{1.6}$$

although continuous on this interval, is *not* a solution on this interval. For, since equation (1.5) is of second order, a solution on an interval must, by definition, be a function with a continuous derivative on that interval. Note that the curve $y = y(x)$ defined by equations (1.6) has a corner at $x = 0$. On the other hand, it is clear that $-x$ *is* a solution of (1.5) on the interval $(-1,0)$. Similarly, x *is* a solution of (1.5) on the interval $(0,1)$.

2 On the Use of Definite Integrals

Let us consider the following problem. Find a solution $y(x)$ of the differential equation

$$y' = e^x \tag{2.1}$$

such that $y(0) = 0$. A correct answer is

$$y(x) = \int_0^x e^x\,dx \qquad (-\infty < x < \infty), \tag{2.2}$$

or, since it does not matter what letter is used for the variable of integration,

$$y(x) = \int_0^x e^t\,dt \qquad (-\infty < x < \infty). \tag{2.3}$$

Our problem may be regarded as solved since it is clear from either (2.2) or (2.3) that $y'(x) = e^x$ and that $y(0) = 0$. Note that if a solution $y(x)$ of (2.1) were required which had the property that $y = 1$ when $x = 0$ [that is, $y(0) = 1$], a correct answer would be

$$y(x) = 1 + \int_0^x e^t\,dt. \tag{2.4}$$

It is fortunate, perhaps, but accidental that we may, if we choose, rewrite the solution (2.2) and (2.3) as

$$y(x) = e^x - 1. \tag{2.5}$$

A solution of the differential equation

$$y' = e^{x^2},$$

which has the property that $y = 0$ when $x = 0$, is, similarly,

$$y(x) = \int_0^x e^{t^2}\,dt \qquad (-\infty < x < \infty). \tag{2.6}$$

Equation (2.6) constitutes a complete and valid answer to our problem, even though we cannot carry out the indicated formal integration in the ordinary elementary sense. For further information concerning the nature of the function defined by equation (2.6) we might resort to one of various approximate methods—perhaps Simpson's rule, or power series expansions.

It should be emphasized, however, that any difficulties we may encounter in approximating to the integral in question affects not at all the validity of the answer (2.6). Indeed, even to evaluate the function $e^x - 1$ in (2.5) when $x = 2$, for example, leads us just as surely to approximate methods. Fortunately, the approximate values of e^x have been tabulated in a number of places, and so we feel a kind of relative familiarity with this function.

EXERCISES

Verify that the following differential equations have the indicated solutions. Where no interval is given the interval $-\infty < x < \infty$ is to be understood.

1. $y'' - y = 0, \qquad e^x.$

2. $y' = 1 + y^2, \qquad \tan x \quad \left(-\frac{\pi}{2} < x < \frac{\pi}{2}\right).$

3. $y'' - 3y' + 2y = 2, \qquad 1 + 3e^{2x}.$

4. $xy' - y = 0, \qquad cx$ (c constant).

5. $x^2y'' - 2xy' + 2y = 0, \qquad c_1x + c_2x^2$ (c_1, c_2 constants).

Determine constants a and b so that the differential equations in Exercises 6 and 7 have the given solutions.

6. $y'' + ay' + by = 0, \qquad e^x, e^{2x}.$

7. $x^2y'' + axy' + by = 0, \qquad x^2, x^3.$

8. Verify that $c_1 \sin ax + c_2 \cos ax$, where c_1, c_2, and a are constants, is a solution of the differential equation $y'' + a^2y = 0$ over every interval of the x-axis.

9. Is the function $\sin \frac{1}{x}$ a solution of the differential equation $x^2y'' + 2xy' + x^{-2}y = 0$ on the interval $0 < x < 7$? On the interval $-1 \le x \le 1$? Why?

10. Is the function $\frac{1}{x}$ a solution of the differential equation $xy' + y = 0$ on the interval $-1 \le x \le 1$? Why?

11. Show that a solution $y(x)$ of the equation $y' - 3xy = 0$, with the property that $y(1) = 1$, is $y(x) = e^{(3/2)(x^2-1)}$.

3 The Fundamental Existence Theorem

The proof of the fundamental existence theorem is given in Chapter 9. In this chapter we give statements of the theorem of a kind which can be readily understood by the student—an understanding well worth achieving. It is suggested that after a first reading of Theorem 3.1, for example, the student check the examples which follow it very carefully before reading the theorem a second time.

We shall first state a form of the theorem as it applies to a differential equation of first order.

Theorem 3.1. *Let $f(x,y)$ and $f_y(x,y)$ be continuous functions of the variables x and y in a region R of the xy-plane containing the point (x_0,y_0). If a constant h is taken positive and sufficiently small, there exists one and only one solution $y(x)$ of the differential equation*

$$y' = f(x,y) \tag{3.1}$$

on the interval $x_0 \le x \le x_0 + h$ with the property that $y(x_0) = y_0$.

The following examples will clarify the use of the theorem.

Example. Consider the differential system

$$y' = y \tag{3.2}$$

$$y(0) = 1. \tag{3.3}$$

That is, we seek a solution $y(x)$ of equation (3.2) which satisfies condition (3.3). In this example

$$f(x,y) = y,$$
$$f_y(x,y) = 1,$$

and this function $f(x,y)$ clearly satisfies the hypotheses of the theorem throughout the xy-plane. In particular, we may apply the theorem in any region containing the point (0,1). According to Theorem 3.1, there exists one and only one solution $y(x)$ of (3.2) satisfying (3.3). We note by inspection that e^x is a solution of (3.2). Further, it satisfies (3.3). Since there is only one such solution, according to Theorem 3.1, e^x is the solution we seek.

If the point had been (0,0), the unique solution through this point would have been the *null* solution $y(x) = 0$.

The following example illustrates what may happen when the hypotheses of the theorem do not hold. (See Fig. 4.1 on page 90.)

Example. Consider the differential equation

$$y' = -\frac{1}{x}y. \tag{3.4}$$

Here the hypotheses of the theorem fail to hold for the right-hand member of (3.4) along the line $x = 0$. Every solution of (3.4) has the form $y = \frac{c}{x}$, where c is a constant (see Fig. 4.1). Thus, all solutions except the null solution become infinite as x tends to zero. Note also that there is no solution through the point $(0,a)$ $(a \neq 0)$.* If $x_0 \neq 0$, the unique solution of (3.4) through the point (x_0,y_0) is seen to be

$$y(x) = x_0y_0x^{-1}.$$

A similar equation is the differential equation

$$y' = \frac{1}{x}y. \tag{3.5}$$

* By "solution through a point (x_0, y_0)" is meant a solution $y(x)$ with the property that the curve $y = y(x)$ passes through the point (x_0, y_0).

All solutions of this equation are of the form $y = cx$, where c is a constant. It will be seen that again no solution goes through the point $(0,a)$ $(a \neq 0)$, whereas all solutions pass through the origin. Through every point (x_0,y_0) $(x_0 \neq 0)$, however, there passes exactly one solution $y(x)$ of (3.5). This solution is $y(x) = x_0^{-1}y_0x$.

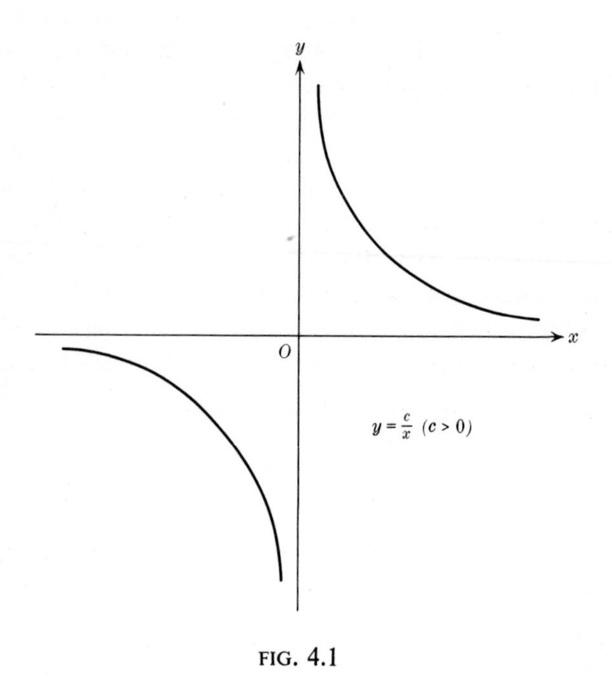

FIG. 4.1

Next, we state a form of the existence theorem as it applies to a differential equation of second order. The alterations necessary for the extension to differential equations of higher order will be clear.

Theorem 3.2. *Let $f(x,y,z)$, $f_y(x,y,z)$, and $f_z(x,y,z)$ be continuous functions of the variables x, y, z in some three-dimensional region R containing the point (x_0,y_0,z_0). If h is taken positive and sufficiently small, there exists one and only one solution $y(x)$ of the differential equation*

$$y'' = f(x\ y,y')$$

on the interval $x_0 \leq x \leq x_0 + h$ *such that* $y(x_0) = y_0$ *and* $y'(x_0) = z_0$.

The following examples will illustrate Theorem 3.2.

Example. Consider the differential system

$$y'' + y = 0,$$
$$y(0) = 0,$$
$$y'(0) = 2.$$

In this case, $f(x,y,z) = -y$, and the point (x_0,y_0,z_0) is the point (0,0,2). Since $f_y(x,y,z) = -1$, and $f_z(x,y,z) = 0$, the conditions of Theorem 3.2 are satisfied for all points (x,y,z). Note that $2 \sin x$ is a solution of the differential system. According to the fundamental existence theorem (Theorem 3.2), there is only one solution having this property; therefore, the solution we seek is $2 \sin x$.

Example. Consider the differential system

$$\begin{aligned} y'' + 2xy' + x^{-2}y &= 0, \\ y(1) &= 0, \\ y'(1) &= 0. \end{aligned} \tag{3.6}$$

In this case $f(x,y,z)$ is the function $-2xz - x^{-2}y$, for $f(x,y,y')$ then becomes $-2xy' - x^{-2}y$. Here,

$$f_y(x,y,z) = -x^{-2}, \qquad f_z = -2x,$$

and so the conditions of Theorem 3.2 are met in any region in which $x \neq 0$. From (3.6) we observe that the point (x_0,y_0,z_0) of the theorem is, in this instance, (1,0,0), and Theorem 3.2 guarantees a unique solution of the system (3.6). Note that $y(x) \equiv 0$, is, first, a solution of the differential equation (obvious by inspection) and, second, a solution such that $y(1) = 0$ and $y'(1) = 0$. According to Theorem 3.2 there is only one solution having this property. Hence, the solution we seek is identically zero.

Note. In the case of *linear* differential equations

$$y^{(n)} + a_1(x)y^{(n-1)} + \cdots + a_{n-1}(x)y' + a_n(x)y = f(x),$$

where $a_1(x), a_2(x), \ldots, a_n(x)$, and $f(x)$ are continuous on an interval $a \leq x \leq b$, it may be shown that the solution guaranteed by the fundamental existence theorem is defined over the entire interval $a \leq x \leq b$.

EXERCISES

1. Given the differential equation

$$y'' + a(x)y' + b(x)y = 0,$$

where $a(x)$ and $b(x)$ are continuous on the interval $a \leq x \leq b$, what can be said of a solution $y(x)$ whose graph $y = y(x)$ is tangent to the x-axis at a point of the interval?

2. Given the differential system

$$y' = 1 + y^2,$$
$$y(0) = 0,$$

show that it possesses a solution on the interval $0 \leq x < \frac{\pi}{2}$, but not on any interval $0 \leq x \leq h$, where $h \geq \frac{\pi}{2}$. (*Hint.* Guess the unique solution of the system.)

3. Given that every solution of the differential equation $y'' + y = 0$ can be written in the form $c_1 \sin x + c_2 \cos x$, where c_1 and c_2 are constants, decide whether or not there exist solutions of the following differential systems. When a solution exists, is it unique?

(a) $y'' + y = 0,$
$y(0) = 1,$
$y'(0) = 0.$

(b) $y'' + y = 0,$
$y(0) = 0,$
$y(\pi) = 1.$

(c) $y'' + y = 0,$
$y(0) = 1,$
$y(\pi) = -1.$

(d) $y'' + y = 0,$
$y(-\pi) = 0,$
$y(0) = 0.$

(e) $y'' + y = 0,$
$y(0) = 2,$
$y''(0) = -2.$

4. Show that every solution $y(x)$ of the differential system

$$\begin{aligned} y'' + y &= 0, \\ y(0) &= 0, \end{aligned}$$

has the property that $y(\pi) = 0$.

5. Find the unique solution of the differential system

$$\begin{aligned} y'' - 2y' + 2y &= 0, \\ y(0) &= 0, \\ y'(0) &= 2. \end{aligned}$$

6. Find the unique solution of the differential system

$$\begin{aligned} x^2y'' + xy' + y &= \log x, \\ y(1) &= 0, \\ y'(1) &= 2. \end{aligned}$$

7. Given the differential equation of Exercise 1, what can be said of two solutions which are tangent to each other at a point (x_0, y_0)?

ANSWERS

1. $y(x) \equiv 0$.

3. (a) $y(x) = \cos x$ (uniquely).
(b) No solution.
(e) $y(x) = 2 \cos x + c_1 \sin x$.

5. $2e^x \sin x$.

6. $\log x + \sin \log x$.

5

Linear Differential Equations

Linear differential equations form the simplest as well as probably the most important large class of differential equations. Of these, those of second order are of especial theoretical and practical interest. For these reasons an attempt has been made to display the mathematical analysis in this chapter in considerable detail.

1 Definitions; the Fundamental Existence Theorem

By a linear differential equation of order n we shall mean an equation of the form

(1.1)
$$a_0(x)y^{(n)} + a_1(x)y^{(n-1)} + \cdots + a_{n-1}(x)y' + a_n(x)y = f(x),$$

where $a_0(x) \not\equiv 0$. In order that we may have a reasonable amount of continuity at our disposal we shall always suppose that the functions $a_0(x)$, $a_1(x), \ldots, a_n(x)$, $f(x)$ are continuous on an interval (a,b) and that $a_0(x) \neq 0$ on this interval. The interval (a,b) may be either of finite or of infinite length and may be open or closed. It will be recalled that a solution $y(x)$ over (a,b) will have the property, according to our earlier definition, that it together with its derivatives $y'(x), y''(x), \ldots, y^{(n-1)}(x)$ will be continuous on this interval. It follows from (1.1) that $y^{(n)}(x)$ will then also be continuous on the interval (a,b).

We state next the fundamental existence theorem as it applies to (1.1).

Theorem 1.1. *Let* $x = x_0$ *be a point of the interval* (a,b) *and let* $c_0, c_1, c_2, \ldots, c_{n-1}$ *be an arbitrary set of* n *real numbers. There then exists one and only one solution* $y(x)$ *of* (1.1) *with the property that*

$$y(x_0) = c_0, \qquad y'(x_0) = c_1, \qquad \ldots, \qquad y^{(n-1)}(x_0) = c_{n-1}.$$

Further, this solution is defined over the entire interval (a,b).

Thus, at any point $x = x_0$ of the interval (a,b) we may prescribe the values of $y(x), y'(x), \ldots, y^{(n-1)}(x)$ quite arbitrarily, and there will then exist precisely one solution over the whole interval which at the point $x = x_0$ assumes the prescribed values.

For example, suppose the interval (a,b) is the interval $0 \leq x \leq 1$ and that $n = 3$. Then at the point $x = \frac{1}{3}$ we may prescribe that $y = \sqrt{2}$, $y' = \pi^2$, $y'' = 10^{10}$, and the theorem asserts the existence of one and exactly one solution $y(x)$ taking on these values at $x = \frac{1}{3}$. This solution will, further, be defined at every point of the interval $0 \leq x \leq 1$, and $y(x)$, $y'(x)$, $y''(x)$, and $y'''(x)$ will be continuous functions at each point of this interval.

Recall that a function $f(x)$ which together with its first n derivatives is continuous on an interval (a,b) is said to be of class C^n on this interval. Thus, a solution of (1.1) is by definition of class C^{n-1}, and it follows from (1.1) that it is also of class C^n on (a,b).

It is important to note that if we discover (no matter how) a solution $y(x)$ of class C^n on (a,b) which satisfies the conditions

$$y(x_0) = c_0, \qquad y'(x_0) = c_1, \qquad \ldots, \qquad y^{(n-1)}(x_0) = c_{n-1},$$

we have found *the* solution we seek. For $y(x)$ will obviously be *a* solution of our problem, but by Theorem 1.1 there is exactly one such solution; hence, $y(x)$ is *the* solution.

If $f(x) \equiv 0$ on (a,b), equation (1.1) becomes

$$(1.2) \quad a_0(x)y^{(n)} + a_1(x)y^{(n-1)} + \cdots + a_{n-1}(x)y' + a_n(x)y = 0.$$

We say that (1.2) is *homogeneous*.

Corollary. A solution $y(x)$ *of* (1.2) *with the property that at a point* $x = x_0$ *of* (a,b)

$$(1.3) \quad y(x_0) = 0, \quad y'(x_0) = 0, \quad \ldots, \quad y^{(n-1)}(x_0) = 0$$

is identically zero on (a,b).

The proof of the corollary is extremely simple. We note that $y(x) = 0$ is first of all *a* solution of (1.2) which satisfies (1.3). By the fundamental existence theorem it is the *only* solution with this property. The proof is complete.

The student will readily verify that if $y_1(x)$ and $y_2(x)$ are any two solutions of (1.2), the *linear combination** $c_1y_1(x) + c_2y_2(x)$, where c_1 and c_2 are constants, is also a solution of (1.2). In the same fashion it can readily be seen that a linear combination of any number of solutions of (1.2) is a solution of (1.2).

EXERCISE

Prove that if $y_1(x)$ and $y_2(x)$ are solutions of (1.2), so is $c_1y_1(x) + c_2y_2(x)$, where c_1 and c_2 are arbitrary constants.

2 Linear Dependence and Linear Independence

For the remainder of this chapter we shall confine our statements of theorems and their proofs to the important case $n = 2$. The student, if he is interested, will experience no difficulty in extending the theorems to the general case.

The concepts of *linear dependence* and *linear independence* are basic in what follows. Two solutions $u_1(x)$ and $u_2(x)$ are said to be *linearly dependent* if there exist constants c_1 and c_2, not both zero, such that

$$c_1u_1(x) + c_2u_2(x) \equiv 0 \qquad [x \text{ on } (a,b)].$$

If $u_1(x)$ and $u_2(x)$ are not linearly dependent, they are said to be *linearly independent*.

* Recall the footnote on p. 16.

Theorem 2.1. *There exist two linearly independent solutions* $y_1(x)$ *and* $y_2(x)$ *of the equation*

$$a_0(x)y'' + a_1(x)y' + a_2(x)y = 0 \tag{2.1}$$

with the property that every solution $y(x)$ *of* (2.1) *may be written in the form*

$$y(x) = c_1y_1(x) + c_2y_2(x), \tag{2.2}$$

where c_1 *and* c_2 *are suitably chosen constants.*

Before we prove Theorem 2.1, let us recall that we have assumed that $a_0(x)$, $a_1(x)$, and $a_2(x)$ are continuous and $a_0(x) \neq 0$ on the interval (a,b).

To prove the theorem, let $x = x_0$ be a point of (a,b) and let $y_1(x)$ and $y_2(x)$ be the solutions (guaranteed by the fundamental existence theorem) with the properties

$$\begin{aligned} y_1(x_0) &= 1, \qquad & y_2(x_0) &= 0, \\ y_1'(x_0) &= 0, \qquad & y_2'(x_0) &= 1. \end{aligned} \tag{2.3}$$

We shall first prove that $y_1(x)$ and $y_2(x)$ are linearly independent. Suppose they were not. There would then exist constants c_1 and c_2, not both zero, such that

$$c_1y_1(x) + c_2y_2(x) \equiv 0, \tag{2.4}$$

and, hence, such that

$$c_1y_1'(x) + c_2y_2(x) \equiv 0 \tag{2.5}$$

on (a,b). The identities (2.4) and (2.5) would hold, in particular, when $x = x_0$; that is,

$$\begin{aligned} c_1y_1(x_0) + c_2y_2(x_0) &= 0, \\ c_1y_1'(x_0) + c_2y_2'(x_0) &= 0. \end{aligned} \tag{2.6}$$

Applying (2.3) to (2.6), we see that $c_1 = 0$ and $c_2 = 0$, contrary to the hypothesis on c_1 and c_2. From this contradiction we infer that $y_1(x)$ and $y_2(x)$ are linearly independent.

To complete the proof of the theorem, let $y(x)$ be an arbitrary solution of (2.1). We wish to show that $y(x)$ may be written as a linear combination of $y_1(x)$ and $y_2(x)$. To that end consider the solution

$$Y(x) = y(x) - y(x_0)y_1(x) - y'(x_0)y_2(x).$$

Note that $Y(x)$ *is*, indeed, a solution, for it is a linear combination of solutions. We shall show that $Y(x)$ is a solution such that $Y(x_0) = 0$, $Y'(x_0) = 0$. It will follow from the corollary to Theorem 1.1 that $Y(x) \equiv 0$, and the proof will be complete. Note that

$$\begin{aligned} Y(x_0) &= y(x_0) - y(x_0)y_1(x_0) - y'(x_0)y_2(x_0) = 0, \\ Y'(x_0) &= y'(x_0) - y(x_0)y_1'(x_0) - y'(x_0)y_2'(x_0) = 0. \end{aligned} \tag{2.7}$$

The proof is complete. The "suitably chosen constants" referred to in the statement of the theorem have the values

$$c_1 = y(x_0), \qquad c_2 = y'(x_0).$$

Theorem 2.1 permits us quite properly to call $c_1y_1(x) + c_2y_2(x)$, where c_1 and c_2 are constants, the *general solution* of (2.1). For every such linear combination of solutions is a solution of (2.1) and, conversely, every solution of (2.1) may be put in this form.

If $y_1(x)$ and $y_2(x)$ are solutions of (2.1), the determinant

$$w(x) = \begin{vmatrix} y_1(x) & y_2(x) \\ y_1'(x) & y_2'(x) \end{vmatrix} = y_1(x)y_2'(x) - y_2(x)y_1'(x),$$

known as the *wronskian** of the two solutions, enables us to decide very simply whether or not the solutions $y_1(x)$ and $y_2(x)$ are linearly dependent.

Theorem 2.2. *Two solutions $y_1(x)$ and $y_2(x)$ of* (2.1) *are linearly dependent if and only if their wronskian is identically zero.*

We shall prove the sufficiency of the condition first; that is, we

* $-w(x)$ is also known as "the" wronskian of $y_1(x)$ and $y_2(x)$. The apparent ambiguity will not present any difficulty in what follows.

shall suppose $w(x)$ to be identically zero and prove that the solutions are linearly dependent. We have then

$$\begin{vmatrix} y_1(x) & y_2(x) \\ y_1'(x) & y_2'(x) \end{vmatrix} \equiv 0. \tag{2.8}$$

It follows that if $x = x_0$ is any point of (a,b),

$$\begin{vmatrix} y_1(x_0) & y_2(x_0) \\ y_1'(x_0) & y_2'(x_0) \end{vmatrix} = 0. \tag{2.9}$$

There then exist constants c_1 and c_2, not both zero, such that

$$\begin{aligned} c_1y_1(x_0) + c_2y_2(x_0) &= 0, \\ c_1y_1'(x_0) + c_2y_2'(x_0) &= 0. \end{aligned} \tag{2.10}$$

Consider the solution $c_1y_1(x) + c_2y_2(x)$. According to (2.10) this solution and its derivative are zero when $x = x_0$; hence, $c_1y_1(x) + c_2y_2(x) \equiv 0$. The proof of the sufficiency is complete.

To prove the necessity of the condition, we assume that there exist constants c_1 and c_2, not both zero, such that

$$c_1y_1(x) + c_2y_2(x) \equiv 0. \tag{2.11}$$

We wish to prove that the wronskian $w(x) \equiv 0$. From (2.11) we have

$$c_1y_1'(x) + c_2y_2'(x) \equiv 0. \tag{2.12}$$

Let $x = x_0$ be an arbitrary point of (a,b). The identities (2.11) and (2.12) hold, in particular, when $x = x_0$. There thus exist constants c_1 and c_2, not both zero, such that equations (2.10) hold. It follows that the determinant of the coefficients of c_1 and c_2 must be zero; that is, (2.9) must hold. But $x = x_0$ was an arbitrary point of (a,b), and (2.8) must hold throughout (a,b).

The proof of the theorem is complete.

Theorem 2.3. *The wronskian is either identically zero or never zero on* (a,b).

First, let us remind ourselves that the interval (a,b) may be either open or closed at either end point of the interval, but in all cases it is an interval in which the functions $a_0(x)$, $a_1(x)$, and $a_2(x)$ of equation (2.1) are continuous with $a_0(x) \neq 0$.

To prove the theorem, note that

$$\begin{aligned} w'(x) &= \begin{vmatrix} y_1'(x) & y_2'(x) \\ y_1'(x) & y_2'(x) \end{vmatrix} + \begin{vmatrix} y_1(x) & y_2(x) \\ y_1''(x) & y_2''(x) \end{vmatrix} \\ &= y_1(x)y_2''(x) - y_2(x)y_1''(x) \\ &= y_1(x)\left[-\frac{a_1}{a_0}y_2'(x) - \frac{a_2}{a_0}y_2(x)\right] \\ &\qquad\qquad - y_2(x)\left[-\frac{a_1}{a_0}y_1'(x) - \frac{a_2}{a_0}y_1(x)\right] \\ &= -\frac{a_1}{a_0}w(x). \end{aligned}$$

Thus, $w(x)$ is a solution of a first-order homogeneous linear differential equation, and according to the corollary in Section 1, $w(x) \equiv 0$ if it is zero at any point of (a,b).

We conclude this section with the following result.

Theorem 2.4. *If $y_1(x)$ and $y_2(x)$ are any pair of linearly independent solutions of equation* (2.1), *every solution $y(x)$ of* (2.1) *may be written in the form*

$$y(x) = c_1y_1(x) + c_2y_2(x),$$

where c_1 and c_2 are suitably chosen constants.

The proof is left to the student as an exercise.

EXERCISES

1. Show that $\sin x$ and $\cos x$ are linearly independent solutions of $y'' + y = 0$.

2. Show that $y_1(x) = \sin x$ and $y_2(x) = \sin x - \cos x$ are linearly independent solutions of $y'' + y = 0$. Determine constants c_1 and c_2 so that the solution

$$\sin x + 3 \cos x \equiv c_1 y_1(x) + c_2 y_2(x).$$

3. Find two linearly independent solutions of the equation

$$x^2 y'' + xy' + 4y = 0 \qquad (x > 0).$$

4. Find the solution of the differential system

$$\begin{aligned} x^2 y'' - xy' + 2y &= 0, \\ y(-1) &= 0, \\ y'(-1) &= 1. \end{aligned}$$

5. Show that linearly independent solutions of

$$y'' - 2y' + 2y = 0$$

are $e^x \sin x$ and $e^x \cos x$. What is the general solution? Find the solution $y(x)$ with the property that $y(0) = 2$, $y'(0) = -3$. Find another pair of linearly independent solutions.

6. Show that if a is a positive constant, linearly independent solutions of $y'' + a^2 y = 0$ are $\sin ax$ and $\cos ax$. What is the general solution?

7. Prove Theorem 2.4.

8. Show that on the interval $0 < x < \infty$, $\sin \frac{1}{x}$ and $\cos \frac{1}{x}$ are linearly independent solutions of the equation $x^4 y'' + 2x^3 y' + y = 0$. Note that $x = 0$ is a singular point of the differential equation. Sketch the former solution on the interval $0 < x < \frac{1}{\pi}$. Find the solution $y(x)$ of the differential equation with the property that $y\left(\frac{1}{\pi}\right) = 1$, $y'\left(\frac{1}{\pi}\right) = -1$.

9. Show that $\sin x^2$ and $\cos x^2$ are linearly independent solutions of the differential equation $xy'' - y' + 4x^3 y = 0$. Show that their wronskian has a zero at $x = 0$, but is not identically zero. Why does this not contradict Theorem 2.3?

10. Define solutions $s(x)$ and $c(x)$ of the differential equation $y'' + y = 0$ by the conditions $s(0) = 0$, $s'(0) = 1$, $c(0) = 1$, $c'(0) = 0$. Prove the well-known theorems (a) $s'(x) \equiv c(x)$; (b) $s^2(x) + c^2(x) \equiv 1$, without use of trigonometry.

11. Refer to Exercise 10 and without use of trigonometry prove that

$$s(x + a) = s(x)c(a) + c(x)s(a).$$

12. Refer to Exercise 10 and without use of trigonometry prove that

$$c(2x) = c^2(x) - s^2(x).$$

ANSWERS

3. $\sin \log x^2$, $\cos \log x^2$.

4. $x \sin \log(-x)$.

3 Variation of Parameters

We now turn our attention to the differential equation

$$a_0(x)y'' + a_1(x)y' + a_2(x)y = f(x), \tag{3.1}$$

where, as usual, $a_0(x)$, $a_1(x)$, $a_2(x)$, and $f(x)$ are continuous with $a_0(x) \neq 0$ on an interval (a,b). With (3.1) we associate the corresponding homogeneous equation

$$a_0(x)y'' + a_1(x)y' + a_2(x)y = 0. \tag{3.2}$$

Equation (3.2), as we have seen, has a general solution in the form

$$c_1y_1(x) + c_2y_2(x), \tag{3.3}$$

where $y_1(x)$ and $y_2(x)$ are linearly independent solutions of (3.2) and c_1 and c_2 are arbitrary constants. We are now prepared to prove the following result concerning the general solution of (3.1).

Theorem 3.1. *If* $y_0(x)$ *is any one solution of* (3.1), *the general solution of* (3.1) *may be written in the form*

$$y_0(x) + c_1y_1(x) + c_2y_2(x),$$

where $y_1(x)$ *and* $y_2(x)$ *are linearly independent solutions of* (3.2) *and* c_1 *and* c_2 *are arbitrary constants.*

Thus, to find the general solution of (3.1), we first find the general solution of (3.2). Next, we determine a particular solution of (3.1) by some convenient method. The sum of the two is the general solution of (3.1).

Before proving the theorem let us illustrate its use. Consider the differential equation

$$y'' + y = 1. \tag{3.1)'$$

The associated homogeneous equation is

$$y'' + y = 0. \tag{3.2)'$$

The general solution of (3.2)′ is

$$c_1 \sin x + c_2 \cos x.$$

By inspection, we observe that $y = 1$ is a particular solution of (3.1)′. Thus, the general solution of (3.1)′ is

$$1 + c_1 \sin x + c_2 \cos x,$$

where c_1 and c_2 are arbitrary constants.

We return now to the proof of the theorem. Suppose that $y(x)$ is an arbitrary solution of (3.1), and consider the function $Y(x) = y(x) - y_0(x)$. By hypothesis, we have

$$a_0 y''(x) + a_1 y'(x) + a_2 y(x) \equiv f(x),$$

$$a_0 y_0''(x) + a_1 y_0'(x) + a_2 y_0(x) \equiv f(x).$$

Subtracting these two identities, we have

$$a_0(y - y_0)'' + a_1(y - y_0)' + a_2(y - y_0) \equiv 0.$$

Thus, $Y(x) = y(x) - y_0(x)$ is a solution of (3.2) and may therefore be written in the form

$$Y(x) \equiv c_1 y_1(x) + c_2 y_2(x).$$

That is,

$$y(x) \equiv y_0(x) + c_1 y_1(x) + c_2 y_2(x),$$

as was to have been proved.

Ordinarily we cannot hope to find, by inspection, the one solution of (3.1) which we need. Fortunately, if we can solve (3.2), the method of *variation of parameters* always produces a particular solution of (3.1). This may be established as follows. Suppose $y_1(x)$ and $y_2(x)$ are linearly independent solutions of the corresponding homogeneous equation (3.2). We shall try to determine functions $u_1(x)$ and $u_2(x)$ such that

$$y_0(x) = u_1(x)y_1(x) + u_2(x)y_2(x)$$

is a particular solution of (3.1), and such that

$$u_1'(x)y_1(x) + u_2'(x)y_2(x) = 0. \tag{3.4}$$

[It is the auxiliary condition (3.4) which leads to the name "variation of parameters."] To that end substitute $y_0(x)$ in (3.1), and, using (3.4), obtain

$$u_1'(x)y_1'(x) + u_2'(x)y_2'(x) = \frac{f(x)}{a_0(x)}. \tag{3.5}$$

Equations (3.4) and (3.5) may be solved for $u_1'(x)$ and $u_2'(x)$:

$$u_1'(x) = -\frac{y_2(x)f(x)}{a_0(x)w(x)}, \qquad u_2'(x) = \frac{y_1(x)f(x)}{a_0(x)w(x)}, \tag{3.6}$$

where $w(x) = y_1(x)y_2'(x) - y_1'(x)y_2(x)$ is the wronskian of $y_1(x)$ and $y_2(x)$. Equations (3.6) are readily solved for $u_1(x)$ and $u_2(x)$:

$$u_1(x) = -\int_{x_0}^{x} \frac{y_2(t)f(t)}{a_0(t)w(t)}\,dt, \qquad u_2(x) = \int_{x_0}^{x} \frac{y_1(t)f(t)}{a_0(t)w(t)}\,dt.$$

The point $x = x_0$ may be any convenient point of (a,b). A particular solution of (3.1) is then

$$y_0(x) = u_1(x)y_1(x) + u_2(x)y_2(x),$$

which may be written in the symmetric form

$$y_0(x) = \int_{x_0}^{x} \begin{vmatrix} y_1(t) & y_2(t) \\ y_1(x) & y_2(x) \end{vmatrix} \frac{f(t)}{a_0(t)w(t)}\,dt. \tag{3.7}$$

It will be noted that $w(t) \neq 0$ on (a,b).

Example. Using variation of parameters, find the general solution of

$$y'' + y = x. \tag{3.8}$$

Here the general solution of the corresponding homogeneous equation is $c_1 \cos x + c_2 \sin x$, and $f(x) = x$, $a_0(x) = 1$, $w(x) = 1$. Equations (3.4) and (3.5) become

$$u_1'(x) \cos x + u_2'(x) \sin x = 0,$$

$$u_1'(x)(-\sin x) + u_2'(x) \cos x = x.$$

Hence,

$$u_1'(x) = -x \sin x, \qquad u_2'(x) = x \cos x,$$

and $u_1(x)$ and $u_2(x)$ may be taken as

$$u_1(x) = x \cos x - \sin x, \qquad u_2(x) = x \sin x + \cos x.$$

A particular solution $y_0(x) = u_1 y_1 + u_2 y_2$ is then $y_0(x) = x$. The general solution is $x + c_1 \cos x + c_2 \sin x$.

We could have obtained the particular solution by substituting directly in (3.7), or, better yet, we could in this case have guessed it by inspection of (3.8).

EXERCISES

1. Find the general solution of $y'' + y = 2 - x$ both by guessing a particular solution and by finding a particular solution by variation of parameters.

2. Find a solution as in Exercise 1 for $y'' - 3y' + 2y = 2$.

3. Find a solution as in Exercise 1 for $y'' + 4y = \sin x$.

4. Find a solution as in Exercise 1 for $y'' + 4y = e^x$.

5. Using the method of variation of parameters, find the general solution of $y'' + y = \tan x$.

6. Using the method of variation of parameters, find the general solution of $y'' + y = \sec x$.

7. Use the method of variation of parameters to find the general solution of $y'' + y = 2 \sin x$.

8. Prove that (3.7) provides a solution of (3.1) by substituting the solution in (3.1). The reversibility of the steps leading to (3.7) will be seen to provide an alternate proof.

ANSWERS

1. $2 - x + c_1 \sin x + c_2 \cos x$.

2. $1 + c_1 e^x + c_2 e^{2x}$.

3. $\frac{1}{3} \sin x + c_1 \sin 2x + c_2 \cos 2x$.

4. $\frac{1}{5} e^x + c_1 \sin 2x + c_2 \cos 2x$.

5. $c_1 \sin x + c_2 \cos x - \cos x \log |\sec x + \tan x|$.

6. $c_1 \sin x + c_2 \cos x + x \sin x + \cos x \log |\cos x|$.

7. $c_1 \sin x + c_2 \cos x - x \cos x$.

4 The Adjoint Differential Equation

In Chapter 1 we verified that

$$z(x) = \frac{1}{a_0(x)} e^{\int [a_1(x)/a_0(x)]\, dx} \tag{4.1}$$

is an integrating factor of the first-order linear differential equation

$$a_0(x)y' + a_1(x)y = f(x). \tag{4.2}$$

This integrating factor might have been obtained by seeking a function $z(x)$ such that

$$z(x)[a_0(x)y' + a_1(x)y] \equiv \frac{d}{dx}[r(x)y], \tag{4.3}$$

where as usual we assume $a_0(x)$, $a_0'(x)$, $a_1(x)$ continuous and $a_0(x) \neq 0$ on an interval (a,b). The function $r(x)$ is also to be determined. Clearly, from (4.3), we desire to determine $z(x)$ and $r(x)$ such that

$$z(x)a_0(x) = r(x), \qquad r'(x) = z(x)a_1(x). \tag{4.4}$$

These equations lead at once to the differential equation

$$[z(x)a_0(x)]' - z(x)a_1(x) = 0 \tag{4.5}$$

for the determination of $z(x)$. Equation (4.5) is a first-order linear homogeneous equation, a solution of which is given by (4.1). The function $r(x)$ is then given by the first of equations (4.4)

If we write

$$L_1(y) = a_0(x)y' + a_1(x)y,$$

$$M_1(z) = -(a_0z)' + (a_1z),$$

$M_1(z)$ is said to be the *adjoint* of $L_1(y)$. The differential equation $L_1(y) = 0$, that is,

$$a_0(x)y' + a_1(x)y = 0,$$

is said to be *self-adjoint* if $L_1(y) \equiv -M_1(y)$. This will be true if

$$a_0'(x) = 2a_1(x);$$

that is, if the differential equation $L_1(y) = 0$ can be written in the form

$$a_0(x)y' + \tfrac{1}{2}a_0'(x)y = 0.$$

Let us proceed in the same fashion with the second-order linear differential equation

$$L(y) \equiv a_0(x)y'' + a_1(x)y' + a_2(x)y = 0. \tag{4.6}$$

We then seek a function $z(x)$ such that

$$z(x)[a_0(x)y'' + a_1(x)y' + a_2(x)y] \equiv \frac{d}{dx}[k(x)y' + m(x)y]. \tag{4.7}$$

By the identity (4.7) is meant a formal identity in the quantities x, y, y', y''. The functions $k(x)$ and $m(x)$ are to be determined as well as $z(x)$. We have the following equations for the determination of these functions:

$$\begin{aligned} a_0(x)z(x) &= k(x), \\ a_1(x)z(x) &= k'(x) + m(x), \\ a_2(x)z(x) &= m'(x). \end{aligned} \tag{4.8}$$

These equations lead at once to the differential equation

$$M(z) \equiv [a_0(x)z]'' - [a_1(x)z]' + [a_2(x)z] = 0 \tag{4.9}$$

for the determination of the function $z(x)$. The functions $k(x)$ and $m(x)$ are then readily determined from the first two of equations (4.8). The expression $M(z)$ is called the *adjoint* of $L(y)$.

When $L(y) \equiv M(y)$, the equation

$$L(y) \equiv a_0(x)y'' + a_1(x)y' + a_2(x)y = 0 \tag{4.10}$$

is said to be *self-adjoint*. It will be seen that the differential equation (4.10) is self-adjoint if and only if

$$a_1(x) = a_0'(x). \tag{4.11}$$

When (4.11) holds, the differential equation (4.10) can be written in the form

$$[r(x)y']' + p(x)y = 0, \tag{4.12}$$

where we have written $r(x) = a_0(x)$ and $p(x) = a_2(x)$.

If $r(x)$, $r'(x)$, and $p(x)$ are continuous and $r(x) > 0$ on an interval (a,b), the equation (4.12) can be written in the form

$$r(x)y'' + r'(x)y'(x) + p(x)y = 0,$$

where the coefficients are continuous and the coefficient of y'' is positive on (a,b). Conversely, every equation

$$a(x)y'' + b(x)y' + c(x)y = 0, \tag{4.13}$$

where $a(x)$, $b(x)$, and $c(x)$ are continuous and $a(x) > 0$ on (a,b), can be written in the form (4.12), that is, in self-adjoint form. We multiply both members of (4.13) by the function

$$\frac{1}{a(x)} e^{\int [b(x)/a(x)]\, dx}.$$

Then

$$r(x) = e^{\int [b(x)/a(x)]\,dx},$$

and

$$p(x) = \frac{c(x)}{a(x)} e^{\int [b(x)/a(x)]\,dx}.$$

Example. Find the adjoint of $L(y) = 2y'' - 3y' + 2y$. We have at once

$$\begin{aligned} M(z) &= (2z)'' - (-3z)' + (2z) \\ &= 2z'' + 3z' + 2z. \end{aligned}$$

Example. Put the differential equation

$$x^2y'' + xy' + y = 0 \qquad (x > 0)$$

in self-adjoint form. We multiply both members of the equation by

$$\frac{1}{x^2} e^{\int dx/x} = \frac{1}{x},$$

and we have

$$(xy')' + \frac{1}{x} y = 0.$$

Example. Put the differential equation

$$y'' + a^2y = 0 \qquad (a > 0)$$

in self-adjoint form. The solution is immediate since the equation may be written in the form $(y')' + a^2y = 0$.

Example. Find functions $z(x)$, $k(x)$, and $m(x)$ such that

$$z(x)[x^2y'' - 2xy' + 2y] \equiv \frac{d}{dx}[k(x)y' + m(x)y].$$

The function $z(x)$ can be found by solving equation (4.9) with $a_0 = x^2$, $a_1 = -2x$, $a_2 = 2$. We have

$$(x^2z)'' + (2xz)' + (2z) = 0,$$

or

$$x^2z'' + 6xz' + 6z = 0.$$

Linearly independent solutions of this equation are x^{-2} and x^{-3}. Accordingly, we may take

$$z(x) = \frac{1}{x^2},$$

$$k(x) = 1,$$

$$m(x) = -\frac{2}{x}$$

[choosing $z(x) = x^{-3}$, or any linear combination $c_1x^{-2} + c_2x^{-3}$, would similarly provide a solution to the problem]. This information would enable us to solve the differential equation

$$x^2y'' - 2xy' + 2y = 0,$$

for an equivalent equation is then

$$\frac{d}{dx}\left[y' - \frac{2}{x}y\right] = 0.$$

It follows that

$$y' - \frac{2}{x}y = -c_1 \qquad (c_1 \text{ constant}).$$

An integrating factor for this first-order linear differential equation is readily found to be x^{-2}. Thus,

$$(x^{-2}y)' = -c_1x^{-2},$$

and

$$y = c_1x + c_2x^2.$$

Unfortunately, the adjoint equation is ordinarily quite as difficult to solve as the original equation, so we are not provided in this fashion with a useful method of solving linear differential equations of second order.

Reduction of the order of a differential equation. When a solution $y_1(x) \not\equiv 0$ of a second-order linear differential equation

$$a(x)y'' + b(x)y' + c(x)y = 0$$

is known, a second linearly independent solution may be found by means of the substitution

$$y = y_1(x)v. \tag{4.14}$$

Before demonstrating this result we shall apply the method to an example.

Example. It is readily verified that e^x is a solution of the differential equation

$$y'' - y = 0. \tag{4.15}$$

We perform the substitution

$$y = e^x v \tag{4.14$'$}$$

obtaining

$$e^x v'' + 2e^x v' = 0,$$

or,

$$p' + 2p = 0 \qquad (p = v').$$

The last equation is a linear differential equation of first order in p. It has the solution

$$p = e^{-2x},$$

and from (4.14)′ we have

$$y = e^x(e^{-2x}) = e^{-x}$$

as a solution of (4.15). It is clearly linearly independent of the given solution e^x.

To prove that the method always provides a second linearly independent solution it is convenient to suppose the given equation to be written in self-adjoint form:

$$r(x)y'' + r'(x)y' + p(x)y = 0. \tag{4.16}$$

The substitution $y = y_1(x)v$ yields

$$ry_1v'' + (2ry_1' + r'y_1)v' + (ry_1'' + r'y_1' + py_1)v = 0.$$

Since y_1 is given to be a solution of (4.16), the coefficient of v is zero. Writing $q = v'$, we have

$$ry_1q' + (2ry_1' + r'y)_1q = 0.$$

It follows at once that a solution of this equation is

$$q = \frac{1}{r(x)y_1^2(x)} = v'.$$

Accordingly, a solution of (4.16) is $y_1(x)v$ or

$$y_1(x)\int_a^x \frac{dx}{r(x)y_1^2(x)}. \tag{4.17}$$

The proof that $y_1(x)$ and the solution (4.17) are linearly independent is not difficult and is left to the student as an exercise.

EXERCISES

1. Put the following differential equations in self-adjoint form:

(a) $xy'' - y' + x^2y = 0$;
(b) $k(x)y'' + m(x)y = 0$;
(c) $y'' - 3y' + 2y = 0$;
(d) $y'' + (\cot x)y' + (\csc x)y = 0$;
(e) $x^2y'' + xy' + (x^2 - n^2)y = 0$;
(f) $(1 - x^2)y'' - 2xy' + (n^2 + n)y = 0$;
(g) $x^2y'' + bxy' + cy = 0$.

2. Find a function $z(x)$ such that

(a) $z(x)[y'' + y] \equiv \frac{d}{dx}[k(x)y' + m(x)y]$;

(b) $z(x)[y'' - y] \equiv \frac{d}{dx}[k(x)y' + m(x)y]$;

(c) $z(x)[y'' + 3y' + 2y] \equiv \frac{d}{dx}[k(x)y' + m(x)y]$.

3. Given that one solution of $y'' + a^2y = 0$ is $\sin ax$, find a second linearly independent solution, using the method of the text.

4. Given that one solution of $y'' - 3y' + 2y = 0$ is e^x, find a second linearly independent solution, using the method of the text.

5. Given that one solution of $y'' - 2y' + 2y = 0$ is $e^x \sin x$, find a second linearly independent solution, using the method of the text.

6. Show that the solution (4.17) is linearly independent of the given solution $y_1(x)$.

7. If $r(x) > 0$ is of class C' on the interval $a \leq x \leq b$, show that linearly independent solutions of the differential equation

$$[r(x)y']' + \frac{1}{r(x)}y = 0 \tag{4.18}$$

are

$$\sin \int_{x_0}^{x} \frac{dt}{r(t)}, \qquad \cos \int_{x_0}^{x} \frac{dt}{r(t)} \qquad (a \leq x_0 < x \leq b).$$

8. Use Exercise 7 to solve the differential equation

$$xy'' - y' + x^3 y = 0 \qquad (x > 0).$$

[*Hint.* First write the differential equation in the form (4.18).]

9. Given that one solution of $y'' - 4y' + 4y = 0$ is e^{2x}, use the method of the text to find a second linearly independent solution.

10. Do the same as in Exercise 9 when the differential equation is $y'' - 2ay' + a^2 y = 0$, and the given solution is e^{ax} $(a \neq 0)$.

ANSWERS

1. (a) $[(1/x)y']' + y = 0$;
(c) $(e^{-3x}y')' + 2e^{-3x}y = 0$;
(g) $(x^b y')' + cx^{b-2}y = 0$.

2. (a) $z(x) = \sin x$,
$k(x) = \sin x$,
$m(x) = -\cos x$.

4. e^{2x}.

5. $e^x \cos x$.

8. $c_1 \sin (x^2/2) + c_2 \cos (x^2/2)$.

6

Further Applications

1 The Deflection of Beams

Imagine a carpenter carrying a long piece of lumber on his shoulder. That piece of lumber is a *beam*, and it is *deflected*—that is, it bends downward in front of and behind the carpenter's shoulder. Imagine two men picking up a length of "two-by-four," one man at each end—the two-by-four will sag in the middle. That too is a deflected beam. If the two-by-four were *very* long, an effort to pick it up by the ends would result in its breaking—the *elastic limit* of the beam would have been exceeded.

In this section we shall be concerned with the deflection of beams occurring well within their elastic limits. Roughly speaking, we shall seek equations of the curves into which beams are bent by the force of gravity when they are supported at one or both ends.

First let us describe the kind of beam we shall be considering. The beam will have an axis of symmetry AB running the length of the beam (see Fig. 6.1). Every plane perpendicular to the axis of symmetry will have the same cross-section. We shall suppose that there is a vertical plane through the axis of symmetry with respect to which the beam is symmetric. Finally, we assume that the beam is made of homogeneous material.

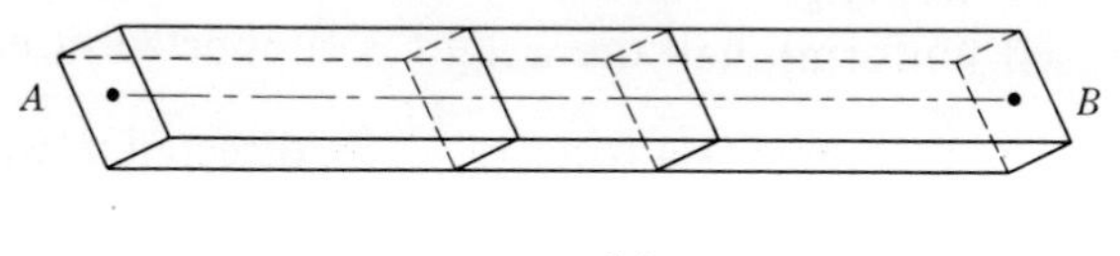

FIG. 6.1

When such a beam is picked up by the ends, the axis of symmetry will be bent as shown by the dotted line in Fig. 6.2. It is

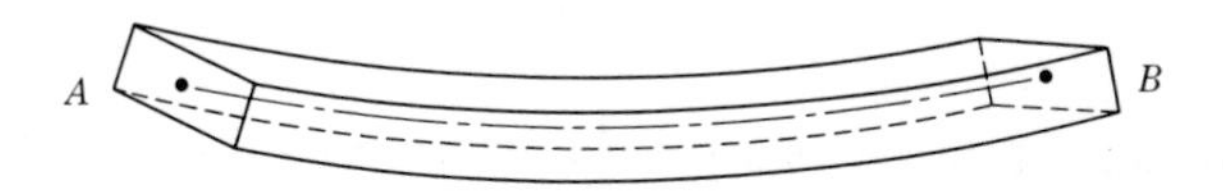

FIG. 6.2

the equation of this so-called *elastic curve* which we seek. To that end, we take an x-axis through the original axis of symmetry,

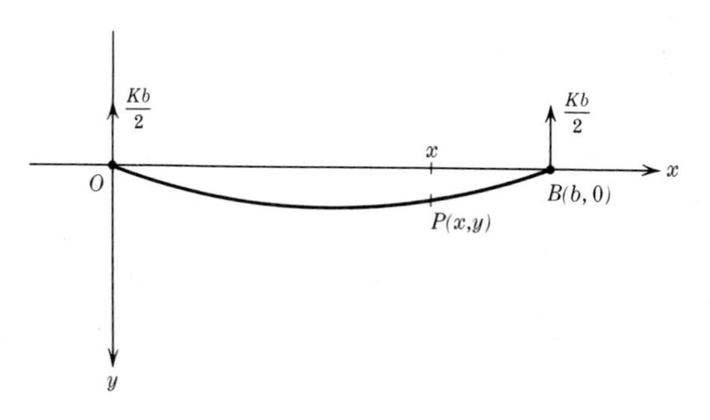

FIG. 6.3

putting the endpoint A at the origin. The y-axis is taken as indicated in Fig. 6.3, where we have indicated also the elastic curve when the beam is supported at both ends.

Call the length of the beam b, and choose a point x $(0 < x < b)$ on OB. Next, mark the corresponding point $P(x,y)$ on the elastic curve. If k is the weight of a unit length of the beam (which we have supposed uniform), half the weight is supported at each end of the beam; that is, there is a force of $\frac{kb}{2}$ lb. directed upward at O and at B.

Consider next the first moments about x of the forces to the left of x. The moment due to the force $\frac{kb}{2}$ at O is

$$\frac{kb}{2}x,$$

while the weight of the segment Ox, which is kx, exerts a moment in the opposite direction in the amount of

$$kx\frac{x}{2}.$$

The algebraic sum of these moments is

$$M(x) = \frac{kx^2}{2} - \frac{kbx}{2}, \tag{1.1}$$

where we have taken downward moments as positive and upward moments as negative. The student may verify that we would have obtained the same result if we had considered the segment xB to the right of x.

Next, we borrow a result from the theory of the strength of materials which states that the *bending moment* $M(x)$ is given by the formula

$$M(x) = EI\frac{y''}{(1 + y'^2)^{3/2}}, \tag{1.2}$$

where E is a constant depending on the material in the beam (*Young's modulus*) and I is the moment of inertia of the cross-section of the beam at x with respect to the line parallel to the

x-axis through the center of gravity of the cross-section. It will be noted that the quantity

$$\frac{y''}{(1 + y'^2)^{3/2}}$$

is the curvature of the elastic curve at x. The product EI is known as the *flexural rigidity* of the beam.

We assume EI to be constant. Since we shall be concerned with relatively small deflections, $|y'|$ will be small (less than unity), and y'^2 will be smaller still. It is customary to add the simplifying assumption that y'^2 is negligible. Equation (1.2) then has the simple form

$$M(x) = EIy''.$$

We combine this equation with (1.1), obtaining the differential equation

$$EIy'' = \frac{kx^2}{2} - \frac{kbx}{2} \tag{1.3}$$

for the elastic curve.

We wish to find a solution $y(x)$ of this differential equation subject to the conditions

$$y(0) = y(b) = 0.$$

This is easily computed to be

$$y(x) = \frac{k}{24EI}(x^4 - 2bx^3 + b^3x). \tag{1.4}$$

The maximum deflection of the beam occurs at $x = \dfrac{b}{2}$ (from the symmetry—or the calculus). It is found to be

$$\frac{5kb^4}{384EI}.$$

The beam of Fig. 6.3, which is supported at both ends, is known as a *simply supported beam.*

Cantilever beams. When a beam is rigidly supported at one end and the other end is free to move (Fig. 6.4), the beam is called

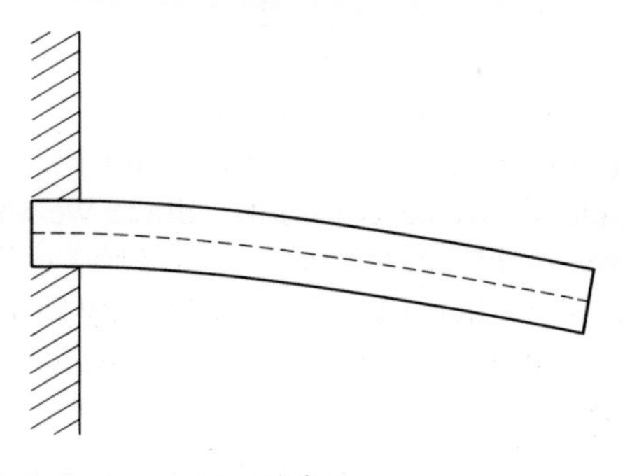

FIG. 6.4

a *cantilever beam.* The axis of symmetry is shown along an x-axis in Fig. 6.5, and the corresponding elastic curve is dotted on the graph.

Let x be a point of OB $(0 < x < b)$, and compute the first moment of xB about the point x. Its weight is $k(b - x)$, and its first moment (downward) is

$$k(b - x)\frac{b - x}{2}.$$

Again we set

$$EIy'' = \frac{k}{2}(b - x)^2,$$

and we wish to find a solution of this differential equation subject to the conditions

$$y(0) = y'(0) = 0.$$

This solution is readily computed to be

$$y(x) = \frac{k}{24EI}(x^4 - 4bx^3 + 6b^2x^2).$$

The deflection of the free end is found by setting $x = b$. It is

$$\frac{kb^4}{8EI}.$$

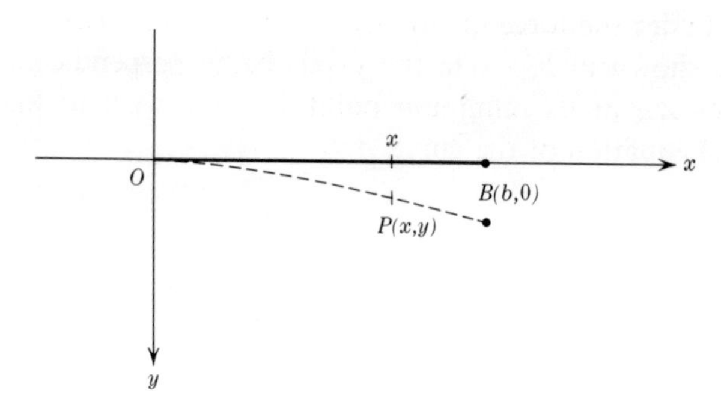

FIG. 6.5

EXERCISES

1. Suppose a cantilever beam has negligible weight and that a weight of w lb. is hung from the free end. Find an equation of the elastic curve and the deflection of the free end.

2. Suppose the cantilever beam of Exercise 1 weighs k lb. per unit of length. Find an equation of the elastic curve and the deflection of the free end.

3. Suppose the simply supported beam of the text has a weight of w lb. suspended at the midpoint. Find an equation of the elastic curve and its maximum deflection. Interpret the answer when k is set equal to zero.

ANSWERS

1. $y = \frac{wx^2}{6EI}(3b - x); \frac{wb^3}{3EI}.$

2. $y = \frac{wx^2}{6EI}(3b - x) + \frac{kx^2}{24EI}(6b^2 - 4bx + x^2); \frac{wb^3}{3EI} + \frac{kb^4}{8EI}.$

2 Suspended Cables

Consider a flexible, inextensible cable or rope suspended from two points A and B, not necessarily at the same level, which hangs at rest under the force of gravity (see Fig. 6.6). Take x- and y-axes as shown in Fig. 6.6, the y-axis being perpendicular to the curve of AB at its minimum point V. We wish to find a differential equation of the curve AB.

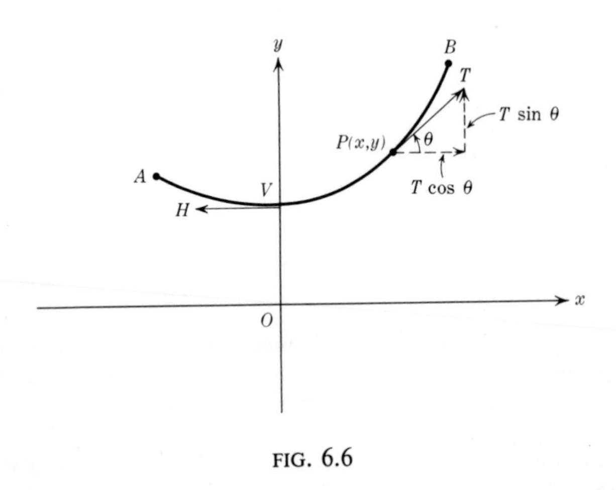

FIG. 6.6

Let $P(x,y)$ be an arbitrary point of the curve, and consider the arc VP. This segment will be in equilibrium under the force of tension T at P, the tension H at V, and the vertical loading W on VP. The tension T and the horizontal force H act along tangents to the curve at P and V, respectively. We regard the vertical loading W on VP as being due to the weight of the cable plus any other weights supported by the cable. Thus, W will vary from point to point.

We resolve T into a horizontal component $T\cos\theta$ and a vertical component $T\sin\theta$. If the density of the load is denoted by $\delta(x)$, then the total vertical load W on the segment VP of the curve is given by the integral

$$W = \int_0^x \delta(x)\,dx. \tag{2.1}$$

Since the arc VP is in equilibrium the algebraic sum of the horizontal and of the vertical forces acting must in each case be zero.

Accordingly,

$$T \cos \theta - H = 0,$$
$$T \sin \theta - W = 0.$$

Elimination of T between these equations yields

$$\tan \theta = \frac{W}{H}.$$

But since $\tan \theta = \frac{dy}{dx}$ we have

$$\frac{dy}{dx} = \frac{W}{H} \tag{2.2}$$

as a differential equation of the curve of AB. We note that H is a constant. As noted above, W is a function of x. It will be useful to differentiate both members of (2.2). We have

$$\frac{d^2y}{dx^2} = \frac{1}{H}\frac{dW}{dx}. \tag{2.3}$$

Example. Suppose the weight of a suspended cable is negligible and that it supports a uniform roadway as indicated in Fig. 6.7

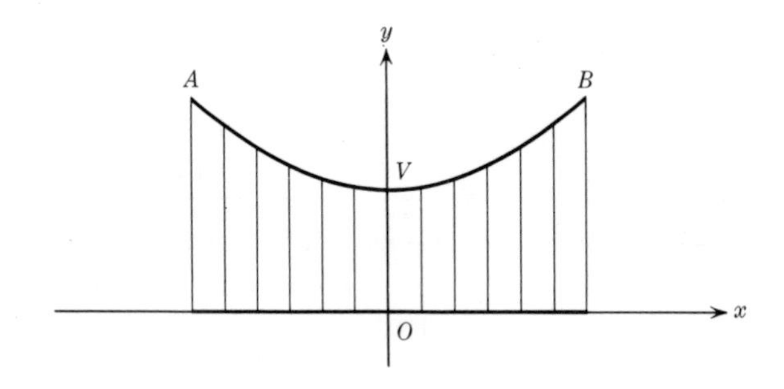

FIG. 6.7

(this is the situation in determining the shape of a cable for a suspension bridge, when the weights of the cable and vertical struts are very small compared with the weight of the roadway). By a uniform roadway is meant one in which the weight per linear foot is constant; that is, $\delta(x)$ is a constant δ, and from (2.1) we have

$$\frac{dW}{dx} = \delta.$$

Equation (2.3) becomes

$$y'' = \frac{\delta}{H}. \tag{2.4}$$

If the coordinates of V are $(0,c)$, we desire a solution of (2.4) subject to the boundary conditions

$$y(0) = c, \qquad y'(0) = 0.$$

The desired solution is readily seen to be the parabola

$$y = \frac{\delta}{2H}x^2 + c. \tag{2.5}$$

Suppose, in particular, that the dimensions of the suspension bridge are as indicated in Fig. 6.8. In this case, when $x = 0$,

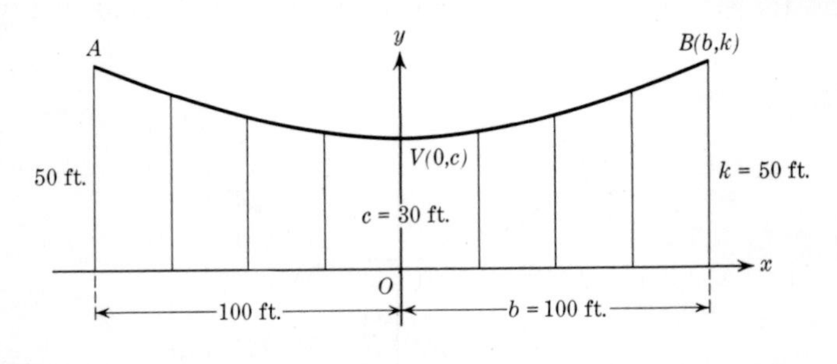

FIG. 6.8

$y = 30$, and when $x = 100$, $y = 50$; consequently, the coefficients in (2.5) can be determined, and the parabola has the equation

$$y = 0.002x^2 + 30.$$

Example. Suppose the cross-section of the cable in Fig. 6.6 is uniform, and that the only load on the cable is due to its own weight. In this case, the change in weight per unit of *arc length* is constant; that is,

$$\frac{dW}{ds} = k,$$

where k is the weight of a unit length of the cable. But

$$\frac{dW}{ds} = \frac{dW}{dx}\frac{dx}{ds};$$

hence,

$$\frac{dW}{dx} = k\frac{ds}{dx} = k\sqrt{1 + \left(\frac{dy}{dx}\right)^2}.$$

Equation (2.3) becomes

$$y'' = \frac{k}{H}\sqrt{1 + y'^2}. \tag{2.6}$$

We note that neither of the quantities x and y appears in this equation. If we set $p = y'$, we have

$$p' = \frac{k}{H}\sqrt{1 + p^2},$$

or

$$\frac{dp}{\sqrt{1 + p^2}} = m\,dx \qquad \left(m = \frac{k}{H}\right).$$

The variables are separated in this differential equation. An integration yields

$$\log\left(p + \sqrt{1 + p^2}\right) = mx + C_1.$$

We shall take $y = c$ and $p = y' = 0$, when $x = 0$; thus, $C_1 = 0$, and we have

$$p + \sqrt{1 + p^2} = e^{mx}.$$

It follows that

$$1 + p^2 = (e^{mx} - p)^2 = e^{2mx} - 2pe^{mx} + p^2.$$

Accordingly,

$$p = \frac{dy}{dx} = \frac{1}{2}(e^{mx} - e^{-mx}),$$

and, recalling that $y = c$ when $x = 0$, we obtain

$$y = \frac{1}{2m}(e^{mx} + e^{-mx}) + \left(c - \frac{1}{m}\right). \tag{2.7}$$

It is customary to choose the x-axis so that

$$c = \frac{1}{m}.$$

Equation (2.7) becomes

$$y = \frac{1}{2m}(e^{mx} + e^{-mx}) \qquad \left(m = \frac{k}{H}\right), \tag{2.8}$$

which can be written

$$y = \frac{1}{m}\cosh mx.$$

The curve represented by equation (2.8) is called a *catenary*. It is of considerable interest to scientists and engineers as well as to mathematicians. It may be shown, for example, by means of the calculus of variations, that if an arc of a curve AB, as in Fig. 6.9, is rotated about the x-axis, the area of the surface of revolution so generated will be smallest when AB is a segment of catenary (provided A and B are not too far apart!).

Suppose the points A and B of the catenary (2.8) are on the same level and that A and B are $2b$ units apart. If the slope of the catenary at B is λ (>0), then

$$m = \frac{1}{b}\log(\lambda + \sqrt{\lambda^2 + 1}). \tag{2.9}$$

The demonstration of (2.9) is left as an exercise for the student.

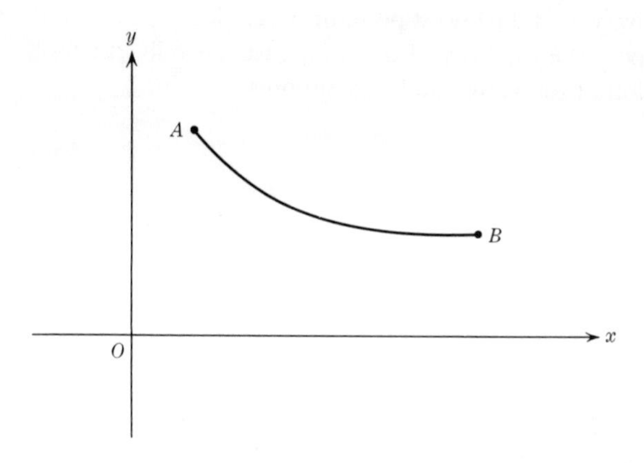

FIG. 6.9

EXERCISES

1. Derive equation (2.9).

2. Refer to equation (2.9) and find an equation of the catenary when the slope at B is $\frac{3}{4}$, and A and B are 100 units apart.

3. Refer to Fig. 6.8, and suppose that $c = 40$ ft., $k = 60$ ft., $b = 100$ ft. Determine an equation of the cable. Plot the curve on the interval $-100 \leq x \leq 100$.

4. Solve as in Exercise 3 when $c = 50$ ft., $k = 80$ ft., $b = 100$ ft.

5. A cable weighs $\frac{1}{2}$ lb. per foot. It is suspended from two supports which are at the same level and are 200 ft. apart. The slope of the cable at one support is $\frac{5}{12}$. Find an equation of the curve of the cable. What is the tension at the vertex?

6. The cable of a suspension bridge is of negligible weight compared with the weight of the roadway it supports. The cable supports are at the same level $2b$ ft. apart. The supports are k ft. above the roadway, and the lowest point of the cable is c ft. above the roadway. Suppose the roadway of the bridge weighs δ lb. per foot. Find the tension at the vertex and at a support.

ANSWERS

2. $y = \dfrac{25}{\log 2}(2^{x/50} + 2^{-x/50})$.

3. $y = 0.002x^2 + 40$.

5. $y = \dfrac{50}{\log(3/2)}\left[\left(\dfrac{3}{2}\right)^{x/100} + \left(\dfrac{3}{2}\right)^{-x/100}\right]; \dfrac{50}{\log(3/2)}$.

6. $H = \dfrac{\delta b^2}{2(k-c)}$; $T = \dfrac{\delta b}{2(k-c)}\sqrt{b^2 + 4(k-c)^2}$.

3 Simple Electric Circuits

In this section we study the use of second-order linear differential equations in describing the flow of electricity in a simple circuit. Such a circuit is shown schematically in Fig. 6.10. In this circuit an electromotive force E causes electricity to flow in a circuit of *inductance* L against a resistance R, depositing an electrostatic charge on one plate of a *capacitor* C. (A capacitor consists of two plates separated by an insulating material. When an electrostatic charge is deposited on one plate of a capacitor an equal charge opposite in sign appears on the other plate.) Quantity of electricity q is measured in *coulombs*. The *current* i is the rate of flow of electricity; that is,

$$i = \frac{dq}{dt}, \tag{3.1}$$

where i is measured in *amperes*, q in coulombs, and t in seconds.

Electrical inductance is analogous to mass in a mechanical system, and resistance is the analogue of friction. The standard unit of inductance is the *henry* and that of resistance is the *ohm*. The capacity of a capacitor is measured in *farads*. When an inductance L, resistance R, and a capacitance C (L, R, C constants)

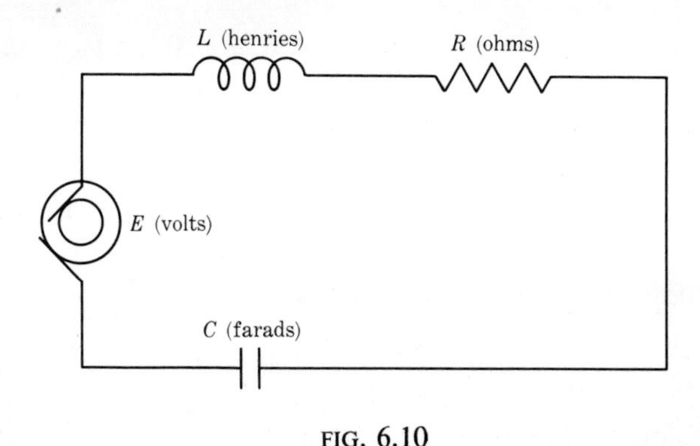

FIG. 6.10

are connected in series, as shown in Fig. 6.10, it is a consequence of what are known as Kirchhoff's laws* that

$$L\frac{d^2q}{dt^2} + R\frac{dq}{dt} + \frac{1}{C}q = E. \tag{3.2}$$

Differentiation of (3.2) with respect to t yields

$$L\frac{d^2i}{dt^2} + R\frac{di}{dt} + \frac{1}{C}i = \frac{dE}{dt}, \tag{3.3}$$

inasmuch as $i = \dfrac{dq}{dt}$.

Example. Suppose that a capacitor of capacity 0.01 farad is being charged by a constant electromotive force of 100 volts through an inductance of 0.02 henry against a resistance of 10

* An exposition of these laws may be found in most elementary physics textbooks.

ohms. In this case, equation (3.2) becomes

$$(3.2)' \qquad 0.02\frac{d^2q}{dt^2} + 10\frac{dq}{dt} + 100q = 100.$$

Let us suppose further that when $t = 0$, $q = 0$, and $i = 0$. We have then to solve the second-order linear differential equation (3.2)′ with constant coefficients subject to the boundary conditions $t = 0$, $q = 0$, $i = 0$.

We note that a particular solution of (3.2)′ is $q = 1$, and that the corresponding homogeneous equation has indicial roots which are the solution of the quadratic equation

$$(3.4) \qquad 0.02m^2 + 10m + 100 = 0.$$

Roots of equation (3.4) are seen to be

$$m = \frac{-5 \pm \sqrt{23}}{0.02} = 50(-5 \pm \sqrt{23}),$$

or

$$m = -10, -490 \text{ (approximately).}$$

The general solution of equation (3.2)′ is, then,

$$q = 1 + c_1e^{-10t} + c_2e^{-490t}.$$

Applying the boundary conditions we have $c_1 = -\frac{49}{48}$, $c_2 = \frac{1}{48}$; hence,

$$(3.5) \qquad q = 1 - \tfrac{49}{48}e^{-10t} + \tfrac{1}{48}e^{-490t},$$

and

$$(3.6) \qquad i = \frac{dq}{dt} = \frac{490}{48}(e^{-10t} - e^{-490t}).$$

Graphs of q and i as functions of t are given in Fig. 6.11 and 6.12. It will be observed that the charge on the capacitor rapidly approaches 1 coulomb and that the current rises quickly to a peak and then decreases rapidly (see Exercise 1).

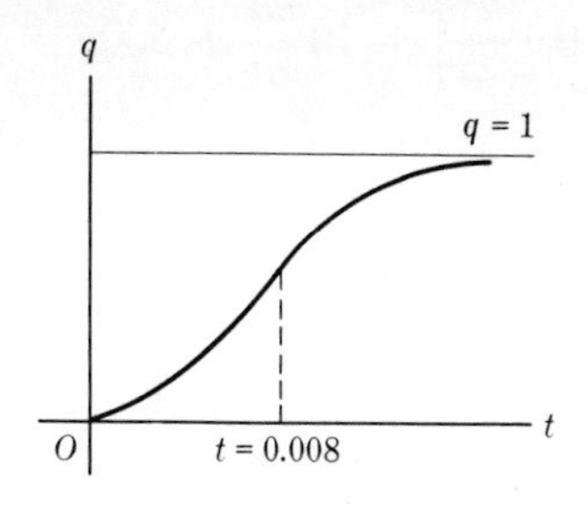

FIG. 6.11

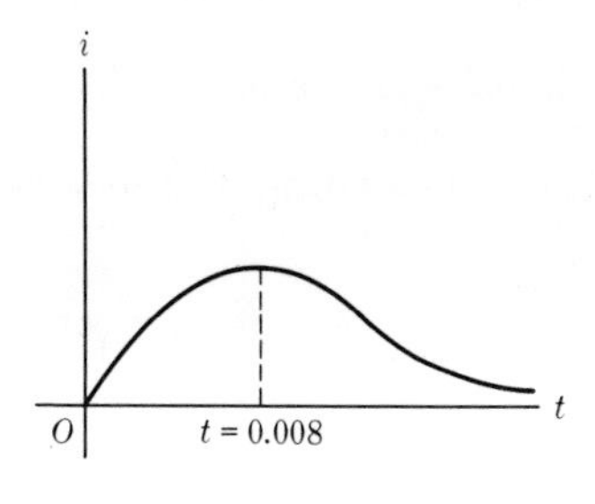

FIG. 6.12

Example. Suppose $L = 0.1$ henry, $R = 10$ ohms, $C = 0.002$ farad, and $E = 50 \sin \omega t$ volts, where ω is a positive constant. Again we suppose that when $t = 0$, $q = 0$ and $i = 0$.

It will be observed in this example that E is a pulsating variable force. Equation (3.2) and its boundary conditions become the differential system

$$0.1 \frac{d^2q}{dt^2} + 10 \frac{dq}{dt} + 500q = 50 \sin \omega t, \tag{3.2$''$}$$

$$t = 0, \qquad q = 0, \qquad i = 0.$$

To solve this system we note that the corresponding homogeneous equation

$$0.1 \frac{d^2q}{dt^2} + 10 \frac{dq}{dt} + 500q = 0$$

has the general solution

$$e^{-50t}(c_1 \cos 50t + c_2 \sin 50t).$$

Accordingly, when $\omega = 50$, the phenomenon of resonance will be encountered (unlike the situation in most mechanical systems, resonance can be a very useful phenomenon—albeit a dangerous one for amateur tinkerers—in electronics).

When $\omega \neq 50$, a particular solution of (3.2)″ of the form

$$q = A \sin \omega t + B \cos \omega t \qquad (A,\ B \text{ constant})$$

can be found. After some computation we find that

$$A = \frac{500(1 - 5000\omega^2)}{(1 - 5000\omega^2)^2 + (100\omega)^2}, \quad B = -\frac{50{,}000\omega}{(1 - 5000\omega^2)^2 + (100\omega)^2}.$$

The general solution of the differential equation is then

(3.7)
$$q = A \sin \omega t + B \cos \omega t + e^{-50t}(c_1 \cos 50t + c_2 \sin 50t) \ (\omega \neq 50).$$

The constants c_1 and c_2 can be determined by the boundary conditions. They are

$$c_1 = -B, \qquad c_2 = -\frac{A\omega + 50B}{50}.$$

It will be seen that the contribution to the solution (3.7) of the quantity

(3.8)
$$e^{-50t}(c_1 \cos 50t + c_2 \sin 50t)$$

becomes very small very quickly as t increases. For this reason the quantity (3.8) is called the *transient* in the system. The quantity

$$A \sin \omega t + B \cos \omega t,$$

on the other hand, is called the *steady-state solution* of the system. The current i is again obtained from the formula

$$i = \frac{dq}{dt}.$$

Two other definitions may be added. The quantity

$$X = L\omega - \frac{1}{C\omega}$$

is called the *reactance* in the circuit, and

$$Z = \sqrt{R^2 + X^2}$$

is called the *impedance*.

EXERCISES

1. Use equation (3.6) to compute the maximum value of i in the first example.

2. Discuss the simple circuit in which (all quantities are given in standard units)
(a) $L = 0.01$, $R = 10$, $C = 0.02$, $E = 50$;
(b) $L = 0.1$, $R = 20$, $C = \frac{1}{360}$, $E = 50 \sin 50t$;
(c) $L = 0.1$, $R = 10$, $C = 0.002$, $E = 50 \sin 50t$.
Assume that $q = i = 0$, when $t = 0$.

3. Discuss the simple circuit in which (all quantities are given in standard units)
(a) $L = 0.01$, $R = 20$, $C = 0.02$, $E = 100$;
(b) $L = 0.2$, $R = 10$, $C = \frac{1}{625}$, $E = 100 \sin 100t$;
(c) $L = 0.2$, $R = 10$, $C = \frac{1}{625}$, $E = 100 \sin 50t$.
Assume that $q = i = 0$, when $t = 0$.

ANSWERS

1. $10(\frac{1}{7})^{1/24} = 9.2$ amperes.

7

Systems of Differential Equations

1 The Existence Theorem

In this chapter we shall begin with the study of systems of linear differential equations; that is, systems of the type

$$
\begin{aligned}
\frac{dx_1}{dt} &= a_{11}(t)x_1 + a_{12}(t)x_2 + \cdots + a_{1n}(t)x_n,\\
\frac{dx_2}{dt} &= a_{21}(t)x_1 + a_{22}(t)x_2 + \cdots + a_{2n}(t)x_n,\\
&\cdots\cdots\cdots\cdots\cdots,\\
\frac{dx_n}{dt} &= a_{n1}(t)x_1 + a_{n2}(t)x_2 + \cdots + a_{nn}(t)x_n.
\end{aligned}
\tag{1.1}
$$

We have taken t (which will often represent *time*) as the independent variable, and the variables $x_1, x_2, \ldots, x_n$ are the unknowns. We shall suppose that the functions $a_{ij}(t)$ are continuous on an interval $I: a \leq t \leq b$.

By a *solution* $x(t)$ of such a system is meant a column of functions

$$
\begin{matrix}
x_1(t)\\
x_2(t)\\
\vdots\\
x_n(t),
\end{matrix}
\tag{1.2}
$$

each of class C' in I, which simultaneously satisfy (1.1).

The fundamental existence theorem (see Chapter 9) when applied to this system may be shown to lead to the following result.

Theorem 1.1. *If* $a_1, a_2, \ldots, a_n$ *is an arbitrary set of constants and if* t_0 *is any point of the interval I, there exists one and only one solution of* (1.1) *with the property that*

$$x_1(t_0) = a_1, \qquad x_2(t_0) = a_2, \qquad \ldots, \qquad x_n(t_0) = a_n.$$

Corollary. A solution (1.2) *of* (1.1) *with the property that at some point* t_0 *of I*

$$x_1(t_0) = x_2(t_0) = \cdots = x_n(t_0) = 0$$

is identically zero; that is,

$$x_1(t) \equiv x_2(t) \equiv \cdots \equiv x_n(t) \equiv 0.$$

The proof of the corollary is easy and is left to the student.

We note that if $u(t)$ and $v(t)$ are two solutions (columns) of (1.1), so is $c_1u(t) + c_2v(t)$, where c_1 and c_2 are any constants.

It is frequently desirable to transform a simple linear differential equation of order n into a system of the type (1.1). This can be accomplished as follows. Suppose the given differential equation is

$$\frac{d^nx}{dt^n} = a_1(t)\frac{d^{n-1}x}{dt^{n-1}} + a_2(t)\frac{d^{n-2}x}{dt^{n-2}} + \cdots + a_{n-1}(t)\frac{dx}{dt} + a_n(t)x, \tag{1.3}$$

where the functions $a_i(t)$ are continuous on the interval I. If we set

$$x_1 = x, \qquad x_2 = \frac{dx}{dt}, \qquad x_3 = \frac{d^2x}{dt^2}, \qquad \ldots, \qquad x_n = \frac{d^{n-1}x}{dt^{n-1}}, \tag{1.4}$$

equation (1.3) is transformed under (1.4) into the system

$$\frac{dx_1}{dt} = x_2,$$

$$\frac{dx_2}{dt} = x_3,$$

$$\cdots$$

$$\frac{dx_{n-1}}{dt} = x_n,$$

$$\frac{dx_n}{dt} = a_1(t)x_n + a_2(t)x_{n-1} + \cdots + a_n(t)x_1.$$

Thus, a system (1.1) may properly be regarded as a generalization of a single linear differential equation of order n.

For the remainder of this section we shall assume $n = 3$ in order to simplify slightly the presentation of the proofs. The alterations required for the general case will be quite evident.

We shall, on occasion, use dots to denote differentiation with respect to t; thus,

$$\dot{x} = \frac{dx}{dt}, \qquad \ddot{x} = \frac{d^2x}{dt^2}, \qquad \dot{a}(t) = \frac{d}{dt}a(t).$$

When $n = 3$, the system (1.1) becomes

$$(1.1)' \qquad \begin{aligned} \frac{dx_1}{dt} &= a_{11}(t)x_1 + a_{12}(t)x_2 + a_{13}(t)x_3, \\ \frac{dx_2}{dt} &= a_{21}(t)x_1 + a_{22}(t)x_2 + a_{23}(t)x_3, \\ \frac{dx_3}{dt} &= a_{31}(t)x_1 + a_{32}(t)x_2 + a_{33}(t)x_3, \end{aligned}$$

and a solution $x(t)$ becomes the column

$$(1.2)' \qquad \begin{matrix} x_1(t) \\ x_2(t) \\ x_3(t). \end{matrix}$$

Three solutions $u(t)$, $v(t)$, $w(t)$ are said to be *linearly dependent* if there exist constants c_1, c_2, c_3, not all zero, such that

$$(1.5) \qquad c_1u(t) + c_2v(t) + c_3w(t) \equiv 0.$$

Condition (1.5) is interpreted as follows. Let the components of $u(t)$, $v(t)$, $w(t)$ be given, respectively, by the columns

$$\begin{matrix} u_1(t) & v_1(t) & w_1(t) \\ u_2(t) & v_2(t) & w_2(t) \\ u_3(t), & v_3(t), & w_3(t). \end{matrix}$$

Then (1.5) is equivalent to the three conditions

$$\begin{aligned} c_1u_1(t) + c_2v_1(t) + c_3w_1(t) &\equiv 0, \\ c_1u_2(t) + c_2v_2(t) + c_3w_2(t) &\equiv 0, \\ c_1u_3(t) + c_2v_3(t) + c_3w_3(t) &\equiv 0. \end{aligned} \tag{1.5$'$}$$

Solutions not linearly dependent are said to be *linearly independent.*

Theorem 1.2. *There exist three linearly independent solutions of* (1.1)$'$. *Every solution of the system can be written as a linear combination of these three solutions.*

The solutions $u(t)$, $v(t)$, $w(t)$ defined, respectively, by the conditions

$$\begin{matrix} u_1(t_0) = 1, & v_1(t_0) = 0, & w_1(t_0) = 0, & \\ u_2(t_0) = 0, & v_2(t_0) = 1, & w_2(t_0) = 0, & \\ u_3(t_0) = 0, & v_3(t_0) = 0, & w_3(t_0) = 1 & (a \leq t_0 \leq b), \end{matrix} \tag{1.6}$$

are readily shown to be linearly independent. For, if constants c_1, c_2, c_3, not all zero, exist such that (1.5)$'$ holds, these conditions would hold in particular when $t = t_0$. But this is impossible. [Note that the solutions $u(t)$, $v(t)$, $w(t)$ defined by (1.6) *do* exist, because of Theorem 1.1.]

It remains to prove that every solution $x(t)$ of (1.1)$'$ may be written as a linear combination of $u(t)$, $v(t)$, $w(t)$. We shall show that if $x_1(t)$, $x_2(t)$, $x_3(t)$ are the components of $x(t)$, then

$$x(t) \equiv x_1(t_0)u(t) + x_2(t_0)v(t) + x_3(t_0)w(t);$$

that is,

$$x_i(t) \equiv x_1(t_0)u_i(t) + x_2(t_0)v_i(t) + x_3(t_0)w_i(t).$$

First, note that $X(t)$, with components

$$X_i(t) = x_i(t) - [x_1(t_0)u_i(t) + x_2(t_0)v_i(t) + x_3(t_0)w_i(t)],$$

is a solution of (1.1)′. This solution has the property that

$$X_1(t_0) = X_2(t_0) = X_3(t_0) = 0.$$

Thus, by the corollary to Theorem 1.1, $X_i(t) \equiv 0$. The proof of the theorem is complete.

EXERCISES

1. Prove the corollary to Theorem 1.1.

2. Prove that if $u(t)$, $v(t)$, $w(t)$ are any three linearly independent solutions of (1.1)′, every solution of the system may be written as a linear combination of these three solutions.

3. Prove that any four solutions of (1.1)′ are linearly dependent.

4. Given the system of differential equations

$$\frac{dx}{dt} = \frac{1}{2}x + \frac{1}{2}z,$$

$$\frac{dz}{dt} = -\frac{3}{2}x + \frac{5}{2}z,$$

show that each column below provides a solution of the system:

$$\begin{matrix} e^t & e^{2t} \\ e^t & 3e^{2t}. \end{matrix}$$

Are the solutions linearly dependent?

5. Given the system

$$\frac{dx_1}{dt} = \frac{t}{t-1}x_2 + \frac{1}{1-t}x_3,$$

$$\frac{dx_2}{dt} = \frac{1}{t(1-t)}x_2 + \frac{1}{t(t-1)}x_3,$$

$$\frac{dx_3}{dt} = \frac{2}{1-t}x_2 + \frac{2}{t-1}x_3,$$

show that the columns

$$\begin{matrix} 1 & t & 1 \\ 0 & 1 & t \\ 0, & 1, & t^2 \end{matrix}$$

are linearly independent solutions. Hence, show that the columns

$$\begin{matrix} t+2 & 0 & t-1 & t+1 \\ t+1 & t & 1-t & 1 \\ t^2+1, & t^2, & (1-t)(1+t), & 1 \end{matrix}$$

are also solutions. Are they linearly independent?

6. Show that the four solutions

$$\begin{matrix} u: & v: & w: & z: \\ 1 & t & 1 & t+2 \\ 0 & 1 & t & t+1 \\ 0, & 1, & t^2, & t^2+1 \end{matrix}$$

of the system in Exercise 5 are linearly dependent by finding four constants c_1, c_2, c_3, c_4, not all zero, such that

$$c_1 u + c_2 v + c_3 w + c_4 z \equiv 0.$$

2 Fundamental Systems of Solutions

In this section, as in Section 1, we shall devote our attention to the system (1.1)′ as a representative of the more general system (1.1).

Let the columns

$$\begin{matrix} u_1(t) & v_1(t) & w_1(t) \\ u_2(t) & v_2(t) & w_2(t) \\ u_3(t), & v_3(t), & w_3(t) \end{matrix}$$

be solutions $u(t)$, $v(t)$, and $w(t)$, respectively, of (1.1)′ and form the determinant

$$\Delta(t) = \begin{vmatrix} u_1(t) & v_1(t) & w_1(t) \\ u_2(t) & v_2(t) & w_2(t) \\ u_3(t) & v_3(t) & w_3(t) \end{vmatrix}.$$

Note that

$$
(2.1)\quad \begin{aligned}
\Delta(t) &= \begin{vmatrix} \dot{u}_1(t) & \dot{v}_1(t) & \dot{w}_1(t) \\ u_2(t) & v_2(t) & w_2(t) \\ u_3(t) & v_3(t) & w_3(t) \end{vmatrix} + \begin{vmatrix} u_1(t) & v_1(t) & w_1(t) \\ \dot{u}_2(t) & \dot{v}_2(t) & \dot{w}_2(t) \\ u_3(t) & v_3(t) & w_3(t) \end{vmatrix} \\
&\quad + \begin{vmatrix} u_1(t) & v_1(t) & w_1(t) \\ u_2(t) & v_2(t) & w_2(t) \\ \dot{u}_3(t) & \dot{v}_3(t) & \dot{w}_3(t) \end{vmatrix}.
\end{aligned}
$$

From (1.1)′ we see that

$$
(2.2)\quad \begin{aligned}
\dot{u}_i &= a_{i1}u_1 + a_{i2}u_2 + a_{i3}u_3, \\
\dot{v}_i &= a_{i1}v_1 + a_{i2}v_2 + a_{i3}v_3, \\
\dot{w}_i &= a_{i1}w_1 + a_{i2}w_2 + a_{i3}w_3 \qquad (i = 1, 2, 3).
\end{aligned}
$$

If the dot quantities in the determinants (2.1) are replaced by the equivalent quantities given by (2.2), it is readily seen that

$$\dot{\Delta}(t) \equiv [a_{11}(t) + a_{22}(t) + a_{33}(t)]\Delta(t).$$

Accordingly, $\Delta(t)$ is a solution of the linear differential equation

$$\dot{x} = [a_{11}(t) + a_{22}(t) + a_{33}(t)]x.$$

It follows that $\Delta(t)$ is either never zero or is identically zero. Indeed,

$$\Delta(t) = \Delta(t_0)e^{\int_{t_0}^{t} [a_{11}(t) + a_{22}(t) + a_{33}(t)]\, dt},$$

where t_0 is any point of the interval $a \leq t \leq b$.

A system of three solutions of (1.1)′ with the property that $\Delta(t) \not\equiv 0$ is called a *fundamental system* of solutions.

EXERCISES

1. Prove that a necessary and sufficient condition that three solutions of (1.1)′ be linearly independent is that they form a fundamental system.

2. Compute $\Delta(t)$ for the system of solutions given for Exercise 4, Section 1, and thus verify that

$$\dot{\Delta}(t) \equiv [a_{11}(t) + a_{22}(t)]\Delta(t).$$

3. Compute $\Delta(t)$ for one of the systems of three solutions given for Exercise 5, Section 1, and thus verify that

$$\dot{\Delta}(t) \equiv [a_{11}(t) + a_{22}(t) + a_{33}(t)]\Delta(t).$$

Does this example invalidate the conclusion of the text that $\Delta(t)$ is either identically zero or never zero?

3 Linear Systems with Constant Coefficients; Matrix Notation

We shall confine our remarks to the system

$$\begin{aligned} \frac{dx_1}{dt} &= a_{11}x_1 + a_{12}x_2, \\ \frac{dx_2}{dt} &= a_{21}x_1 + a_{22}x_2, \end{aligned} \tag{3.1}$$

where a_{11}, a_{12}, a_{21}, and a_{22} are constants. The following examples will illustrate the techniques of solving such a system.

Example. Solve the system

$$\begin{aligned} \frac{dx_1}{dt} &= \frac{1}{2}x_1 + \frac{1}{2}x_2, \\ \frac{dx_2}{dt} &= -\frac{3}{2}x_1 + \frac{5}{2}x_2. \end{aligned} \tag{3.2}$$

Let us attempt to determine constants A, B, and λ such that the column

$$\begin{matrix} Ae^{\lambda t} \\ Be^{\lambda t} \end{matrix}$$

is a solution of (3.2). If we substitute these functions for x_1 and x_2, respectively, in (3.2), we see that A, B, and λ must satisfy the equations

$$\begin{aligned} (\tfrac{1}{2} - \lambda)A + \tfrac{1}{2}B &= 0, \\ -\tfrac{3}{2}A + (\tfrac{5}{2} - \lambda)B &= 0. \end{aligned} \tag{3.3}$$

If solutions A and B, not both zero, of equations (3.3) exist, it is necessary and sufficient that

$$\begin{vmatrix} \frac{1}{2} - \lambda & \frac{1}{2} \\ -\frac{3}{2} & \frac{5}{2} - \lambda \end{vmatrix} = 0. \tag{3.4}$$

Equation (3.4) is readily seen to be equivalent to

$$\lambda^2 - 3\lambda + 2 = 0,$$

the roots of which are 1 and 2. If we set $\lambda = 1$ in (3.3), we obtain

$$\begin{aligned} -\frac{A}{2} + \frac{B}{2} &= 0, \\ -\frac{3A}{2} + \frac{3B}{2} &= 0. \end{aligned} \tag{3.5}$$

These simultaneous equations are consistent, and we may choose as solutions of them any pair of numbers different from zero satisfying them. An obvious choice is $A = B = 1$. This leads to the solution

$$\begin{matrix} e^t \\ e^t. \end{matrix}$$

If we had chosen any other pair of numbers A, B satisfying (3.5), we would simply have obtained a constant times this solution.

In a similar way the root $\lambda = 2$ leads to the equations

$$\begin{aligned} -\frac{3A}{2} + \frac{B}{2} &= 0, \\ -\frac{3A}{2} + \frac{B}{2} &= 0. \end{aligned}$$

A nontrivial solution of this system is $A = 1$, $B = 3$, and the corresponding solution of (3.2) is

$$\begin{matrix} e^{2t} \\ 3e^{2t}. \end{matrix}$$

Every solution of (3.2) may then be written in the form

$$\begin{matrix} c_1e^t + c_2e^{2t}, \\ c_1e^t + 3c_2e^{2t}, \end{matrix} \tag{3.6}$$

where c_1 and c_2 are constants. Since, conversely, for every choice of the constants c_1 and c_2 the column (3.6) is a solution, it is appropriate to refer to (3.6) as the *general solution* of (3.2).

Example. Solve the system

$$\begin{aligned} \frac{dx_1}{dt} &= 3x_1 - x_2, \\ \frac{dx_2}{dt} &= x_1 + x_2. \end{aligned} \tag{3.7}$$

The substitution in (3.7) of the column

$$\begin{matrix} Ae^{\lambda t} \\ Be^{\lambda t} \end{matrix}$$

leads in this case to the equations

$$\begin{aligned} (3 - \lambda)A - \quad\quad B &= 0, \\ A + (1 - \lambda)B &= 0, \end{aligned} \tag{3.8}$$

and the determinantal equation

$$\begin{vmatrix} 3 - \lambda & -1 \\ 1 & 1 - \lambda \end{vmatrix} = 0. \tag{3.9}$$

The roots of (3.9) are seen to be $\lambda = 2, 2$. Setting $\lambda = 2$ in (3.8), we determine the nontrivial solution $A = B = 1$ and the corresponding solution

$$\begin{matrix} e^{2t} \\ e^{2t} \end{matrix} \tag{3.10}$$

of the system (3.7). Since the roots of (3.9) are equal, we cannot employ the second root of this quadratic equation to obtain a second linearly independent solution of (3.7). The situation here is similar to that which arose when we solved a linear differential equation of second order whose corresponding indicial equation possessed a repeated root (see Chapter 2, Section 2). This similarity might suggest that a second solution of (3.7) could be obtained by multiplying the solution (3.10) by t:

$$\begin{matrix} te^{2t} \\ te^{2t}. \end{matrix}$$

It is easy to see, however, by testing these functions in (3.7), that they do not provide a solution. A more promising scheme is to attempt to determine functions $u(t)$ and $v(t)$ such that

$$\begin{matrix} e^{2t}u(t) \\ e^{2t}v(t) \end{matrix}$$

is a solution. Upon substituting these functions for x_1 and x_2, respectively, in (3.7), we find

$$\begin{aligned} \dot{u} &= u - v, \\ \dot{v} &= u - v. \end{aligned}$$

It follows that $\dot{u} = \dot{v}$, and hence that $u = v + c_1$. Thus, $c_1 = u - v = \dot{u} = \dot{v}$; hence, $u = c_1 t + c_2$, $v = c_1 t + (c_2 - c_1)$. We choose $c_2 = 0$, $c_1 = 1$, and we have the solution

$$\begin{matrix} te^{2t} \\ (t - 1)e^{2t} \end{matrix} \tag{3.11}$$

of (3.7). The solutions (3.10) and (3.11) may be proved to be linearly independent by computing the determinant

$$\Delta(t) = \begin{vmatrix} e^{2t} & te^{2t} \\ e^{2t} & (t - 1)e^{2t} \end{vmatrix} = -e^{4t}.$$

Since $\Delta(t) \not\equiv 0$, the solutions are linearly independent.

The general solution of equations (3.7) is, accordingly,

$$\begin{matrix} c_1e^{2t} + c_2te^{2t} \\ c_1e^{2t} + c_2(t - 1)e^{2t}. \end{matrix}$$

A somewhat shorter—and less enlightening—procedure after obtaining the solution (3.10) would be to determine constants a, b, f, g such that

$$\begin{matrix} (at + b)e^{2t} \\ (ft + g)e^{2t} \end{matrix}$$

is a solution. This can be accomplished by substituting these functions in (3.7).

Example. Solve the system

$$\begin{aligned} \frac{dx_1}{dt} &= 3x_1 + 2x_2, \\ \frac{dx_2}{dt} &= -x_1 + x_2. \end{aligned} \tag{3.12}$$

The substitution in (3.12) of the column

$$\begin{matrix} Ae^{\lambda t} \\ Be^{\lambda t} \end{matrix}$$

leads to the equations

$$\begin{aligned} (3 - \lambda)A + 2B &= 0, \\ -A + (1 - \lambda)B &= 0, \end{aligned} \tag{3.13}$$

and the determinantal equation

$$\begin{vmatrix} 3 - \lambda & 2 \\ -1 & 1 - \lambda \end{vmatrix} = 0. \tag{3.14}$$

The roots λ of (3.14) are $2 + i$ and $2 - i$. The substitution of $\lambda = 2 + i$ in (3.13) leads to the nontrivial solution $A = 1 + i$, $B = -1$ of (3.13) and the solution

$$\begin{matrix} (1 + i)e^{(2+i)t} \\ -e^{(2+i)t} \end{matrix} \tag{3.15}$$

of (3.12). The solution (3.15) can be rewritten, using the familiar relationship

$$e^{(a+ib)t} = e^{at}(\cos bt + i \sin bt),$$

in the form

$$\begin{aligned} &e^{2t}[(\cos t - \sin t) + i(\cos t + \sin t)], \\ &-e^{2t}[\cos t + i \sin t]. \end{aligned}$$

The real part of this solution,

$$\begin{aligned} &e^{2t}(\cos t - \sin t) \\ &-e^{2t} \cos t, \end{aligned} \tag{3.16}$$

must then also be a solution. So also is the imaginary part

$$\begin{aligned} &e^{2t}(\cos t + \sin t) \\ &-e^{2t} \sin t. \end{aligned} \tag{3.17}$$

The solutions (3.16) and (3.17) may, of course, be tested directly in (3.12). The computation of

$$\Delta(t) = \begin{vmatrix} e^{2t}(\cos t - \sin t) & e^{2t}(\cos t + \sin t) \\ -e^{2t} \cos t & -e^{2t} \sin t \end{vmatrix} = e^{4t}$$

shows that the solutions (3.16) and (3.17) are linearly independent.

The general solution of (3.12) is, accordingly,

$$\begin{aligned} &c_1e^{2t}(\cos t - \sin t) + c_2e^{2t}(\cos t + \sin t) \\ &-c_1e^{2t} \cos t - c_2e^{2t} \sin t. \end{aligned}$$

Since the root $\lambda = 2 + i$ of (3.14) yielded the general solution of (3.12), we can gain nothing by the substitution of the second root $\lambda = 2 - i$ of (3.14).

The three examples above illustrate all the possibilities for a system (3.1) since the roots λ of the corresponding determinantal equation

$$\begin{vmatrix} a_{11} - \lambda & a_{12} \\ a_{21} & a_{22} - \lambda \end{vmatrix} = 0$$

fall into one of the three following categories:

1. Roots real and distinct.
2. Roots real and equal.
3. Roots conjugate complex.

The substitution of

$$Ae^{\lambda t}$$

$$Be^{\lambda t}$$

$$Ce^{\lambda t}$$

in a system of three linear differential equations with constant coefficients leads to similar analysis. The student should experience no difficulty in carrying out the details.

Matrix notation. We may consider the column

$$x = \begin{bmatrix} x_1 \\ x_2 \\ \vdots \\ x_n \end{bmatrix}$$

as an n-dimensional vector the kth component of which is x_k. It may also be regarded as an $n \times 1$ matrix. If the components are functions of t on $I: a \leq t \leq b$, the column becomes a *vector-valued* function on I, since each value of t on the interval determines a vector x. The vector-valued function is said to be continuous on I if each component is continuous on I.

The derivative with respect to t of the vector x is the vector

$$\dot{x} = \begin{bmatrix} \dot{x}_1 \\ \dot{x}_2 \\ \vdots \\ \dot{x}_n \end{bmatrix}.$$

The sum of two vectors x and y is the vector

$$x + y = \begin{bmatrix} x_1 + y_1 \\ x_2 + y_2 \\ \vdots \\ x_n + y_n \end{bmatrix},$$

where y_k $(k = 1, 2, \ldots, n)$ is, of course, the kth component of y. The integral of a vector-valued function $x(t)$ is the vector

$$\int_a^b x(t)\,dt = \begin{bmatrix} \int_a^b x_1(t)\,dt \\ \int_a^b x_2(t)\,dt \\ \vdots \\ \int_a^b x_n(t)\,dt \end{bmatrix}.$$

If c is any real number, the vector cx is the vector whose kth component is cx_k. Two vectors x and y are said to be equal if and only if $x_k = y_k$ $(k = 1, 2, \ldots n)$. The null vector 0 is the vector each of whose components is zero. The *norm* $\|x\|$ of a vector x may be defined in a number of ways. The usual definition is

$$\|x\| = (x_1^2 + x_2^2 + \cdots + x_n^2)^{1/2}.$$

For purposes of matrix differential equations theory, however, a very useful definition is*

$$\|x\| = \sum_1^n |x_i|.$$

* For this definition and for more on matrix differential equations see Richard Bellman, *Introduction to Matrix Analysis*, McGraw-Hill, New York (1960).

If we designate by $A(t)$ the matrix

$$A(t) = \begin{pmatrix} a_{11}(t) & a_{12}(t) & \dots & a_{1n}(t) \\ a_{21}(t) & a_{22}(t) & \dots & a_{2n}(t) \\ \cdot & \cdot & \cdot & \cdot \\ a_{n1}(t) & a_{n2}(t) & \dots & a_{nn}(t) \end{pmatrix},$$

the product $A(t)x$ of the matrices $A(t)$ and x is precisely the right-hand member of (1.1), and the system (1.1) can then be written

$$\frac{dx}{dt} = A(t)x. \tag{3.18}$$

We say that $A(t)$ is a *continuous* matrix if each element $a_{ij}(t)$ is continuous. A solution of (3.18) is then a vector-valued function $x(t)$—that is, a column such as (1.2).

Theorem 1.1 can now be translated as follows:

Suppose $A(t)$ is continuous on $I: a \leq t \leq b$, let t_0 be any point of I, and let

$$a = \begin{bmatrix} a_1 \\ a_2 \\ \vdots \\ a_n \end{bmatrix}$$

be an arbitrary constant vector (or $n \times 1$ matrix). There then exists one and only one solution $x(t)$ of the (matrix) differential system

$$\frac{dx}{dt} = A(t)x,$$

$$x(t_0) = a.$$

EXERCISES

Find the general solutions of the given systems of differential equations.

1. $\dfrac{dx_1}{dt} = x_2, \qquad \dfrac{dx_2}{dt} = -2x_1 + 3x_2.$

2. $\dfrac{dx_1}{dt} = -3x_1 + 4x_2, \qquad \dfrac{dx_2}{dt} = -2x_1 + 3x_2.$

3. $\dfrac{dx_1}{dt} = x_2, \qquad \dfrac{dx_2}{dt} = -x_1 + 2x_2.$

4. $\dfrac{dx_1}{dt} = 4x_1 - x_2, \qquad \dfrac{dx_2}{dt} = 4x_1.$

5. $\dfrac{dx_1}{dt} = 12x_1 - 5x_2, \qquad \dfrac{dx_2}{dt} = 30x_1 - 13x_2.$

6. $\dfrac{dx_1}{dt} = -2x_2, \qquad \dfrac{dx_2}{dt} = x_1 + 2x_2.$

7. $\dfrac{dx_1}{dt} = x_1 - 2x_2, \qquad \dfrac{dx_2}{dt} = 4x_1 + 5x_2.$

8. $\dfrac{dx}{dt} = 4x - 2z, \qquad \dfrac{dz}{dt} = 4x.$

9.
$$\frac{dx_1}{dt} = 2x_1 + x_2 - 2x_3,$$
$$\frac{dx_2}{dt} = 3x_2 - 2x_3,$$
$$\frac{dx_3}{dt} = 3x_1 + x_2 - 3x_3.$$

10.
$$\frac{dx_1}{dt} = x_2,$$
$$2\frac{dx_2}{dt} = -3x_1 + 6x_2 - x_3,$$
$$\frac{dx_3}{dt} = -x_1 + x_2 + x_3.$$

11.
$$\frac{dx_1}{dt} = 3x_1 - 3x_2 + x_3,$$
$$\frac{dx_2}{dt} = 2x_1 - x_2,$$
$$\frac{dx_3}{dt} = x_1 - x_2 + x_3.$$

12. Solve the matrix differential system

$$\frac{dx}{dt} = A(t)x$$

when

(a) $A(t) = \begin{pmatrix} \frac{1}{2} & \frac{1}{2} \\ -\frac{3}{2} & \frac{5}{2} \end{pmatrix}, \qquad x(0) = \begin{bmatrix} 1 \\ 1 \end{bmatrix};$

(b) $A(t) = \begin{pmatrix} 0 & 1 \\ -2 & 3 \end{pmatrix}, \qquad x(0) = \begin{bmatrix} 0 \\ 1 \end{bmatrix};$

(c) $A(t) = \begin{pmatrix} 0 & 2 & 0 \\ -1 & 3 & 0 \\ 0 & 0 & 3 \end{pmatrix}, \qquad x(0) = \begin{bmatrix} 0 \\ 1 \\ 1 \end{bmatrix}.$

ANSWERS

1. $c_1e^t + c_2e^{2t}$,
$c_1e^t + 2c_2e^{2t}$.

2. $c_1e^t + 2c_2e^{-t}$,
$c_1e^t + c_2e^{-t}$.

3. $c_1e^t + c_2te^t$,
$c_1e^t + c_2(t + 1)e^t$.

4. $c_1e^{2t} + c_2te^{2t}$,
$2c_1e^{2t} + c_2(2t - 1)e^{2t}$.

5. $c_1e^{2t} + c_2e^{-3t}$,
$2c_1e^{2t} + 3c_2e^{-3t}$.

6. $2c_1e^t \cos t + 2c_2e^t \sin t$,
$c_1e^t (\sin t - \cos t) - c_2e^t (\sin t + \cos t)$.

7. $c_1e^{3t} \cos 2t + c_2e^{3t} \sin 2t$,
$c_1e^{3t} (\sin 2t - \cos 2t) - c_2e^{3t} (\sin 2t + \cos 2t)$.

8. $c_1e^{2t} \cos 2t + c_2e^{2t} \sin 2t$,
$c_1e^{2t} (\cos 2t + \sin 2t) + c_2e^{2t} (\sin 2t - \cos 2t)$.

9. $c_1e^t + c_2e^{-t} + c_3e^{2t}$,
$c_1e^t + c_2e^{-t} + 2c_3e^{2t}$,
$c_1e^t + 2c_2e^{-t} + c_3e^{2t}$.

10. $c_1e^t + c_2te^t + c_3e^{2t}$,
$c_1e^t + c_2(1 + t)e^t + 2c_3e^{2t}$,
$c_1e^t + c_2(2 + t)e^t + c_3e^{2t}$.

11. $c_1e^t + c_2e^t(2 \cos t - \sin t) + c_3e^t (\cos t + 2 \sin t)$,
$c_1e^t + 2c_2e^t \cos t + 2c_3e^t \sin t$,
$c_1e^t + c_2e^t \cos t + c_3e^t \sin t$.

12. (a) $x = \begin{bmatrix} e^t \\ e^t \end{bmatrix}$;

(b) $x = \begin{bmatrix} e^{2t} - e^t \\ 2e^{2t} - e^t \end{bmatrix}$;

(c) $x = \begin{bmatrix} 2e^{2t} - 2e^t \\ 2e^{2t} - e^t \\ e^{3t} \end{bmatrix}$.

4 The Phase Plane

The linear differential equations

$$\frac{dx}{dt} = a_1x + b_1y, \qquad \frac{dy}{dt} = a_2x + b_2y, \tag{4.1}$$

where a_1, b_1, a_2, and b_2 are constants and t is regarded as time, are of fundamental importance in the study of nonlinear differential equations. We regard t as a parameter and study the curves defined by equations (4.1) in the xy-plane, that is, in the *phase plane*.

The point $x = 0$, $y = 0$ at which both $\frac{dx}{dt}$ and $\frac{dy}{dt}$ vanish, that is, where

$$\left(\frac{dx}{dt}\right)^2 + \left(\frac{dy}{dt}\right)^2 = 0,$$

is called a *critical point* of the system (4.1). Note that if the determinant

$$\begin{vmatrix} a_1 b_1 \\ a_2 b_2 \end{vmatrix} = a_1 b_2 - a_2 b_1$$

is not equal to 0, the origin is the only critical point of the system (4.1).

We seek a solution of (4.1) in the form

$$\begin{aligned} x &= Ae^{\lambda t} \\ y &= Be^{\lambda t}, \end{aligned} \tag{4.2}$$

where A, B, and λ are suitably chosen constants (see Section 3). When the substitution (4.2) is made in equations (4.1) we have

$$\begin{aligned} A(a_1 - \lambda) + Bb_1 &= 0, \\ Aa_2 + B(b_2 - \lambda) &= 0. \end{aligned} \tag{4.3}$$

Equations (4.3) will possess solutions A and B not both zero if and only if λ is a root of the *characteristic equation*

$$\begin{vmatrix} a_1 - \lambda & b_1 \\ a_2 & b_2 - \lambda \end{vmatrix} = 0. \tag{4.4}$$

This equation can be rewritten in the form

$$\lambda^2 - (a_1 + b_2)\lambda + (a_1 b_2 - a_2 b_1) = 0. \tag{4.5}$$

The roots λ_1 and λ_2 of this quadratic equation are known as *characteristic roots.* If equation (4.5) is written as

$$\lambda^2 - p\lambda + q = 0, \tag{4.6}$$

where

$$p = a_1 + b_2, \qquad q = a_1 b_2 - a_2 b_1,$$

we note that

$$p = \lambda_1 + \lambda_2, \qquad q = \lambda_1 \lambda_2.$$

The discriminant Δ of equation (4.6) is given by

$$\begin{aligned}\Delta &= p^2 - 4q \\ &= (a_1 - b_2)^2 + 4a_2b_1.\end{aligned}$$

The behavior of the solutions (4.2) of equations (4.1) depends in a fundamental way on the nature of the roots of equation (4.6). Let us examine these solutions more carefully.

If λ is set equal to λ_1 in the first of equations (4.3) and if we designate by A_1 and B_1, respectively, any corresponding nontrivial solution A and B of (4.3), we have

$$A_1(a_1 - \lambda_1) + B_1b_1 = 0. \tag{4.7}$$

Similarly,

$$A_2(a_1 - \lambda_2) + B_2b_1 = 0, \tag{4.8}$$

where A_2 and B_2 are any nontrivial solution of (4.3) corresponding to the characteristic root λ_2. If both members of equation (4.7) are multiplied by $-A_2$ and both members of (4.8) are multiplied by A_1 and the results are added, we have

$$b_1(A_1B_2 - A_2B_1) = (\lambda_2 - \lambda_1)A_1A_2. \tag{4.9}$$

A similar treatment of the second of equations (4.3) yields

$$a_2(A_1B_2 - A_2B_1) = (\lambda_1 - \lambda_2)B_1B_2. \tag{4.10}$$

It follows readily from (4.9) and (4.10) that if $\lambda_1 \neq \lambda_2$, then

$$A_1B_2 - A_2B_1 \neq 0.$$

If $\lambda_1 \neq \lambda_2$, linearly independent solutions of (4.1) are furnished by the columns

$$\begin{matrix} A_1e^{\lambda_1 t} & A_2e^{\lambda_2 t} \\ B_1e^{\lambda_1 t}, & B_2e^{\lambda_2 t}. \end{matrix} \tag{4.11}$$

The general solution of (4.1) may then be written in the form

$$\begin{aligned} x &= c_1A_1e^{\lambda_1 t} + c_2A_2e^{\lambda_2 t}, \\ y &= c_1B_1e^{\lambda_1 t} + c_2B_2e^{\lambda_2 t}, \end{aligned} \tag{4.12}$$

where c_1 and c_2 are arbitrary constants.

The curves in the phase plane (xy-plane) satisfy at each point the differential equation

$$(a_2x + b_2y)\,dx = (a_1x + b_1y)\,dy; \tag{4.13}$$

accordingly, by the fundamental existence theorem, there is one and only one curve through each point of the plane, except possibly the origin.

A number of cases which arise are illustrated below by examples. Careful examination of these examples will indicate that the methods employed are quite general.

Case I. $q < 0$. In this case the characteristic roots λ_1 and λ_2 are real and of opposite signs. As an example, consider the system

$$\frac{dx}{dt} = x - y, \qquad \frac{dy}{dt} = -2x. \tag{4.14}$$

The characteristic equation is readily seen to be

$$\begin{vmatrix} 1-\lambda & -1 \\ -2 & -\lambda \end{vmatrix} = \lambda^2 - \lambda - 2 = 0,$$

and the characteristic roots are $\lambda_1 = -1$, $\lambda_2 = 2$. The general solution may be written in the form

$$x = c_1e^{-t} + c_2e^{2t}, \qquad y = 2c_1e^{-t} - c_2e^{2t}. \tag{4.15}$$

Consider first the case when $c_2 = 0$ and $c_1 \neq 0$. The points (x,y) lie along the line $y = 2x$, and as t varies from an arbitrary value t_0 to ∞, the point (x,y) moves toward the origin as a limit. Similarly, if $c_2 \neq 0$ and $c_1 = 0$, the point (x,y) moves along the line $y = -x$ away from the origin, as t varies from an arbitrary value t_0 to ∞.

Either by solving the differential equation (4.13) or by eliminating the parameter t in equation (4.15) we find that the curves represented by (4.15) have the equation

$$(x + y)^2(y - 2x) = k, \tag{4.16}$$

where k is a constant. It is clear from equation (4.16) that the lines $x + y = 0$ and $y - 2x = 0$ are asymptotes of the family

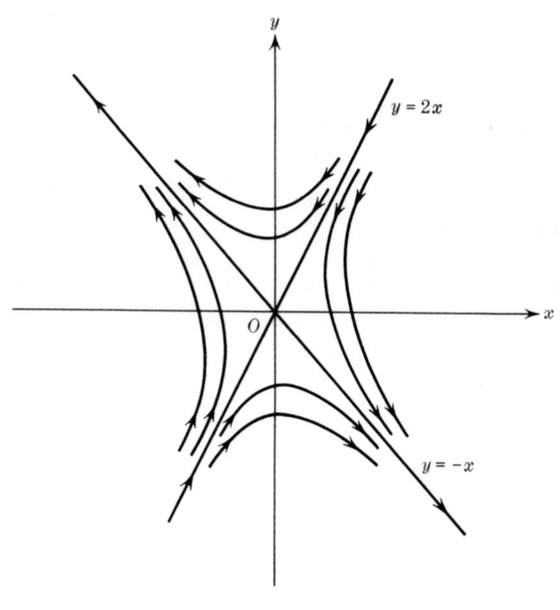

($q < 0$, saddle point)

FIG. 7.1

(4.16). This can also be observed from equations (4.15). For, when t is very large and positive, the first terms in the right-hand members of (4.15) are very small, and these equations are approximately $x = c_2e^{2t}$, $y = -c_2e^{2t}$; that is, the point (x,y) is close to the line $y = -x$. Similarly, when t is numerically large but negative, the point (x,y) is near the line $y = 2x$.

Note that the curves (4.15) have slopes given by the formula

$$\frac{dy}{dx} = \frac{2x}{y - x}.$$

This follows from (4.14). Thus, the *trajectories*—the curves (4.15)—have the property that all have horizontal tangents where they cross the y-axis. Further, they have vertical tangents at the points where they cross the line $y = x$, and all have slope -2 at their x-intercepts. It is clear from (4.15) that if neither c_1 nor c_2 is zero, a point (x,y) moving along a trajectory cannot approach the origin.

Typical trajectories in the phase-plane are shown in Fig. 7.1. The arrowheads on the curves indicate the direction of motion of a point (x,y) along the trajectories.

The critical point at the origin in this case ($q < 0$) is frequently called a *saddle point*.

Case II. $q > 0, \Delta > 0$. In this case the characteristic roots λ_1 and λ_2 are real, unequal, and are either both positive or both negative. Consider the system

$$\begin{aligned} \frac{dx}{dt} &= -\frac{7}{4}x + \frac{1}{4}y, \\ \frac{dy}{dt} &= \frac{3}{4}x - \frac{5}{4}y. \end{aligned} \tag{4.17}$$

The characteristic equation is

$$\lambda^2 + 3\lambda + 2 = 0,$$

and the characteristic roots are $\lambda_1 = -1$, $\lambda_2 = -2$. It is easily seen that the general solution of (4.17) can be written

$$\begin{aligned} x &= c_1e^{-t} + c_2e^{-2t}, \\ y &= 3c_1e^{-t} - c_2e^{-2t}. \end{aligned} \tag{4.18}$$

If $c_1 = 0$, and $c_2 \neq 0$, the point (x,y) moves along the line $y = -x$ and moves toward the origin as t increases. If $c_1 \neq 0$, and $c_2 = 0$, the point (x, y) moves along the line $y = 3x$ and moves toward the origin as t increases.

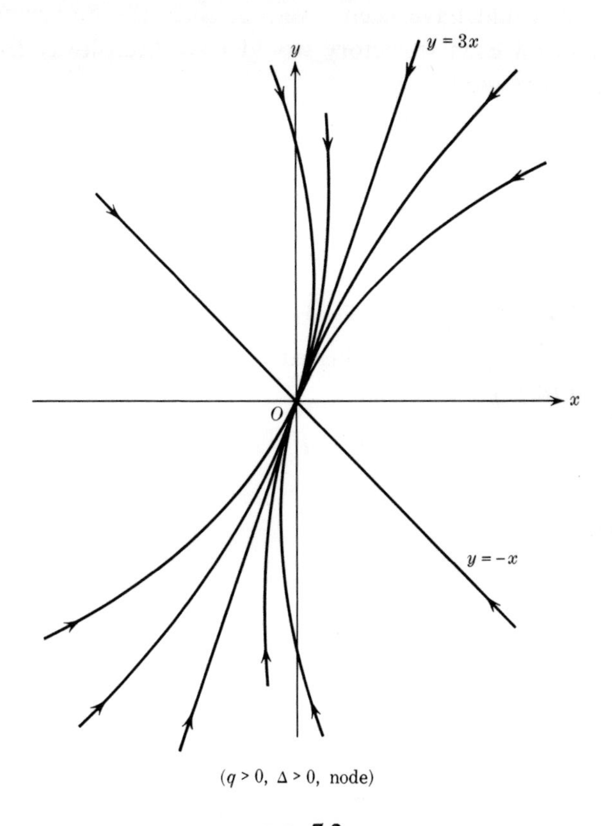

($q > 0$, $\Delta > 0$, node)

FIG. 7.2

If the parameter t is eliminated from equation (4.18) or if equation (4.13) is solved, the family of trajectories is given by the equation

$$(x + y)^2 = k(y - 3x). \tag{4.19}$$

These curves are seen to be tangent to the line $y = 3x$ at the origin (they are parabolas in this particular example, with the lines $2x + 2y + k = 0$ as their axes of symmetry). The critical point at the origin in this case ($q > 0$, $\Delta > 0$) is called a *node*.

If the characteristic roots λ_1 and λ_2 had both been positive, the picture would have been similar, but the arrows on the trajectories in Fig. 7.2 would have been reversed, since the movement of a point (x,y) on each trajectory would have been away from the origin as t increased.

Case III. $\Delta < 0, p \neq 0$. In this case, the characteristic roots λ_1 and λ_2 are conjugate imaginary numbers, and the critical point at the origin is called a *focus*. We set

$$\lambda_1 = \alpha + i\beta,$$
$$\lambda_2 = \alpha - i\beta \qquad (\alpha\beta \neq 0).$$

It will be desirable to obtain real solutions from the solutions (4.11) and (4.12). If we set

$$A = a + ib,$$
$$B = c + id,$$

the solution

$$Ae^{\lambda_1 t}$$
$$Be^{\lambda_1 t}$$

becomes

$$(a + ib)e^{\alpha t}(\cos \beta t + i \sin \beta t),$$
$$(c + id)e^{\alpha t}(\cos \beta t + i \sin \beta t).$$

It follows that linearly independent solutions are given by the columns

$$\begin{matrix} e^{\alpha t}(a \cos \beta t - b \sin \beta t) & e^{\alpha t}(b \cos \beta t + a \sin \beta t) \\ e^{\alpha t}(c \cos \beta t - d \sin \beta t) & e^{\alpha t}(d \cos \beta t + c \sin \beta t), \end{matrix} \tag{4.20}$$

and that the general solution can be written

$$\begin{aligned} x &= e^{\alpha t}[c_1(a \cos \beta t - b \sin \beta t) + c_2(b \cos \beta t + a \sin \beta t)], \\ y &= e^{\alpha t}[c_1(c \cos \beta t - d \sin \beta t) + c_2(d \cos \beta t + c \sin \beta t)], \end{aligned} \tag{4.21}$$

where c_1 and c_2 are arbitrary constants. These equations can be written in the form

$$x = e^{\alpha t}[(ac_1 + bc_2) \cos \beta t + (ac_2 - bc_1) \sin \beta t],$$
(4.22)
$$y = e^{\alpha t}[(cc_1 + dc_2) \cos \beta t + (cc_2 - dc_1) \sin \beta t].$$

A moderate amount of algebra will verify that $ad - bc \neq 0$. For, if this were not so, a solution of equations (4.1) would clearly be $y = kx$, for some choice of the real constant k. It would follow that

$$a_2 = k(b_1k + a_1 - b_2),$$

and hence that the discriminant $\Delta \geq 0$, contrary to hypothesis. Further, it is easily verified that the determinant of the coefficients of $\cos \beta t$ and $\sin \beta t$ in (4.22),

$$e^{2\alpha t}\begin{vmatrix} ac_1 + bc_2 & ac_2 - bc_1 \\ cc_1 + dc_2 & cc_2 - dc_1 \end{vmatrix} = e^{2\alpha t}(bc - ad)(c_1^2 + c_2^2),$$

is zero if and only if $c_1 = c_2 = 0$. It follows that there is no value of t which will make both x and y zero if $c_1^2 + c_2^2 \neq 0$, inasmuch as $\sin \beta t$ and $\cos \beta t$ cannot vanish for the same value of t.

Consider now the illustrative example

$$\frac{dx}{dt} = x - y,$$
(4.23)
$$\frac{dy}{dt} = x + y.$$

The characteristic roots are $\lambda_1 = 1 + i$, $\lambda_2 = 1 - i$, and the general solution may be written in the form

$$x = e^t(c_1 \cos t + c_2 \sin t)$$
(4.24)
$$y = e^t(c_1 \sin t - c_2 \cos t).$$

The family of curves represented by (4.24) in the phase plane have the equation

(4.25) $$\sqrt{x^2 + y^2} = ce^{\text{arc tan } y/x},$$

where c is an arbitrary constant. The form of this equation suggests the introduction of polar coordinates ρ and θ. Since in polar coordinates,

$$\rho = \sqrt{x^2 + y^2},$$

$$\tan \theta = \frac{y}{x},$$

equation (4.25) becomes

$$\rho = ce^{\theta},$$

which is the equation of a spiral.

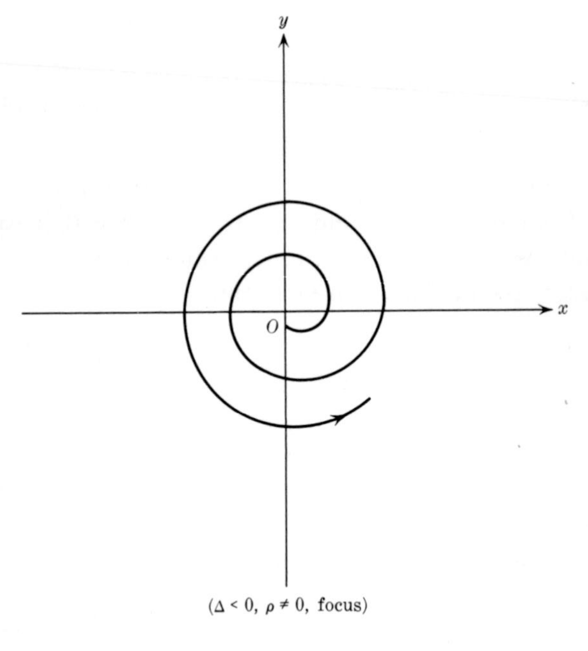

($\Delta < 0$, $p \neq 0$, focus)

FIG. 7.3

The situation is described in Fig. 7.3. The motion is away from the critical point because the real part α of the characteristic roots is positive [note the factor $e^{\alpha t}$ in equations (4.22)]. If the real part α of the characteristic roots were negative, the arrow would be reversed in Fig. 7.3.

Exceptional cases. The cases that remain are interesting from a mathematical point of view, but less so from a physical point of view. For example, consider the case $\Delta < 0$, $p = 0$. Typical is the system

$$\frac{dx}{dt} = 4x + 5y, \qquad \frac{dy}{dt} = -5x - 4y. \tag{4.26}$$

The characteristic equation is

$$\begin{vmatrix} 4 - \lambda & 5 \\ -5 & -4 - \lambda \end{vmatrix} = \lambda^2 + 9 = 0,$$

and the characteristic roots are $\lambda_1 = 3i$, $\lambda_2 = -3i$. If the coefficients in (4.26) are regarded as numbers from a physical problem, the slightest change in any of them will cause $p \neq 0$.

In this case, the general solution may be written in the form

$$x = c_1(5 \cos 3t) + c_2(5 \sin 3t), \qquad y = c_1(-4 \cos 3t - 3 \sin 3t) + c_2(3 \cos 3t - 4 \sin 3t). \tag{4.27}$$

The trajectories in the phase plane have the equation

$$5x^2 + 8xy + 5y^2 = c^2,$$

which gives a family of concentric curves (here ellipses) having the origin as center. The critical point at the origin when $\Delta < 0$, $p = 0$, is called a *center* (see Fig. 7.4, page 162).

The discussion of the case $\Delta < 0$ is complete. In addition we have analyzed the cases $\Delta > 0$, $q \neq 0$. There remain

1. $(\Delta > 0)$, $q = 0$, $p \neq 0$,
2. $\Delta = 0$, $p \neq 0$,
3. $(\Delta = 0)$, $q = 0$, $p = 0$.

These cases are left to the student as exercises.

More general systems. Consider the system

$$\frac{dx}{dt} = f(x,y), \qquad \frac{dy}{dt} = g(x,y), \tag{4.28}$$

where $f(x,y)$ and $g(x,y)$ are analytic functions of the variables

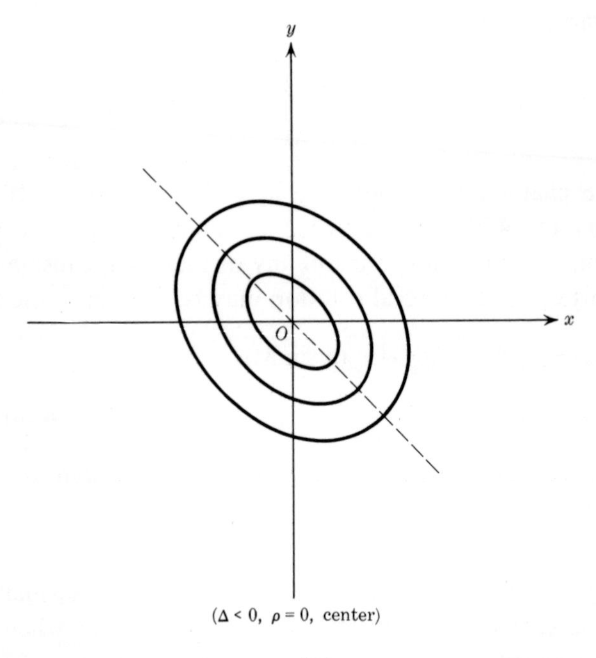

FIG. 7.4

(x,y) neighboring the origin. Suppose (without loss in generality) that

$$f(0,0) = 0,$$
$$g(0,0) = 0.$$

To say that f and g are analytic near the origin is equivalent to saying that each may be expanded in a Taylor series which represents the function near the origin; that is,

$$
(4.29)\qquad
\begin{aligned}
\frac{dx}{dt} &= a_1x + b_1y + a_{11}x^2 + a_{12}xy + a_{22}y^2 + F(x,y),\\
\frac{dy}{dt} &= a_2x + b_2y + b_{11}x^2 + b_{12}xy + b_{22}y^2 + G(x,y),
\end{aligned}
$$

where $F(x,y)$ and $G(x,y)$ involve only third and higher powers of x and y (together). When the linear terms in (4.29) provide a sufficiently close approximation to the function $f(x,y)$ and $g(x,y)$ near the origin, the study of the solutions of the equations

$$
(4.30)\qquad
\begin{aligned}
\frac{dx}{dt} &= a_1x + b_1y,\\
\frac{dy}{dt} &= a_2x + b_2y
\end{aligned}
$$

frequently is very useful in providing an approximation to the behavior of solutions of (4.28) near the origin. Equations (4.30) are called *the equations of variation* of the system (4.28).

In the applications, phase-plane study arises frequently in connection with second-order nonlinear differential equations

$$
(4.31)\qquad \frac{d^2x}{dt^2} = f\left(x, \frac{dx}{dt}\right).
$$

We set $v = \dfrac{dx}{dt}$ and we have, on the one hand, the system

$$
(4.32)\qquad
\begin{aligned}
\frac{dx}{dt} &= v,\\
\frac{dv}{dt} &= f(x,v).
\end{aligned}
$$

If the function $f(x,v)$ has the expansion

$$
f(x,v) = a_1x + b_1v + (\text{terms of higher order}),
$$

the equations of variation of the system (4.32) are the system

$$\frac{dx}{dt} = v,$$

$$\frac{dv}{dt} = a_1x + b_1v,$$

which can be studied by the methods of this chapter.

On the other hand, a differential equation of the trajectories in the phase-plane is the first-order equation

$$v\frac{dv}{dx} = f(x,v).$$

The last equation can be studied by any methods appropriate for differential equations of first-order.*

EXERCISES

1. Discuss the system

$$\frac{dx}{dt} = x + y,$$

$$\frac{dy}{dt} = 3x - y.$$

Sketch typical trajectories.

2. Discuss the system

$$\frac{dx}{dt} = x - y,$$

$$\frac{dy}{dt} = 2x + 4y.$$

Sketch typical trajectories.

3. Discuss the system

$$\frac{dx}{dt} = -x - y,$$

$$\frac{dy}{dt} = x - y.$$

Sketch a typical trajectory.

* For more material on elementary phase-plane analysis see W. Kaplan, *Ordinary Differential Equations*, Addison-Wesley, Reading, Massachusetts (1958).

4. Discuss the system

$$\frac{dx}{dt} = 3x + 5y,$$

$$\frac{dy}{dt} = -5x - 3y.$$

Sketch some typical trajectories.

5. Discuss the following systems, and sketch typical trajectories:

(a) $$\frac{dx}{dt} = x + y,$$

$$\frac{dy}{dt} = 2x + 2y;$$

(b) $$\frac{dx}{dt} = x - 2y,$$

$$\frac{dy}{dt} = 2x + 5y;$$

(c) $$\frac{dx}{dt} = 6x - 9y,$$

$$\frac{dy}{dt} = 4x - 6y.$$

6. Discuss the following systems, and sketch typical trajectories:

(a) $$\frac{dx}{dt} = 2x + y,$$

$$\frac{dy}{dt} = -5x - 4y;$$

(b) $$\frac{dx}{dt} = x - 3y,$$

$$\frac{dy}{dt} = 4x - 6y;$$

(c) $$\frac{dx}{dt} = 3x - 5y,$$

$$\frac{dy}{dt} = 2x + y;$$

(d) $\dfrac{dx}{dt} = 3x - 13y,$

$\dfrac{dy}{dt} = x - 3y;$

(e) $\dfrac{dx}{dt} = x + y,$

$\dfrac{dy}{dt} = -3x - 3y;$

(f) $\dfrac{dx}{dt} = -x - y,$

$\dfrac{dy}{dt} = x - 3y;$

(g) $\dfrac{dx}{dt} = x,$

$\dfrac{dy}{dt} = y;$

(h) $\dfrac{dx}{dt} = 2x - 4y,$

$\dfrac{dy}{dt} = x - 2y.$

7. The differential equation

$$\frac{d^2x}{dt^2} + \mu(x^2 - 1)\frac{dx}{dt} + x = 0 \qquad (\mu \text{ a positive constant})$$

is known as van der Pol's equation. It is of importance in vacuum tube theory. The substitution $v = \dfrac{dx}{dt}$ leads to the pair of equations

$$\text{(4.33)} \qquad \frac{dx}{dt} = v, \qquad \frac{dv}{dt} = -x + \mu(1 - x^2)v.$$

The equations of variation of the system (4.31) are the associated linear equations

$$\text{(4.34)} \qquad \frac{dx}{dt} = v, \qquad \frac{dv}{dt} = -x + \mu v.$$

Discuss the system (4.34) and draw some typical trajectories in the xv-plane (the phase-plane). Divide your discussion into three cases according as $\mu < 2$, $\mu = 2$, $\mu > 2$.

ANSWERS

1. $\lambda = 2, -2$; saddle point.

2. $\lambda = 2, 3$; node.

3. $\lambda = -1 \pm i$; focus.

4. $\lambda = 4i, -4i$; center.

5. (a) $\lambda = 0,3$; (b) $\lambda = 3,3$; (c) $\lambda = 0,0$.

5 Nonlinear Differential Systems

An enormous number of practical problems in the control of electrical, mechanical, thermal, and other engineering systems may be reduced to the study of a system of differential equations of the type

$$\begin{aligned} \frac{dx_1}{dt} &= X_1(x_1, x_2, \ldots, x_n, t), \\ \frac{dx_2}{dt} &= X_2(x_1, x_2, \ldots, x_n, t), \\ &\cdots\cdots\cdots \\ \frac{dx_n}{dt} &= X_n(x_1, x_2, \ldots, x_n, t), \end{aligned} \tag{5.1}$$

where the quantities X_i are functions, not necessarily linear, of the $n + 1$ variables $x_1, x_2, \ldots, x_n, t$. If $x_1, x_2, \ldots, x_n$ are regarded as components of an n-vector x and $X_1, X_2, \ldots, X_n$ as components of an n-vector X, equation (5.1) may be written in abbreviated form as

$$\frac{dx}{dt} = X(x,t). \tag{5.2}$$

When the variable t does not appear formally in the right-hand member of (5.1), the system (5.1) is said to be an *autonomous* system; otherwise, it is called *nonautonomous*. We shall be concerned with autonomous systems. The equations (5.1) then take the form

$$(5.1)' \qquad \begin{aligned} \frac{dx_1}{dt} &= X_1(x_1, x_2, \ldots, x_n), \\ \frac{dx_2}{dt} &= X_2(x_1, x_2, \ldots, x_n), \\ &\cdots\cdots \\ \frac{dx_n}{dt} &= X_n(x_1, x_2, \ldots, x_n), \end{aligned}$$

and we write (5.2) as

$$(5.2)' \qquad \frac{dx}{dt} = X(x).$$

A solution

$$\begin{aligned} x_1 &= x_1(t), \\ x_2 &= x_2(t), \\ &\cdots \\ x_n &= x_n(t) \end{aligned}$$

of (5.1)′ may be regarded either as a curve in the space of the $n + 1$ variables $x_1, x_2, \ldots, x_n, t$ or as a curve in the space of n variables $x_1, x_2, \ldots, x_n$ with t regarded as a parameter. In the latter case (which will be our principal concern), the curve is called a *trajectory* in the *phase space*—the space of the n variables $x_1, x_2, \ldots, x_n$.

For example, the autonomous system

$$(5.3) \qquad \begin{aligned} \frac{dx_1}{dt} &= x_2, \\ \frac{dx_2}{dt} &= -x_1 \end{aligned}$$

has the solution

$$(5.4) \qquad \begin{aligned} x_1 &= \sin t, \\ x_2 &= \cos t. \end{aligned}$$

The solution (5.4) will be recognized as a helix in (x_1, x_2, t)-space, while the corresponding trajectory in the phase space (i.e. the x_1x_2-plane) is the circle $x_1^2 + x_2^2 = 1$. In the latter case t is regarded as a parameter.

Any point $(a_1, a_2, \ldots, a_n)$ that provides a solution of the system of equations

$$\begin{aligned} X_1(x_1, x_2, \ldots, x_n) &= 0, \\ \cdot \quad \cdot \quad \cdot \quad \cdot \quad \cdot \quad \cdot \quad &\cdot \\ X_n(x_1, x_2, \ldots, x_n) &= 0 \end{aligned}$$

is called a *critical point* of the system (5.1)′. It is important to study the behavior of trajectories in the neighborhood of a critical point, and for this purpose it is usually convenient to assume the critical point is at the origin. The translation

$$x_i = a_i + z_i \qquad (i = 1, 2, \ldots, n)$$

transforms the system

$$\frac{dx}{dt} = X(x) \tag{5.5}$$

into the equivalent system

$$\frac{dz}{dt} = Z(z), \tag{5.6}$$

where

$$Z(z) = X(z + z),$$

and a critical point $(a_1, a_2, \ldots, a_n)$ of the system (5.5) becomes the critical point $(0, 0, \ldots, 0)$ of the system (5.6).

EXERCISES

1. Find the solution of the linear system

$$\frac{dx_1}{dt} = x_2,$$

$$\frac{dx_2}{dt} = -4x_1,$$

with the property that $x_1(0) = 0$, $x_2(0) = 1$. Interpret the solution in x_1, x_2, t-space and find the corresponding trajectory in the phase plane.

2. Find the solution of the linear system

$$\frac{dx_1}{dt} = x_1,$$

$$\frac{dx_2}{dt} = 2x_2$$

with the property that $x_1(0) = 1$, $x_2(0) = 1$. Interpret the solution in x_1, x_2, t-space and find the corresponding trajectory in the phase plane.

3. Show that the critical points of the nonlinear system

$$\frac{dx_1}{dt} = 8x_1 - x_2^2,$$

$$\frac{dx_2}{dt} = x_2 - x_1^2$$

are the points (0,0) and (2,4). Transform the system to an equivalent system in which the critical point (2,4) has been translated to the origin.

4. Show that the critical points of the nonlinear system

$$\frac{dx_1}{dt} = 5 - x_1^2 - x_2^2,$$

$$\frac{dx_2}{dt} = x_2 - 2x_1$$

are the points (1,2) and $(-1,-2)$. Transform the system to an equivalent system in which the critical point $(-1,-2)$ has been translated to the origin.

5. Find the critical points of the nonlinear system

$$\frac{dx_1}{dt} = x_1 + x_2 - 5,$$

$$\frac{dx_2}{dt} = x_1x_2 - 6.$$

6. Find the critical points of the nonlinear system

$$\frac{dx_1}{dt} = 293 - x_1^2 - x_2^2,$$

$$\frac{dx_2}{dt} = x_1x_2 - 34.$$

7. Find the critical points of the nonlinear system

$$\frac{dx_1}{dt} = x_1(x_2 + x_3) - 12,$$

$$\frac{dx_2}{dt} = 6 - x_2(x_1 + x_3),$$

$$\frac{dx_3}{dt} = x_3(x_1 + x_2) - 10.$$

ANSWERS

2. $x_1 = e^t$, $x_2 = e^{2t}$; a curve lying on the surface $x_2 = x_1^2$; the curve $x_2 = x_1^2$.

3. The transformation $x_1 = 2 + z_1$, $x_2 = 4 + z_2$ leads to the equivalent system

$$\frac{dz_1}{dt} = 8z_1 - 8z_2 - z_2^2,$$

$$\frac{dz_2}{dt} = z_2 - 4z_1 - z_1^2.$$

6. (4,1,2), (−4,−1,−2).

6 Stability; Liapunov Functions

In this section we shall suppose we are dealing with an autonomous system of the form (5.1)′, where all partial derivatives $\frac{\partial X_i}{\partial x_j}$ exist and are continuous throughout the space of the n variables $x_1, x_2, \ldots, x_n$—that is, throughout the phase space. To simplify our discussion we shall develop the theory for the case $n = 2$ and write (5.1)′ in the form

$$\frac{dx}{dt} = f(x,y), \qquad \frac{dy}{dt} = g(x,y), \tag{6.1}$$

where we now suppose $f(x,y)$ and $g(x,y)$ are of class C' for all x and y, and $f(0,0) = g(0,0) = 0$. The results will, in general, extend readily to n dimensions.

The origin is a critical point of (6.1) and its phase space will be the xy-plane. The fundamental existence theorem will ensure that through each point of the xy-plane, which is not a critical point, there exists a unique trajectory of the system (6.1).

Two (related) questions are of paramount importance in the study of such systems. One is the existence, or not, of *periodic solutions* of the system. That is to say, are any trajectories closed curves? We shall not attempt to deal with this question here.* The second question has to do with *stability* of the trajectories.

We shall suppose that the origin is an *isolated* critical point of the system (6.1)—that is, that a circle can be drawn with the origin as center such that no other critical point of the system lies in the circle. Following LaSalle and Lefschetz we shall say that the critical point at the origin is *stable* whenever for any positive number R there exists a positive number $r \leq R$ such that a trajectory that starts inside the circle $x^2 + y^2 = r^2$ at time t_0 remains inside the circle $x^2 + y^2 = R^2$ for all $t > t_0$ (see Fig. 7.5).

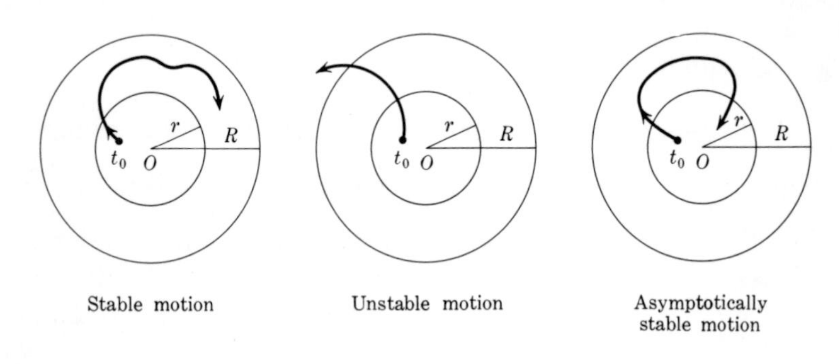

FIG. 7.5

The critical point at the origin will be said to be *asymptotically stable* if it is stable and if there exists a circle $x^2 + y^2 = R_0^2$

* The reader is referred to the fundamental study of J. LaSalle and S. Lefschetz, *Stability by Liapunov's Direct Method, with Applications*, Academic Press, New York (1961) for more information on this and other matters pertaining to the material of this section.

($R_0 > 0$) with the property that every trajectory that starts inside that circle at time t_0 tends to the origin as $t \to +\infty$.

The critical point at the origin will be said to be *unstable* in a region R containing the origin when for any $r > 0$, however small, there is always some point $P(x,y)$ inside the circle $x^2 + y^2 = r^2$ such that a trajectory that starts at P at time t_0 reaches the boundary of R.

Accordingly, the critical point at the origin is stable in Fig. 7.4, unstable in Fig. 7.1 and 7.3, and asymptotically stable in Fig. 7.2. The trajectories in Fig. 7.4 are also examples of periodic motions.

The functions of Liapunov. We are ready to formulate criteria that a critical point have one of the properties defined above. To that end let $V(x,y)$ be a function of class C' in an open region H containing the origin. Suppose $V(0,0) = 0$ and that V is positive at all other points of H. Then V has a minimum at the origin. We say that V is then *positive definite* in H.

We may compute $\dot{V}$ along trajectories of (6.1). We have

$$\dot{V} = \frac{dV}{dt} = \frac{\partial V}{\partial x} f(x,y) + \frac{\partial V}{\partial y} g(x,y).$$

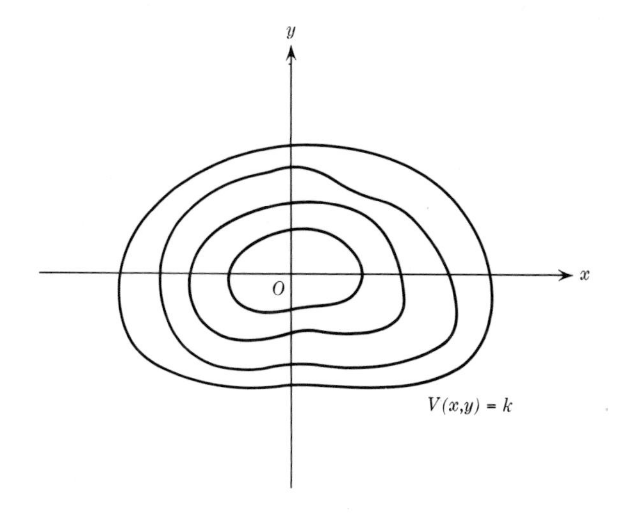

FIG. 7.6

If V is positive definite and $\dot{V} \leq 0$ in H, V is called a *Liapunov function* for the system (6.1) in the region H.

The surface $z = V(x,y)$ is tangent to the xy-plane at the origin, and it is intuitively evident that planes $z = k$ $(k > 0)$ cut this surface in curves that are closed, at least for k sufficiently small, and we shall assume this. The projection of these level curves on the xy-plane will then be a nest of ovals $V(x,y) = k$.

Theorem 6.1. *If there exists a Liapunov function for* (6.1) *in some neighborhood H of the origin, the critical point at the origin is stable.*

To prove the theorem let C be a circle of radius R with center at the origin that lies in H. Choose a k such that the oval $V(x,y) = k$ lies inside C, and then let c be a circle of radius r $(< R)$ with

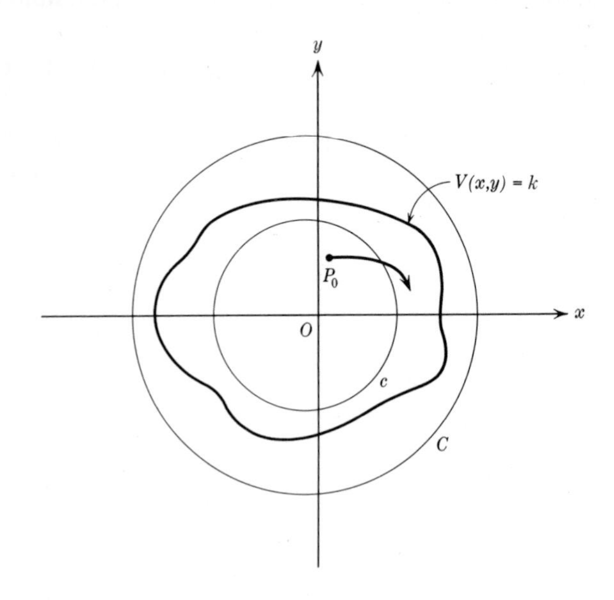

FIG. 7.7

center at the origin that lies inside this oval. Now let a trajectory start at a point $P_0(x_0,y_0)$ inside c at time t_0. Since P_0 lies inside the oval $V(x,y) = k$, it follows* that $V(x_0,y_0) < k$. Further, since $\dot{V} \leq 0$, V never increases, as t increases, along a trajectory. Accordingly, the trajectory commencing at P_0 can never reach the oval $V(x,y) = k$, and consequently cannot reach C.

The proof is complete.

Critique. For the purposes to which Theorem 6.1 is addressed it is convenient to state the hypotheses on the function V as follows:

1. $V(x,y)$ is of class C' in some open region H that contains the origin;
2. $V(0,0) = 0$;
3. $V(x,y) > 0$ at all other points of H;
4. There is a positive number k_0 such that for each $k < k_0$ the equation $V(x,y) = k$ represents a simple closed curve, and the curve $V(x,y) = k_1$ lies wholly within the curve $V(x,y) = k_2$ when $k_1 < k_2 < k_0$;
5. $\dot{V} \leq 0$ on trajectories in H.

Liapunov functions are extensions of the idea of energy functions in mechanics. But to apply Liapunov's idea any function $V(x,y)$ satisfying the hypotheses of the theorem will suffice. In simpler cases we may often guess usable Liapunov functions; in more complicated cases determining a Liapunov function for a given system may be very difficult indeed.

As an example consider the system

$$\frac{dx}{dt} = -y, \qquad \frac{dy}{dt} = x. \tag{6.2}$$

The point (0,0) is the only critical point of the system. A suitable

* This may be argued as follows: $V(x_0,y_0) \neq k$, since P_0 is not on the oval; suppose, then, $V(x_0,y_0) = k_1 > k$. An oval $V(x,y) = k_1$ would then lie wholly within the oval $V(x,y) = k$. But this would contradict the single-valuedness of V in H.

Liapunov function is $V(x,y) = x^2 + y^2$. For, the first four conditions of the critique are easily verified, and

$$\dot{V} = 2x(y) + 2y(-x) = 0.$$

Thus, the critical point at the origin is stable. The trajectories are readily seen to be the family of circles $x^2 + y^2 = a^2$.

Theorem 6.2. *If, in addition to the hypotheses of Theorem* 6.1, $-\dot{V}$ *is positive definite* (*that is,* $\dot{V}$ *is negative definite*), *the critical point at the origin is asymptotically stable.*

In this case, as t increases, V decreases steadily along a trajectory. Accordingly, V approaches a limiting value $k_1 \geq 0$. Because of the continuity of V it is sufficient to show that $k_1 = 0$. Suppose, if possible, that $k_1 > 0$. Then, since the trajectory would not penetrate the oval $V(x,y) = k_1$, the function $\dot{V}$, which is negative definite, would remain negative and bounded away from zero. Consider now the function

$$W(t) = V[x(t), y(t)],$$

—that is, V regarded as a function of t evaluated along the trajectory. $W(t)$ is of class C'. By hypothesis,

$$\lim_{t \to \infty} W(t) = k_1 > 0,$$

and, for t large,

$$\dot{W}(t) \leq -V_0 < 0.$$

But this is impossible. From this contradiction we infer the truth of the theorem.

As an example of the application of Theorem 6.2 consider the system (see Fig. 7.2)

$$\frac{dx}{dt} = -\frac{7}{4}x + \frac{1}{4}y,$$

(6.3)

$$\frac{dy}{dt} = \frac{3}{4}x - \frac{5}{4}y.$$

The origin is the only critical point. A suitable Liapunov function is

$$V(x,y) = 12x^2 + 12xy + 20y^2.$$

The first three conditions of the critique are easily verified. The equations $V(x,y) = k$ $(k > 0)$ represent a family of ellipses in which the fourth condition is satisfied. We compute

$$\dot{V} = -(33x^2 + 47y^2);$$

accordingly, $\dot{V}$ is negative definite along trajectories, and Theorem 6.2 states that the critical point at the origin is asymptotically stable.

It will be observed that an equally good choice (among others) for V would have been $3x^2 + 6xy + 11y^2$.

We conclude with the following theorem on instability.

Theorem 6.3. *Let $V(x,y)$ be of class C' in a region H containing the origin and suppose that $V(0,0) = 0$. If $\dot{V}$ (evaluated along trajectories) is positive definite and if in every neighborhood of the origin there is a point where $V > 0$, then the critical point at the origin is unstable in every circular region centered at O in H.*

The proof is somewhat more difficult than the preceding proofs. To prove the theorem let $R > 0$ be any number such that the circle $x^2 + y^2 = R^2$ lies in H. Choose r such that $0 < r < R$. Draw the circle $x^2 + y^2 = r^2$, and consider a trajectory J that starts at a point P_0 inside the smaller circle at which $V > 0$. Note that $\dot{V} > 0$ at P_0 and consider the function

$$W(t) = V[x(t), y(t)].$$

W is defined on J when t is greater than or equal to some number t_0. $W(t_0) > 0$ and $W'(t) > 0$ for $t \geq t_0$; consequently, W, and hence V, increases along J. Since $V \geq W(t_0) > 0$ on J, J is bounded away from the origin. It follows that $\dot{V}$ has a positive lower bound b on $J(t \geq t_0)$. Accordingly, $W(t)$ is a positive function with $W'(t) \geq b > 0$ for $t \geq t_0$. J cannot then remain inside the circle $x^2 + y^2 = R^2$, for V has a finite bound in $x^2 + y^2 \leq R^2$ which must be exceeded by $W(t)$, as t increases.

Therefore, J must reach the boundary $x^2 + y^2 = R^2$ (actually, it is seen that it will penetrate the boundary), and the instability of the critical point at the origin has been proved.

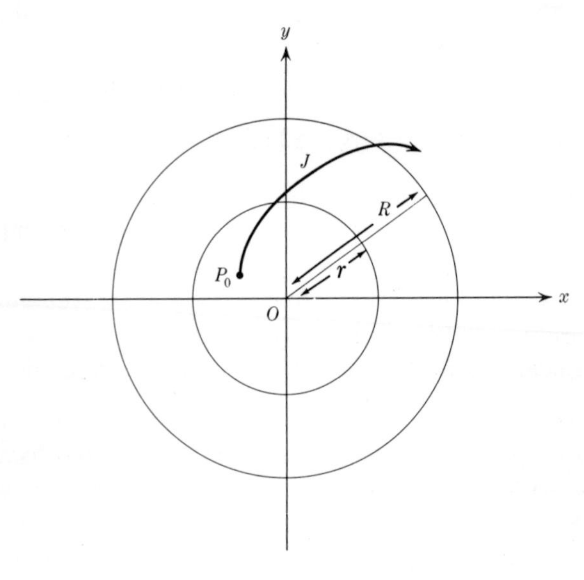

FIG. 7.8

To illustrate the theorem consider the system (see Fig. 7.1)

$$\begin{aligned} \frac{dx}{dt} &= x - y, \\ \frac{dy}{dt} &= -2x. \end{aligned} \tag{6.4}$$

The function $V(x,y) = x^2 - 2xy - y^2$ satisfies the hypotheses of the theorem, for at every point, except the origin, on the line $2x + y = 0$ we note that $V > 0$, and along each trajectory

$$\begin{aligned} \dot{V} &= 2x\dot{x} - 2x\dot{y} - 2y\dot{x} - 2y\dot{y} \\ &= 6x^2 + 2y^2. \end{aligned}$$

Accordingly, the critical point at the origin is unstable in every circular region about the origin.

EXERCISES

1. Find a Liapunov function for each system in Exercise 1–4 of Section 4, and in each case determine the stability or instability of the critical point of the system. [*Hint.* Assume $V = x^2 + kxy + my^2$, where k and m are constants to be determined. Recall that a form $ax^2 + bxy + cy^2$ ($a \neq 0$) is definite if and only if $b^2 - 4ac < 0$.]

2. The substitution $\dot{x} = y$ in van der Pol's equation

$$\ddot{x} + \mu(x^2 - 1)\dot{x} + x = 0$$

leads to the nonlinear system

$$\frac{dx}{dt} = y,$$

$$\frac{dy}{dt} = -\mu(x^2 - 1)y - x.$$

Using $V = x^2 + y^2$ show that the critical point at the origin is asymptotically stable when $\mu < 0$.

3. Discuss the stability of the critical point at the origin of the linear system

$$\frac{dx}{dt} = y,$$

$$\frac{dy}{dt} = -x.$$

4. Discuss the stability of the critical point at the origin of the nonlinear system

$$\frac{dx}{dt} = y + x^3 + xy^2,$$

$$\frac{dy}{dt} = -x + x^2y + y^3.$$

Take $V = x^2 + y^2$.

5. Discuss the stability of some of the systems in Exercises 5 and 6 of Section 4.

6. Show that a necessary and sufficient condition that the critical point of the system

$$\frac{dx}{dt} = ax + by,$$

$$\frac{dy}{dt} = cx + dy \quad (a, b, c, d \text{ constants}, ad - bc \neq 0),$$

be stable is that no root of the characteristic equation

$$\begin{vmatrix} a - \lambda & b \\ c & d - \lambda \end{vmatrix} = 0$$

have a positive real part.

ANSWERS

1. (a) One choice of V is $3x^2 + xy - y^2$, unstable; (b) unstable; (c) stable; (d) stable.

3. Stable.

4. Unstable.

8

Solutions in Power Series

It should be regarded as something of a fortunate accident when a differential equation has a simple neat solution in terms of familiar functions. Frequently, however, a series solution is available. In this chapter we shall develop methods of obtaining solutions in the form of *power series* for a number of types of differential equations for which such solutions exist.

1 Power Series

An infinite series

$$a_0 + a_1(x - a) + a_2(x - a)^2 + \cdots = \sum_0^\infty a_n(x - a)^n,$$

where $a_0, a_1, a_2, \ldots$ are constants, is a *power series*. Such a series evidently converges when $x = a$. If it converges for any other value of x, it converges on an interval

$$-b < x - a < b \qquad (0 < b \leq \infty).$$

On this interval it represents a function $f(x)$, the derivative of which may be obtained by term-by-term differentiation; that is,

$$f'(x) = \sum_0^\infty na_n(x - a)^{n-1} \qquad (-b < x - a < b).$$

It follows that

$$f''(x) = \sum_0^\infty n(n-1)a_n(x-a)^{n-2} \qquad (-b < x - a < b),$$

and so on.

The algebra of power series suggests the following method of solving differential equations. A solution $y(x)$ is assumed in the form

$$y(x) = \sum_0^\infty a_n(x-a)^n,$$

and after this series is substituted for y in the differential equation, coefficients of like powers of $x - a$ on each side of the equation are equated.

Let us see how the method works in a simple example.

Example. Find a power-series solution of the differential system

$$\begin{gathered} y'' + y = 0, \\ y(0) = 0, \qquad y'(0) = 1. \end{gathered} \tag{1.1}$$

We shall try for a solution in powers of $(x - 0) = x$; that is, we shall attempt to determine constants $a_0, a_1, a_2, \ldots$ such that the power series

$$a_0 + a_1x + a_2x^2 + \cdots = \sum_0^\infty a_nx^n$$

is a solution of (1.1). If we assume that (1.1) has a solution in this form and substitute it for y in the differential equation, we have

$$\sum_0^\infty n(n-1)a_nx^{n-2} + \sum_0^\infty a_nx^n \equiv 0,$$

or

$$\sum_0^\infty [(n+2)(n+1)a_{n+2} + a_n]x^n \equiv 0.$$

In order that the power series be identically zero, each of its coefficients must be zero; hence,

$$(n+2)(n+1)a_{n+2} + a_n = 0 \qquad (n = 0, 1, 2, \ldots). \tag{1.2}$$

The boundary conditions in (1.1) determine that $a_0 = 0$ and $a_1 = 1$. From (1.2) we then have $0 = a_2 = a_4 = a_6 = \cdots$, and

$$a_{2n+1} = -\frac{a_{2n-1}}{2n(2n+1)}.$$

Thus,

$$a_3 = -\frac{1}{2\cdot 3}, \qquad a_5 = \frac{1}{2\cdot 3\cdot 4\cdot 5}, \qquad \cdots,$$

and we have determined the power series

$$y = x - \frac{x^3}{3!} + \frac{x^5}{5!} - \cdots. \tag{1.3}$$

This series converges on every finite interval, and consequently provides a solution* of (1.1) for x on the interval $-\infty < x < \infty$. The series (1.3) is seen to be the usual power-series representation of $\sin x$, which was to have been expected.

If $|x|$ is small, the series (1.3) converges very rapidly and lends itself well to computation. Near $x = 100$, however, a great many terms of the series would be required to obtain accuracy to, say, two decimal places. If we were interested, for example, in a series solution $y(x)$ with the property that $y(100) = 2$, $y'(100) = 1$, a more efficient plan would be to attempt to determine the coefficients $a_0, a_1, a_2, \ldots$ so that the power series

$$a_0 + a_1(x - 100) + a_2(x - 100)^2 + \cdots = \sum_0^\infty a_n(x - 100)^n$$

would represent such a solution. The determination of the coefficients is easy in this instance and will be left to the student.

A somewhat more complicated example is the following.

* The student will recognize that it is in some sense fortuitous that mathematicians have happened to assign a name ($\sin x$) to the function represented by the power series (1.3). In some respects the series is more useful than the designation "$\sin x$." We can compute from it, for example. We feel more comfortable about the closed expression $\sin x$, partly because it *is* closed, partly because of relative familiarity with the function so designated, and partly because tables of values of the function are available [tables which are computed from expressions like that in (1.3)].

Example. Find a series solution in powers of $(x - 1)$ of the differential system

$$(1.4)\qquad \begin{aligned} &(4 - x^2)y'' - 2xy' + 12y = 0, \\ &y(1) = -7, \qquad y'(1) = 3. \end{aligned}$$

It will be convenient first to write the coefficients of the differential equation in powers of $(x - 1)$:

$$\begin{aligned} 4 - x^2 &= 3 - 2(x - 1) - (x - 1)^2, \\ -2x &= -2 - 2(x - 1), \\ 12 &= 12. \end{aligned}$$

Equation (1.4) may then be rewritten in the form

(1.4)′

$$[3 - 2(x - 1) - (x - 1)^2]y'' + [-2 - 2(x - 1)]y' + 12y = 0.$$

Next, we try for a solution of the form

$$(1.5)\qquad y = \sum_0^\infty a_n(x - 1)^n.$$

Then

$$(1.6)\qquad \begin{aligned} y' &= \sum_0^\infty na_n(x - 1)^{n-1}, \\ y'' &= \sum_0^\infty n(n - 1)a_n(x - 1)^{n-2}. \end{aligned}$$

The substitution of (1.5) and (1.6) in (1.4)′ leads to the equation

$$(1.7)\qquad \sum_0^\infty (12 - n - n^2)a_n(x - 1)^n - \sum_1^\infty 2n^2a_n(x - 1)^{n-1} + \sum_2^\infty (3n^2 - 3n)a_n(x - 1)^{n-2} = 0.$$

The last equation can then be written in the form

$$(1.8)\quad \sum_{0}^{\infty}(12 - n - n^2)a_n(x - 1)^n - \sum_{0}^{\infty} 2(n + 1)^2 a_{n+1}(x - 1)^n + \sum_{0}^{\infty} 3(n^2 + 3n + 2)a_{n+2}(x - 1)^n = 0,$$

or

$$(1.9)\quad \sum_{0}^{\infty}[3(n + 1)(n + 2)a_{n+2} - 2(n + 1)^2 a_{n+1} - (n - 3)(n + 4)a_n](x - 1)^n = 0.$$

It follows from (1.9) that

$$(1.10)\quad a_{n+2} = \frac{2(n + 1)^2 a_{n+1} + (n - 3)(n + 4)a_n}{3(n + 1)(n + 2)} \qquad (n = 0, 1, 2, \ldots).$$

From the side conditions in (1.4) we have

$$a_0 = -7,$$
$$a_1 = 3.$$

It follows from (1.10), upon setting $n = 0, 1, 2, 3$, successively, that

$$a_2 = 15,$$
$$a_3 = 5,$$
$$a_4 = 0,$$
$$a_5 = 0;$$

consequently, $a_n = 0$ $(n = 4, 5, \ldots)$. Accordingly, the series terminates, and the solution we seek is the polynomial

$$(1.5)'\qquad -7 + 3(x - 1) + 15(x - 1)^2 + 5(x - 1)^3.$$

We note that written in powers of x the solution (1.5)′ becomes $-12x + 5x^3$.

EXERCISES

Find power-series solutions of the following differential systems.

1. $y'' + y = 0,\ y(0) = 1,\ y'(0) = 0$ (in powers of x).

2. $y'' + y = 0$, $y(0) = 1$, $y'(0) = 1$ (in powers of x).

3. $y'' - 3y' + 2y = 0$, $y(0) = 0$, $y'(0) = 1$ (in powers of x).

4. $y'' + 4y' + 4y = 0$, $y(0) = 0$, $y'(0) = 0$ (in powers of x).

5. $(1 - x^2)y'' - 2xy' + 6y = 0$, $y(0) = -1$, $y'(0) = 0$ (in powers of x).

6. $y'' + y = 0$, $y(10) = 0$, $y'(10) = 1$ (in powers of $x - 10$).

7. $y'' - 3y' + 2y = 0$, $y(-4) = 0$, $y'(-4) = 1$ (in powers of $x + 4$).

8. $x^2y'' - xy' + 2y = 0$, $y(1) = 0$, $y'(1) = 1$ (in powers of $x - 1$).

9. $x^2y'' + xy' - 4y = 0$, $y(1) = 0$, $y'(1) = 1$ (in powers of $x - 1$).

10. $x^2y'' - 2xy' + 2y = 0$, $y(-2) = 1$, $y'(-2) = 0$ (in powers of $x + 2$).

ANSWERS

1. $1 - (x^2/2!) + (x^4/4!) - \cdots$.

3. $x + (3x^2/2!) + (7x^3/3!) + (15x^4/4!) + \cdots$.

5. $3x^2 - 1$.

6. $(x - 10) - (1/3!)(x - 10)^3 + (1/5!)(x - 10)^5 - \cdots$.

8. $(x - 1) + [(x - 1)^2/2!] - [2(x - 1)^3/3!] + [4(x - 1)^4/4!] - [10(x - 1)^5/5!] + \cdots$.

2 Alternative Method

For many problems a method other than that given in Section 1 may prove to be simpler.

Example. Consider the differential system

$$(2.1)\qquad \begin{aligned} y'' + y &= 2x - 1,\\ y(1) = 1, &\qquad y'(1) = 3. \end{aligned}$$

Suppose there is a solution $y(x)$ of (2.1) which can be represented as a power series in $(x - 1)$. Then by Taylor's theorem

$$(2.2)\qquad y(x) = y(1) + \frac{y'(1)}{1!}(x - 1) + \frac{y''(1)}{2!}(x - 1)^2 + \cdots.$$

We shall, accordingly, have the series we seek if we can evaluate the constants

$$y(1),\ y'(1),\ y''(1), \ldots. \tag{2.3}$$

The first two terms of this sequence are given by the side conditions in (2.1). From the differential equation we then have that

$$y''(x) = -y(x) + 2x - 1. \tag{2.4}$$

It follows that

$$\begin{aligned} y''(1) &= -y(1) + 1 \\ &= 0. \end{aligned}$$

Next, we differentiate both members of (2.4), obtaining

$$y'''(x) = -y'(x) + 2; \tag{2.5}$$

hence,

$$y'''(1) = -1.$$

We continue the process, differentiating (2.5). This yields

$$y''''(1) = -y''(1) = 0.$$

In this fashion each member of (2.3) may be determined successively, and we have

$$y(x) = 1 + \frac{3}{1!}(x-1) - \frac{1}{3!}(x-1)^3 + \frac{1}{5!}(x-1)^5 - \cdots. \tag{2.6}$$

In this case, if we note that we may write the general solution of the equation $y'' + y = 0$ in the form

$$c_1 \sin (x-1) + c_2 \cos (x-1),$$

the system (2.1) can be solved by inspection. We have

$$y = 2x - 1 + \sin (x-1). \tag{2.7}$$

Clearly, (2.6) is the formal expansion of (2.7) in powers of $(x - 1)$.

This method is likely to be simpler to apply than the method given in Section 1 when the differential equation is nonlinear.

Example. Consider the differential system

$$y' = 1 + y^2,$$
$$y(0) = 0. \tag{2.8}$$

The solution of this system is clearly $\tan x \left(-\frac{\pi}{2} < x < \frac{\pi}{2}\right)$.

Suppose we try to determine the solution $y(x)$ in the form

$$y(x) = y(0) + \frac{y'(0)}{1!}x + \frac{y''(0)}{2!}x^2 + \cdots.$$

If $y(x)$ is assumed to be a solution of (2.8), we have at once

$$\begin{aligned} y'(x) &= 1 + y^2(x), \\ y(0) &= 0, \\ y'(0) &= 1 + y^2(0) = 1. \end{aligned} \tag{2.9}$$

We differentiate (2.9), obtaining

$$y''(x) = 2y(x)y'(x). \tag{2.10}$$

It follows that

$$y''(0) = 0.$$

Similarly,

$$y'''(x) = 2y(x)y''(x) + 2y'^2(x);$$

thus,

$$y'''(0) = 2.$$

The process may be continued indefinitely, and it will yield as many terms of the series as patience and computing facilities permit. We have, after two more differentiations,

$$y(x) = x + \frac{x^3}{3} + \frac{2x^5}{15} + \cdots.$$

The method of Section 1 is slightly more complicated, perhaps, in that it involves squaring a power series. Using that method we would suppose

$$y(x) = \sum_1^\infty a_n x^n,$$

$$y'(x) = \sum_1^\infty n a_n x^{n-1},$$

since a_0 is seen to be zero from (2.8). Then, formally,

$$y^2(x) = a_1^2x^2 + 2a_1a_2x^3 + (a_2^2 + 2a_1a_3)x^4 + 2(a_1a_4 + a_2a_3)x^5 + \cdots.$$

Setting $y'(x) = 1 + y^2(x)$ yields

$$(2.11)\quad a_1 + 2a_2x + 3a_3x^2 + 4a_4x^3 + 5a_5x^4 + \cdots = 1 + a_1^2x^2 + 2a_1a_2x^3 + (a_2^2 + 2a_1a_3)x^4 + \cdots.$$

From (2.11) we have, successively,

$$a_1 = 1, \quad a_2 = 0, \quad a_3 = \tfrac{1}{3}, \quad a_4 = 0, \quad a_5 = \tfrac{2}{15}, \cdots,$$

which agrees with our previous result.

Critique. The general problem of convergence of power series to functions which represent solutions of the differential systems belongs in the realm of the theory of functions of a complex variable. In the examples and exercises in this chapter we are dealing with differential equations of the form

$$(2.12)\quad y^{(n)} = f[x, y, y', \ldots, y^{(n-1)}],$$

where the right-hand member of (2.12) is, in general, a very well-behaved (analytic) function of the $n + 1$ variables indicated. For example, the differential equation

$$(2.13)\quad x^2y'' - 2xy' - 4y = 0,$$

may be written in the form

$$y'' = \frac{2}{x}y' + \frac{4}{x^2}y.$$

Here,

$$f(x,y,y') = \frac{2}{x}y' + \frac{4}{x^2}y,$$

and this function, regarded for the moment as a function of the three independent variables x, y, and y', is very well-behaved provided $x \neq 0$.

The general situation will be clear from the differential equation $y'' = f(x,y,y')$. If $f(x,y,y')$ is well-behaved (analytic) in a region containing the point $x = a$, $y = b$, $y' = c$, there then exists a convergent power-series solution $\sum a_n(x - a)^n$ of the differential system

$$y'' = f(x,y,y'),$$
$$y(a) = b, \qquad y'(a) = c,$$

which is valid on an interval $-k < x - a < k$, where k is some number such that $0 < k \leq \infty$.

In particular, the differential system

$$(2.13)' \qquad \begin{aligned} y'' &= \frac{2}{x}y' + \frac{4}{x^2}y, \\ y(1) &= 0, \qquad y'(1) = 1 \end{aligned}$$

will then possess a convergent power-series solution of the form

$$y(x) = \sum_0^\infty a_n(x - 1)^n$$

for values of x on an interval $-k < x - 1 < k$, where $k > 0$. (In this particular case it can be shown that $k \geq 1$.)

Again, consider the differential system

$$(2.14) \qquad \begin{aligned} y'' &= -\frac{3y'^2}{y}, \\ y(0) &= 1, \qquad y'(0) = \tfrac{1}{4}. \end{aligned}$$

The right-hand member of the differential equation in (2.14) is well-behaved near the point $x = 0$, $y = 1$, $y' = \frac{1}{4}$. Accordingly, there exists a convergent power-series solution of the differential system (2.14) of the form

$$y(x) = \sum_{0}^{\infty} a_n x^n$$

for x on some interval $-k < x < k$ $(0 < k \leq \infty)$.

EXERCISES

1. Find a power-series solution of the differential system

$$yy'' + 3y'^2 = 0,$$
$$y(0) = 1, \qquad y'(0) = \tfrac{1}{4}.$$

2. Find a power-series solution in powers of $(x - 1)$ of the differential system

$$x^2y'' - 2xy' + 2y = 2,$$
$$y(1) = 1, \qquad y'(1) = 1.$$

3. Find a power-series solution of the differential system

$$y'' + 4y' + 3y = 0,$$
$$y(0) = 1, \qquad y'(0) = -1.$$

4. Find a power-series solution of the differential system

$$y'''' - 2y''' + 3y'' - 2y' + 2y = 0,$$
$$y(0) = 0, \qquad y'(0) = 1, \qquad y''(0) = 0, \qquad y'''(0) = -1.$$

Identify the solution.

ANSWERS

1. $1 + \dfrac{x}{2^2} - \dfrac{3x^2}{2^5} + \dfrac{7x^3}{2^7} - \dfrac{77x^4}{2^{11}} + \cdots.$

2. $1 + (x - 1) + (x - 1)^2.$

3 Regular Singular Points

In this section we shall confine our attention to homogeneous linear differential equations of second order. Such a differential equation will be said to possess a *regular* singular point at $x = a$ if it may be written in the form

$$(3.1) \qquad (x - a)^2 p_0(x) y'' + (x - a) p_1(x) y' + p_2(x) y = 0,$$

where $p_0(x)$, $p_1(x)$, and $p_2(x)$ are representable by power series in powers of $(x - a)$ which are valid in a common interval $|x - a| < h$ $(h > 0)$, and where $p_0(x) \neq 0$ in this interval. We shall suppose also that a is real and that the functions $p_i(x)$ are real for real values of x.

Many of the classical differential equations of interest to the physicist as well as to the mathematician may be written in this form. Perhaps the two most famous examples are the following:

$$x^2 y'' + xy' + (x^2 - n^2) y = 0 \qquad \text{(Bessel)},$$

$$(1 - x^2) y'' - 2xy' + n(n + 1) y = 0 \qquad \text{(Legendre)}.$$

The former has a regular singular point at $x = 0$, and the latter has a regular singular point at $x = 1$ and at $x = -1$.

The definition of a regular singular point as formulated above includes as a special case a regular (nonsingular) point. Thus, the differential equation

$$y'' + y = 0$$

has a regular singular point at $x = 1$, for example, for we may write the differential equation in the form

$$(x - 1)^2 y'' + (x - 1)^2 y = 0,$$

where $p_0(x) = 1$, $p_1(x) = 0$, and $p_2(x) = (x - 1)^2$. Accordingly, any theorems which we may state concerning solutions of equations (3.1) in the neighborhood of a regular singular point must be valid also near a nonsingular point of the differential equation. The theorems are of particular interest as they apply to the study of *singular* points which are regular.

The student will recall that the "Euler-type" differential equation

$$(3.2) \qquad ax^2 y'' + bxy' + cy = 0 \qquad (a \neq 0),$$

where a, b, and c are real constants, has a regular singular point at $x = 0$. Indeed, equation (3.2) provides the simplest example of a second-order linear differential equation with a regular singular point, and its study will suggest the correct approach to the study of the more general equation (3.1).

Equation (3.2) was solved in Chapter 2 by means of the substitution $|x| = e^t$. This substitution may also be used profitably to transform equation (3.1). We might also try to solve (3.2) by seeking to determine a solution $|x|^r$, where r is a suitably determined constant. Upon substituting this function for y in (3.2), we see that r must satisfy the quadratic equation

$$ar(r - 1) + br + c = 0. \tag{3.3}$$

Conversely, if r is a root of this quadratic equation, $|x|^r$ is a solution of (3.2). Thus, if r_1 and r_2 are distinct roots (possibly complex) of (3.3), the general solution of (3.2), at least on any interval of the x-axis not containing the origin, may be given the form*

$$c_1|x|^{r_1} + c_2|x|^{r_2}.$$

When $r_1 = r_2$, the general solution becomes

$$c_1|x|^{r_1} + c_2|x|^{r_1} \log |x|.$$

The foregoing analysis suggests that we try to find a solution of equation (3.1) of the form†

$$|x - a|^r P(x), \tag{3.4}$$

* When r_1 and r_2 are conjugate complex numbers, the functions $|x|^{r_1}$ and $|x|^{r_2}$ are known from the theory of functions of a complex variable to be many-valued functions. Using that theory and that of linear differential equations, we can show, nevertheless, that it is correct in this situation to set

$$|x|^{\alpha + i\beta} = |x|^\alpha [\cos (\beta \log |x|) + i \sin (\beta \log |x|)] \qquad (\beta \neq 0,\ x \neq 0),$$

where $|x|^\alpha$ and $\log |x|$ have their usual (unique) definitions as real functions.

† The author's thanks are due to Professor R. H. Bruck, who points out that the formula

$$[|x - a|^r P(x)]' = |x - a|^r [P'(x) + r(x - a)^{-1} f(x)] \qquad (x \neq a)$$

simplifies appreciably the computation in situations of this kind.

where r is a suitably determined constant and $P(x)$ is representable by a power series $\sum_0^\infty c_n(x-a)^n$ in some interval

$$|x-a| < c \qquad (c > 0),$$

and where $P(a) \neq 0$ (that is, $c_0 \neq 0$). If we substitute the function (3.4) for y in equation (3.1) and assume that it provides a solution, we obtain

$$(3.5)\quad (x-a)^2 p_0 P'' + (x-a)(2rp_0 + p_1)P' + [p_0 r(r-1) + rp_1 + p_2]P \equiv 0.$$

In particular, this identity must hold when $x = a$. Thus, if (3.4) provides a solution of equation (3.1), r must be a root of the quadratic equation

$$(3.6)\qquad p_0(a)r(r-1) + p_1(a)r + p_2(a) = 0.$$

Equation (3.6) is known as the *indicial* equation associated with the regular singular point $x = a$ of equation (3.1).

Theorem 3.1. *If the roots r_1 and r_2 of the indicial equation differ by a number which is not an integer, there exist two linearly independent solutions of* (3.1),

$$|x-a|^{r_1}P_1(x) \quad \text{and} \quad |x-a|^{r_2}P_2(x),$$

where $P_1(x)$ and $P_2(x)$ are representable as power series in $(x-a)$ which are valid in the interval $|x-a| < h$ and $P_1(a) \neq 0$, $P_2(a) \neq 0$.

If the difference $r_1 - r_2$ is a positive integer or zero, there exist linearly independent solutions of (3.1),

$$y_1(x) = |x-a|^{r_1}P_1(x),$$
$$y_2(x) = |x-a|^{r_2}P_2(x) + Cy_1(x)\log|x-a|,$$

where the functions $P_1(x)$ and $P_2(x)$ are representable by power series in $(x-a)$ which are valid in the interval $|x-a| < h$ and

$P_1(a) \neq 0$, $P_2(a) \neq 0$. *The constant C is not zero when* $r_1 = r_2$; *if* $r_1 - r_2$ *is a positive integer, C may or may not be zero.**

The proof of the theorem is omitted.†

Since the coefficients of the indicial equation (3.6) are real, its roots are either real and distinct, real and equal, or conjugate complex. For simplicity, we shall suppose henceforth that $a = 0$. Equation (3.1) then becomes

$$(3.1)' \qquad x^2p_0(x)y'' + xp_1(x)y' + p_2(x)y = 0.$$

The student will recognize that then only obvious changes are required for the more general case.

Real Roots. The theorems of this section ensure that there always exists a solution of (3.1)′ of the form

$$(3.7) \qquad y_1(x) = |x|^{r_1} \sum_0^\infty c_n x^n,$$

* Bruck points out that a useful alternate form for $y_2(x)$ is

$$y_2(x) = |x - a|^{r_1}[CP_1(x) \log |x - a| + (x - a)^{-k}P_2(x)],$$

where $k = r_1 - r_2$. We can then often profitably introduce the substitution $y = |x - a|^r{}_1 Y$ initially in the given differential equation.

† The proof of the theorem (due to Fuchs) from which Theorem 3.1 follows is to be found, for example, in L. Bieberbach, *Theorie der Differentialgleichungen*, pp. 206ff., Dover Publications, New York (1944). To verify that the form of Theorem 3.1 is correct (which is the form needed in the real domain), the student should note that the substitution for y in (3.1) of $(x - a)^rP(x)$ and $|x - a|^rP(x)$ when x is real leads in both cases to the same indicial equation (3.6) and to the same differential equation (3.5) which is satisfied by $P(x)$. The existence proof of the original theorem (see Bieberbach, *loc. cit.*) amounts first to demonstrating the existence of a convergent power-series solution $P(x)$ of (3.5) corresponding to the index r_1 which has the greater real part. Obtaining in this fashion the solution

$$y_1(x) = (x - a)^{r_1}P(x),$$

we make the substitution in (3.1) of $y = (x - a)^{r_1}P(x)w$ to determine w and hence a second linearly independent solution. Since for x real we obtain the same differential equation for the determination of w by substituting $|x - a|^{r_1}P(x)w$ for y in (3.1), we see that Theorem 3.1 is a consequence of the theorem of Fuchs.

It should be pointed out that the functions $P_1(x)$ and $P_2(x)$ may be complex functions when the indicial roots r_1 and r_2 are conjugate complex numbers.

where r_1 is the larger of the two roots ($r_1 \geq r_2$), and the series $\sum c_n x^n$ is valid in some interval about $x = 0$. To determine this solution, it is frequently simplest to make the substitution $y = |x|^{r_1} u$ in (3.1)′, obtaining

$$x^2 p_0 u'' + x(2rp_0 + p_1)u' + [p_0 r(r-1) + rp_1 + p_2]u = 0. \tag{3.8}$$

The substitution $u = \sum_0^{\infty} c_n x^n$ leads then to a determination of the coefficients $c_0, c_1, c_2, \ldots$ of the power series. When the coefficients in (3.8) become too complicated or when r_1 is a positive integer, the direct substitution of (3.7) in (3.1) may be simpler.

The solution $y_1(x)$ corresponding to the larger of the two roots of the indicial equation is called a *principal* solution. There are several methods available for computing a solution linearly independent of $y_1(x)$. In any, the computation frequently becomes rather cumbersome. A direct plan—one probably as good as any—is to substitute $y = y_1(x)z$ in (3.1), obtaining

(3.9)
$$xp_0(x)y_1(x)w' + [2xp_0(x)y_1'(x) + p_1(x)y_1(x)]w = 0 \qquad (w = z').$$

This is a linear homogeneous differential equation of the first order in w which may be written as

$$w' + \left[2\frac{y_1'(x)}{y_1(x)} + \frac{p_1(x)}{xp_0(x)}\right]w = 0. \tag{3.9′}$$

Its solution is

$$w = z' = c\frac{1}{y_1^2(x)}e^{-\int \frac{p_1(x)\,dx}{x p_0(x)}}. \tag{3.10}$$

The operations indicated in (3.10) may be carried out in terms of power series. From the result we may compute z as a power series. Finally, the product $y_1(x)z$ yields the desired solution.

Example. The differential equation

$$x^2y'' - 2x^2y' + (\tfrac{1}{4} + x^2)y = 0 \tag{3.11}$$

has a regular singular point at $x = 0$. Here, $p_0(x) = 1$, $p_1(x)$

$= -2x$, $p_2(x) = \frac{1}{4} + x^2$, and the indicial equation associated with the singularity is

$$r^2 - r + \tfrac{1}{4} = 0,$$

the roots of which are $r = \frac{1}{2}, \frac{1}{2}$. According to the theory, there is a solution of the form

$$y_1(x) = |x|^{1/2} \sum_0^\infty c_n x^n \qquad (c_0 \neq 0).$$

The substitution $y = |x|^{1/2}u$ in (3.11) leads to the differential equation

$$x^2u'' + x(1 - 2x)u' + (x^2 - x)u = 0. \tag{3.12}$$

In (3.12), we set

$$u = \sum_0^\infty c_n x^n,$$

$$u' = \sum_0^\infty c_n n x^{n-1},$$

$$u'' = \sum_0^\infty c_n n(n - 1)x^{n-2}$$

obtaining readily

$$(c_1 - c_0)x + \sum_2^\infty [n^2c_n + (1 - 2n)c_{n-1} + c_{n-2}]x^n = 0.$$

Thus,

$$c_1 = c_0, \qquad c_n = \frac{(2n - 1)c_{n-1} - c_{n-2}}{n^2} \qquad (n = 2, 3, \ldots).$$

The constant c_0 may be assigned any value different from zero. Let us set $c_0 = 1$. Then

$$c_0 = 1, \quad c_1 = 1, \quad c_2 = \frac{1}{2}, \quad c_3 = \frac{1}{2\cdot 3}, \quad \ldots, \quad c_n = \frac{1}{n!}, \ldots.$$

We recognize the solution $u(x)$ we have obtained as e^x. Accordingly,

$$y_1(x) = |x|^{1/2}e^x.$$

To find a second linearly independent solution, we may substitute $u = e^x z$ in (3.12) or $y = |x|^{1/2}e^x z$ in (3.11). We choose the former as being the simpler for this problem. We see that z satisfies the differential equation

$$xz'' + z' = 0. \tag{3.13}$$

Linearly independent solutions of (3.13) are 1 and $\log |x|$. The former leads to $y_1(x)$. The latter leads to the solution

$$y_2(x) = |x|^{1/2}e^x \log |x|.$$

The general solution of (3.11) is, consequently,

$$c_1|x|^{1/2}e^x + c_2|x|^{1/2}e^x \log |x|.$$

Example. The differential equation

$$x^2y'' + xy' + (x - 1)y = 0 \tag{3.14}$$

has a regular singular point at $x = 0$. The associated indicial equation is

$$r^2 - 1 = 0,$$

the roots of which are $r = 1, -1$. Accordingly, there is a solution of the form

$$y_1(x) = x \sum_0^\infty c_n x^n = \sum_0^\infty c_n x^{n+1} \qquad (c_0 \neq 0). \tag{3.15}$$

In this case we choose to substitute the series (3.15) in (3.14) directly. We obtain

$$\sum_1^\infty [(n^2 + 2n)c_n + c_{n-1}]x^{n+1} = 0;$$

therefore,

$$c_n = -\frac{c_{n-1}}{n(n+2)} \qquad (n = 1, 2, \ldots). \tag{3.16}$$

Choosing $c_0 = 1$ (any value not equal to zero would be acceptable), we have

$$c_1 = -\frac{2}{1!3!}, \qquad c_2 = \frac{2}{2!4!}, \qquad c_3 = -\frac{2}{3!5!}, \;\ldots\;.$$

We note that

$$c_n = (-1)^n \frac{2}{n!(n+2)!} \qquad (n = 1, 2, \ldots),$$

and that the series (3.15) converges for all x by the test-ratio test [this is seen most quickly by reference to (3.16)]. A principal solution of (3.14) is

$$y_1(x) = x\left[1 + \sum_1^\infty (-1)^n \frac{2}{n!(n+2)!} x^n\right].$$

The substitution $y = y_1(x)z$ leads to equation (3.10), which becomes

$$z' = \frac{c}{y_1^2(x)} e^{-\int \frac{p_1(x)\,dx}{x\,p_0(x)}} = \frac{c}{xy_1^2(x)}$$

$$= \frac{c}{x^3\left[1 + \sum_1^\infty (-1)^n \frac{2}{n!(n+2)!} x^n\right]^2}$$

$$= \frac{c}{x^3}\left(\frac{1}{1 - \frac{x}{3} + \frac{x^2}{24} - \frac{x^3}{360} + \cdots}\right)^2$$

$$= \frac{c}{x^3}\left(1 + \frac{x}{3} + \frac{5x^2}{72} + \frac{13}{1080}x^3 + \cdots\right)^2$$

$$= c\left(\frac{1}{x^3} + \frac{2}{3x^2} + \frac{1}{4x} + \frac{19}{270} + \cdots\right).$$

Thus,

$$z = c_1 + c\left(-\frac{1}{2x^2} - \frac{2}{3x} + \frac{1}{4}\log|x| + \frac{19}{270}x + \cdots\right),$$

and, accordingly, we may take

$$y_2(x) = \frac{c}{4}(\log|x|)y_1(x)$$

$$+ \frac{c}{x}\left(-\frac{1}{2} - \frac{1}{2}x + \frac{29}{144}x^2 + \frac{19}{432}x^3 + \cdots\right) \qquad (c \neq 0).$$

Example. The differential equation

$$(x - 1)^2 y'' + (x - 1)y' + (x - 3)y = 0 \tag{3.17}$$

has a regular singular point at $x = 1$. To solve the differential equation, we might first set $t = x - 1$. Then

$$\frac{dy}{dx} = \frac{dy}{dt} \quad \text{and} \quad \frac{d^2y}{dx^2} = \frac{d^2y}{dt^2}.$$

The resulting differential equation will have a regular singular point at $t = 0$. Let us, however, proceed directly with equation (3.17). The indicial equation associated with the singularity at $x = 1$ is

$$r^2 - 2 = 0, \tag{3.18}$$

and its roots are $\sqrt{2}, -\sqrt{2}$. There exists, then, a solution

$$y_1(x) = |x - 1|^{\sqrt{2}} \sum_0^\infty c_n (x - 1)^n \qquad (c_0 \neq 0)$$

corresponding to the larger root. Here the substitution $y = |x - 1|^{\sqrt{2}} u$ is indicated, and the coefficients c_n may be determined by setting $u = \sum_0^\infty c_n (x - 1)^n$ in the resulting differential equation. Since the difference $\sqrt{2} - (-\sqrt{2})$ is not an integer, a second solution $y_2(x)$ exists which may be represented by the series

$$y_2(x) = |x - 1|^{-\sqrt{2}} \sum_0^\infty b_n (x - 1)^n \qquad (b_0 \neq 0).$$

The substitution $y = v|x - 1|^{-\sqrt{2}}$ in (3.17) will permit the later substitution $v = \sum_0^\infty b_n (x - 1)^n$ and the consequent determination of the numbers b_n.

The case when the indicial roots are conjugate complex numbers is somewhat more complicated and is omitted.*

* For an exposition of this case see the author's *Introduction to the Theory of Differential Equations*, McGraw-Hill, New York (1952).

EXERCISES

Find the general solutions of the following differential equations.

1. $x^2y'' - x(1 + 2x)y' + (1 + x + x^2)y = 0.$

2. $x^2y'' + x(3 - 2x)y' + (1 - 3x + x^2)y = 0.$

3. $4x^2y'' + 8x^2y' + (1 + 4x^2)y = 0.$

4. $x^2y'' - 2xy' + (2 + x^2)y = 0.$

5. $xy'' - y' + 4x^3y = 0.$

6. $(x - 2)^2y'' - 4(x - 2)y' + (x^2 - 4x + 10)y = 0.$

7. $(x - 1)^2y'' + (x - 1)(1 - 2x)y' + (1 - x + x^2)y = 0.$

8. One solution of each of the following (Legendre) differential equations is given. Find a linearly independent solution.

(a) $(1 - x^2)y'' - 2xy' = 0,$ $\quad y_1(x) = 1.$
(b) $(1 - x^2)y'' - 2xy' + 2y = 0,$ $\quad y_1(x) = x.$
(c) $(1 - x^2)y'' - 2xy' + 6y = 0,$ $\quad y_1(x) = \frac{1}{2}(3x^2 - 1).$
(d) $(1 - x^2)y'' - 2xy' + 12y = 0,$ $\quad y_1(x) = \frac{1}{2}(5x^3 - 3x).$

9. Find the general solution of the differential equation

$$x^2y'' + xy' + (x^2 - \tfrac{1}{4})y = 0.$$

10. Find the general solution of the differential equation

$$x^2y'' + 2xy' - \left(2 + \sum_1^\infty x^n\right)y = 0.$$

11. Find the general solution of the differential equation (3.17).

12. Find the general solution of Bessel's equation

$$x^2y'' + xy' + (x^2 - n^2)y = 0,$$

when $n = 0$.

ANSWERS

1. $\left(x + \frac{x^2}{1!} + \frac{x^3}{2!} + \frac{x^4}{3!} + \cdots\right)(c_1 + c_2 \log |x|).$

2. $x^{-1}\left(1 + \frac{x}{1!} + \frac{x^2}{2!} + \frac{x^3}{3!} + \cdots\right)(c_1 + c_2 \log |x|).$

3. $|x|^{1/2}\left(1 - \frac{x}{1!} + \frac{x^2}{2!} - \frac{x^3}{3!} + \cdots\right)(c_1 + c_2 \log |x|).$

4. $c_1\left(x^2 - \frac{x^4}{3!} + \frac{x^6}{5!} - \cdots\right) + c_2\left(x - \frac{x^3}{2!} + \frac{x^5}{4!} - \cdots\right).$

5. $c_1\left(x^2 - \frac{x^6}{3!} + \frac{x^{10}}{5!} - \cdots\right) + c_2\left(1 - \frac{x^4}{2!} + \frac{x^8}{4!} - \frac{x^{12}}{6!} + \cdots\right).$

6. $$(x-2)^2\left\{c_1\left[(x-2) - \frac{(x-2)^3}{3!} + \frac{(x-2)^5}{5!} - \cdots\right] + c_2\left[1 - \frac{(x-2)^2}{2!} + \frac{(x-2)^4}{4!} - \cdots\right]\right\}.$$

7. $$\left[(x-1) + \frac{(x-1)^2}{1!} + \frac{(x-1)^3}{2!} + \frac{(x-1)^4}{3!} + \cdots\right] \times (c_1 + c_2 \log |x-1|).$$

8. (a) $\frac{1}{2}\log\left|\frac{x+1}{x-1}\right|;$

(b) $\frac{1}{2}x\log\left|\frac{x+1}{x-1}\right| - 1;$

(c) $\frac{1}{4}(3x^2 - 1)\log\left|\frac{x+1}{x-1}\right| - \frac{3x}{2};$

(d) $\frac{1}{4}(5x^3 - 3x)\log\left|\frac{x+1}{x-1}\right| - \frac{5}{2}x^2 + \frac{2}{3}.$

9. $c_1|x|^{-1/2}\left(x - \frac{x^3}{3!} + \frac{x^5}{5!} - \cdots\right) + c_2|x|^{-1/2}\left(1 - \frac{x^2}{2!} + \frac{x^4}{4!} - \cdots\right).$

10. $$\left(x + \frac{x^2}{4} + \frac{x^3}{8} + \frac{11}{144}x^4 + \cdots\right) \times \left[c_1 + c_2\left(-\frac{1}{3x^3} + \frac{1}{4x^2} + \frac{1}{16x} - \frac{1}{36}\log x + \cdots\right)\right].$$

11. $$c_1|x-1|^{\sqrt{2}}\left(1 + \frac{1-2\sqrt{2}}{7}(x-1) + \frac{5-3\sqrt{2}}{28}(x-1)^2 + \frac{19\sqrt{2}-27}{84}(x-1)^3 + \cdots\right)$$
$$+ c_2|x-1|^{-\sqrt{2}}\left(1 + \frac{1+2\sqrt{2}}{7}(x-1) + \frac{5+3\sqrt{2}}{28}(x-1)^2 - \frac{19\sqrt{2}+27}{84}(x-1)^3 + \cdots\right).$$

12. $c_1 y_1(x) + c_2\left[y_1(x)\log|x| + \left(\frac{x}{2}\right)^2 - \frac{\frac{1}{1}+\frac{1}{2}}{(2!)^2}\left(\frac{x}{2}\right)^4 + \frac{\frac{1}{1}+\frac{1}{2}+\frac{1}{3}}{(3!)^2}\left(\frac{x}{2}\right)^6 - \cdots\right];$

$$y_1(x) = \sum_0^\infty (-1)^n \frac{1}{(n!)^2}\left(\frac{x}{2}\right)^{2n}.$$

4 On Numerical Solutions

The advent of the giant computer has largely put the calculation of an approximate solution of a differential equation in the realm of numerical analysis and computer programming. It may be well, however, to remind ourselves of some of the processes which may be available to us with the help of a small computing machine or of a slide-rule.

First, a power-series solution may be available to us, and the methods of this chapter will suggest methods of computations. Then, the method of successive approximations (see Chapter 9) is occasionally useful as a practical means of computation. What is known as the Rayleigh-Ritz method* is a powerful method for obtaining approximate solutions to certain differential equations arising in the calculus of variations. There are areas in which Fourier series can be useful. For many purposes, divergent series (asymptotic or semi-convergent series) are more useful as means of computation than are convergent power series.

From the brief observations above the student will realize the enormous scope and complexity of the general problem of computing approximate solutions of a differential equation or of a system of differential equations. Usually such computations are quite time-consuming.

The Cauchy polygon method. It may be helpful to point out a method of approximating a solution of a system of the type

$$\frac{dy}{dx} = f(x,y), \tag{4.1}$$

* See for example, R. Courant and D. Hilbert, *Methods of Mathematical Physics*, vol. 1, Interscience, New York (1953).

$$y(x_0) = y_0, \tag{4.2}$$

which is useful at times.

Note that the differential equation (4.1) provides the slope of the solution of the equation at any point (x,y) on a solution-curve, and that the solving of the system (4.1) and (4.2) means finding the solution of the differential equation which passes through the point (x_0, y_0).

The method will be clear from the following example. Consider the system

$$\frac{dy}{dx} = \frac{-y}{1+x}, \tag{4.1$'$}$$

$$y(0) = 1. \tag{4.2$'$}$$

Suppose we are interested in the solution on the interval $0 \le x \le 1$. The slope of this solution at (0,1) is readily computed from (4.1) to be -1. The interval [0,1] is subdivided into n subintervals.

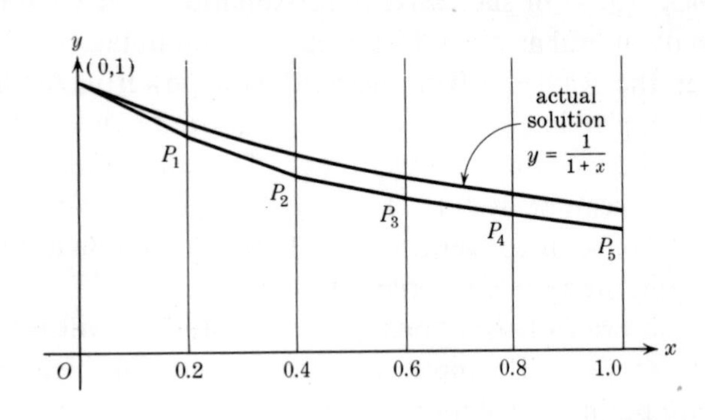

FIG. 8.1

(We have broken the interval into five equal subintervals in Fig. 8.1. In general, the larger n is, the better is the approximation. Also, the subintervals need not be equal.) The straight-line segment through (0,1) with slope -1 has the equation

$$y = 1 - x. \tag{4.3}$$

We take this straight line as the approximation to the solution on the interval $0 < x < 0.2$.

At $x = 0.2$, y is computed from (4.3) to be 0.8. The coordinates of P_1 in Fig. 8.1 are then (0.2,0.8). We now use equation (4.1)′ to compute the slope of the solution through P_1. We find this slope to be $-\frac{2}{3}$. The straight line through P_1 with slope $-\frac{2}{3}$ has the equation

$$y = 0.8 - \tfrac{2}{3}(x - 0.2), \tag{4.4}$$

and this line is taken as the solution of the system (4.1)′ and (4.2)′ on the interval $0.2 < x < 0.4$. When $x = 0.4$, y is found from (4.4) to be 0.67. The coordinates of P_2 are then (0.4,0.67). The process is continued, and points P_3, P_4, P_5 are determined consecutively. To two-place accuracy the coordinates of these points are found to be

$$P_3\colon (0.60,\ 0.57), \qquad P_4\colon (0.80,\ 0.50), \qquad P_5\colon (1.00,\ 0.44).$$

The precise solution of (4.1)′ and (4.2)′ is easily found to be

$$y(x) = \frac{1}{1 + x}. \tag{4.5}$$

We give below a table of comparative values.

x	*Actual y*	*Approx. y*
0.00	1.00	1.00
0.20	0.83	0.80
0.40	0.71	0.67
0.60	0.62	0.57
0.80	0.56	0.50
1.00	0.50	0.44.

It will be seen that the actual values of y are larger than the approximate values computed, and that the errors tend to accumulate. The former is true because the actual solution is concave upward on the interval. The latter observation is typical of the method.

EXERCISES

Use the Cauchy polygon method to compute an approximate solution of each of the following differential systems on the interval indicated. Take n as given and use equal subintervals. Compute to two decimal places accuracy. Draw the polygonal graph and the graph of the actual solution (use large-scale drawings).

1. $\dfrac{dy}{dx} = -\dfrac{y}{x+1}$, $y(0) = 1$, $0 \leq x \leq 1$; $n = 10$.

2. $\dfrac{dy}{dx} = \dfrac{1}{2y}$, $y(0) = 1$, $0 \leq x \leq 1$; $n = 5$.

3. $\dfrac{dy}{dx} = \dfrac{1}{2y}$, $y(0) = 1$, $0 \leq x \leq 1$; $n = 10$.

4. $\dfrac{dy}{dx} = 1 + y$, $y(0) = 0$, $0 \leq x \leq 1$; $n = 5$.

5. $\dfrac{dy}{dx} = 1 + y$, $y(0) = 0$, $0 \leq x \leq 1$; $n = 10$.

9

The Method of Successive Approximations; The Existence Theorem

1 Algebraic Equations

The method of *successive approximations* is an exceedingly important practical method of solving algebraic equations as well as probably the most important theoretical method for solving differential equations. Frequently, it is also very useful as a practical method of solving differential equations.

Let us apply the method first to the trivial problem of solving the equation

$$2x - 1 = x + 1. \tag{1.1}$$

The graphs of the functions $2x - 1$ and $x + 1$ appear in Fig. 9.1, and the steps in the solution of the problem may be followed from the diagram.

First, we guess an approximation x_0 to the solution. Suppose our guess is $x_0 = 4$. We set this value in the right-hand member of (1.1) and compute a new approximation x_1 to x from (1.1), obtaining

$$2x_1 - 1 = 4 + 1,$$

or $x_1 = 3$. This value is put in the right-hand member of (1.1), and a new approximation $x_2 = \frac{5}{2}$ is obtained. It is clear from the geometry of the situation that the sequence

$$x_0, x_1, x_2, \ldots$$

will converge to the correct value, which is 2. This process is equivalent to computing numbers x_n from the *recursion* formulas

$$(1.2)\qquad \begin{aligned} 2x_n - 1 &= x_{n-1} + 1, \\ x_0 &= 4. \end{aligned}$$

We note that if our original guess x_0 had been 5, 10, or 10^{10}, the process would have yielded eventually as good an approximation to the true solution 2 as needed. We observe from Fig. 9.1,

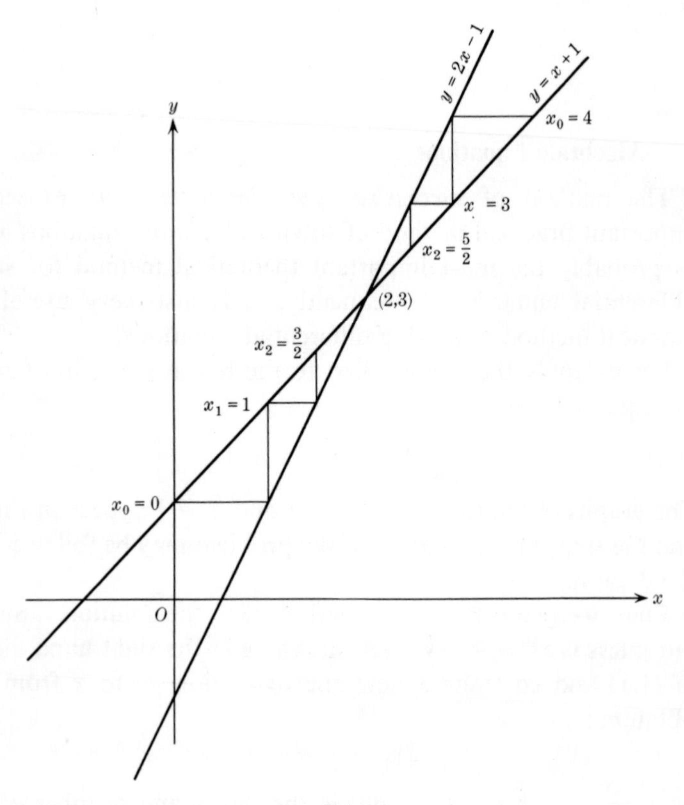

FIG. 9.1

however, that it is desirable for computational reasons to make as good a guess initially as possible.

Again, suppose that our initial guess had been $x_0 = 0$. The sequence of numbers x_n determined from (1.2) is

$$0, 1, \tfrac{3}{2}, \ldots.$$

From Fig. 9.1 we see that this sequence also will converge to the correct value 2.

If we had commenced by inserting the value 4 for x in the left-hand member of (1.1) and computed x_1 from the relation

$$2(4) - 1 = x_1 + 1,$$

we would have obtained $x_1 = 6$, and if we had continued in this fashion using, in effect, the recursion relation

$$2x_{n-1} - 1 = x_n + 1, \tag{1.3}$$

we would have obtained successively the values

$$4, 6, 10, 18, 34, \ldots.$$

It is easy to see that this sequence does not have a finite limit. It will also be apparent from Fig. 9.1 that the sequence so obtained does not approach the limit desired.

Although rules may be given which would enable the student to decide for a given equation which of the two recursion formulas, (1.2) or (1.3), to employ, in practice one more commonly either decides from a rough graph, or makes a guess. If the guess is wrong, this ordinarily becomes clear very quickly, and the correct procedure may then be followed.

If an error in computation is made, the result obtained amounts simply to a new guess, and the process is not invalidated. It may, indeed, actually be speeded up! If, for example, in computing x_1 in the first sequence we had made an error and obtained instead of 3 the value 2.5, we should have improved our approximating sequence.

EXERCISES

Solve the following equations by the method of successive approximations. Compute your answer to three decimal places.

1. $x - 3 = 2x + 2.$

2. $x = 1 + 1/x.$

3. $x = 2 + 2/x.$

4. $x^3 + 2x - 20 = 0.$ (*Hint.* Rewrite in a convenient form.)

5. $x^x = 100.$

6. $2x - 1 = -2x + 1.$ (Take $x_0 = 1$; examine the graphs, and make appropriate alterations of the process in the text.)

ANSWERS

4. 2.470.

5. 3.597.

2 Differential Equations

We shall now apply the method to the differential system

$$y' - 2xy = 0, \quad y(0) = 1. \tag{2.1}$$

We rewrite (2.1) as

$$y = 1 + \int_0^x 2xy\,dx$$

from which we obtain the recursion formula

$$y_n(x) = 1 + \int_0^x 2xy_{n-1}(x)\,dx. \tag{2.2}$$

Since $y(0) = 1$, a convenient guess for $y_0(x)$ is $y_0(x) = 1$. From (2.2) we obtain successively

$$y_1(x) = 1 + x^2,$$

$$y_2(x) = 1 + x^2 + \frac{x^4}{2},$$

$$y_3(x) = 1 + x^2 + \frac{x^4}{2} + \frac{x^6}{6},$$

$$\cdots\cdots\cdots\cdots\cdots$$

The sequence of functions so obtained can be shown to converge to the solution of (2.1) over every finite interval. They are clearly best suited to computation when $|x|$ is not too large.

The student will find it instructive to compute the sequence of functions $y_n(x)$ obtained from (2.2) for various selections of $y_0(x)$.

The method is also available for a system of differential equations. To apply it to the differential system

$$\begin{aligned} \frac{dy}{dx} &= 3y - z, \\ \frac{dz}{dx} &= 2y, \end{aligned} \tag{2.3}$$

$$y(0) = 1, \qquad z(0) = 2,$$

we rewrite the system in the form

$$y = 1 + \int_0^x (3y - z)\, dx,$$

$$z = 2 + \int_0^x 2y\, dx,$$

from which we obtain the recursion formulas

$$y_n(x) = 1 + \int_0^x [3y_{n-1}(x) - z_{n-1}(x)]\, dx,$$

$$z_n(x) = 2 + \int_0^x 2y_{n-1}(x)\, dx.$$

Natural choices of $y_0(x)$ and $z_0(x)$ are

$$y_0(x) = 1, \qquad z_0(x) = 2.$$

The completion of the problem is left to the student as an exercise.

As a practical method of solving differential equations, the use of the method of successive approximations is rather limited, owing to the difficulties which may arise in carrying out the indicated integrations. This is especially true when the differential equations are nonlinear.

EXERCISES

Solve the following differential systems by the method of successive approximations.

1. $y' - 2xy = 0,$
$y(0) = 1.$

(a) Take $y_0(x)$ as $1 + x$;
(b) Take $y_0(x)$ as e^x.

2. $y' = 1 + y^2,$
$y(0) = 0.$

3. $\dfrac{dy}{dx} = 3y - z,$

$\dfrac{dz}{dx} = 2y,$

$y(0) = 1,\ z(0) = 2.$

4. $\dfrac{dy}{dx} = z + x,$

$\dfrac{dz}{dx} = y + x,$

$y(0) = 2,\ z(0) = -2.$

3 The Fundamental Existence Theorem

In this section we shall employ the Picard method of successive approximations to demonstrate the existence of a solution of the following pair of differential equations:

$$\frac{dy}{dx} = f(x,y,z), \qquad \frac{dz}{dx} = g(x,y,z). \tag{3.1}$$

The alterations in the statement of the theorem and in its proof which are required for the case of the general system

$$\frac{dy_1}{dx} = f_1(x,y_1,y_2,\ldots,y_n),$$

$$\frac{dy_2}{dx} = f_2(x,y_1,y_2,\ldots,y_n),$$

$$\cdot \quad \cdot \quad \cdot \quad \cdot \quad \cdot \quad \cdot \quad \cdot$$

$$\frac{dy_n}{dx} = f_n(x,y_1,y_2,\ldots,y_n) \qquad (n = 1, 2, \ldots)$$

will be evident.*

To return to the differential system (3.1), we shall suppose that the functions $f(x,y,z)$ and $g(x,y,z)$ are continuous and bounded in an (open) three-dimensional region $R(x,y,z)$ and that there exist constants A and B such that

$$\begin{aligned} &|f(x,y_1,z_1) - f(x,y_2,z_2)| \leq A|y_1 - y_2| + B|z_1 - z_2|, \\ &|g(x,y_1,z_1) - g(x,y_2,z_2)| \leq A|y_1 - y_2| + B|z_1 - z_2|, \end{aligned} \tag{3.2}$$

where $P_1:(x,y_1,z_1)$ and $P_2:(x,y_2,z_2)$ are two points in R. The constants A and B are understood to be fixed constants, of course, quite independent of the points P_1 and P_2. Conditions (3.2) are called *Lipschitz* conditions.

Let $P_0:(x_0,y_0,z_0)$ be an arbitrary point of R, and let D be a rectangular domain lying in R which is defined by the inequalities

$$x_0 \leq x \leq x_0 + a,$$

$$y_0 - b \leq y \leq y_0 + b,$$

$$z_0 - c \leq z \leq z_0 + c,$$

where a, b, and c are positive constants. Finally, we choose a constant h which satisfies simultaneously the inequalities

$$h \leq a, \qquad h \leq \frac{b}{M}, \qquad h \leq \frac{c}{M},$$

where M is any positive constant such that both

$$|f(x,y,z)| \leq M,$$

$$|g(x,y,z)| \leq M,$$

in R.

* The proof for the case $n = 2$ is in every sense typical of the general case, whereas that for the case $n = 1$ is slightly less so. We have accordingly chosen to provide the former in the text.

Recall that by a solution of a system (3.1) is meant a pair (usually regarded as a column) of functions $y(x)$ and $z(x)$ of class C^1 on some interval of the x-axis which simultaneously satisfy the system on that interval.*

Theorem 3.1. *There exists a unique solution* $y(x)$, $z(x)$ *of* (3.1) *on the interval* $x_0 \leq x \leq x_0 + h$ *with the property that*

$$y(x_0) = y_0, \qquad z(x_0) = z_0.$$

To prove the theorem, we define two sequences of functions $y_0(x), y_1(x), \ldots$ and $z_0(x), z_1(x), \ldots$ by means of the recursion formulas

$$\begin{aligned} y_0(x) &= y_0, \\ y_n(x) &= y_0 + \int_{x_0}^{x} f[x, y_{n-1}(x), z_{n-1}(x)]\, dx, \\ z_0(x) &= z_0, \\ z_n(x) &= z_0 + \int_{x_0}^{x} g[x, y_{n-1}(x), z_{n-1}(x)]\, dx \qquad (n = 1, 2, \ldots). \end{aligned} \tag{3.3}$$

We shall show that these sequences converge, respectively, on the interval $x_0 \leq x \leq x_0 + h$ to the functions $y(x)$ and $z(x)$ of the theorem.

First, we must show that the recursion formulas do indeed define a sequence of functions. (The principal consideration is to be sure that all our operations take place in D.) We shall show that

$$\begin{aligned} |y_n(x) - y_0| &\leq b, \\ |z_n(x) - z_0| &\leq c \qquad (n = 0, 1, 2, \ldots). \end{aligned} \tag{3.4}$$

The proof is accomplished through the use of mathematical induction. Note that relations (3.4) are valid when $n = 0$. Suppose they are valid for $n = 0, 1, \ldots, r - 1$. We shall show that they are then valid for $n = r$. We have

* The student has undoubtedly already observed that the symbols C' and C^1 are used interchangeably in mathematical writing.

$$\begin{aligned}|y_r(x) - y_0| &= \left| \int_{x_0}^{x} f[x, y_{r-1}(x), z_{r-1}(x)]\, dx \right| \\ &\le \int_{x_0}^{x} |f[x, y_{r-1}(x), z_{r-1}(x)]|\, dx \le M \int_{x_0}^{x} dx \\ &= M(x - x_0) \le Mh \le b,\end{aligned}$$

and, similarly, $|z_r(x) - z_0| \le Mh \le c$. Since the continuity of $y_n(x)$ and of $z_n(x)$ on the interval $x_0 \le x \le x_0 + h$ may also be established readily by mathematical induction, the first step in the proof is complete.

Next, consider the two infinite series

$$\begin{aligned}&y_0(x) + [y_1(x) - y_0(x)] + [y_2(x) - y_1(x)] + \cdots, \\ &z_0(x) + [z_1(x) - z_0(x)] + [z_2(x) - z_1(x)] + \cdots,\end{aligned} \tag{3.5}$$

and note that the sums of the first $(n + 1)$ terms of these series are, respectively, $y_n(x)$ and $z_n(x)$. We shall show that both series converge uniformly on the interval $x_0 \le x \le x_0 + h$. To see this, we may verify by mathematical induction that

$$\begin{aligned}|y_n(x) - y_{n-1}(x)| &\le M(A + B)^{n-1} \frac{(x - x_0)^n}{n!}, \\ |z_n(x) - z_{n-1}(x)| &\le M(A + B)^{n-1} \frac{(x - x_0)^n}{n!}\end{aligned} \tag{3.6}$$

$$(n = 1, 2, \ldots).$$

We shall indicate the proof of the former of these two inequalities. The latter may be proved in precisely similar fashion. First, we see that (as in the earlier induction proof)

$$|y_1(x) - y_0(x)| \le M(x - x_0).$$

Suppose then that the inequalities (3.6) are valid for

$$n = 1, 2, \ldots, r - 1.$$

We shall show that they are valid when $n = r$. For,

$$|y_r(x) - y_{r-1}(x)| = \left| \int_{x_0}^{x} [f(x,y_{r-1},z_{r-1}) - f(x,y_{r-2},z_{r-2})]\, dx \right|$$

$$\leq \int_{x_0}^{x} [A|y_{r-1} - y_{r-2}| + B|z_{r-1} - z_{r-2}|]\, dx$$

$$\leq A \int_{x_0}^{x} M(A + B)^{r-2} \frac{(x - x_0)^{r-1}}{(r-1)!}\, dx$$

$$+ B \int_{x_0}^{x} M(A + B)^{r-2} \frac{(x - x_0)^{r-1}}{(r-1)!}\, dx$$

$$= M(A + B)^{r-1} \frac{(x - x_0)^r}{r!}.$$

Since the right-hand members of the inequalities (3.6) are less than

$$\frac{M(A + B)^{n-1}h^n}{n!},$$

each series in (3.5) is dominated by the series whose general term is the right-hand member in (3.6). The last series is readily seen to be a convergent positive term series. The series (3.5) then converge uniformly (and absolutely) to continuous functions $y(x)$ and $z(x)$, respectively; that is

$$\lim_{n \to \infty} y_n(x) = y(x),$$

$$\lim_{n \to \infty} z_n(x) = z(x),$$

uniformly on $x_0 \leq x \leq x_0 + h$.

The next step in the proof is to show that this pair of functions $y(x)$ and $z(x)$ provide a solution of (3.1). First, we note that from

$$y_n(x) = y_0 + \int_{x_0}^{x} f[x,y_{n-1}(x),z_{n-1}(x)]\, dx,$$

$$z_n(x) = z_0 + \int_{x_0}^{x} g[x,y_{n-1}(x),z_{n-1}(x)]\, dx,$$

we have

$$\lim_{n \to \infty} y_n(x) = y_0 + \lim_{n \to \infty} \int_{x_0}^{x} f[x, y_{n-1}(x), z_{n-1}(x)]\, dx$$

and

$$\lim_{n \to \infty} z_n(x) = z_0 + \lim_{n \to \infty} \int_{x_0}^{x} g[x, y_{n-1}(x), z_{n-1}(x)]\, dx.$$

But the *uniform* convergence of the sequences $\{y_n(x)\}$ and $\{z_n(x)\}$ permits us to interchange limits above, and we have

$$\begin{aligned} y(x) &= y_0 + \int_{x_0}^{x} \lim_{n \to \infty} f[x, y_{n-1}(x), z_{n-1}(x)]\, dx, \\ z(x) &= z_0 + \int_{x_0}^{x} \lim_{n \to \infty} g[x, y_{n-1}(x), z_{n-1}(x)]\, dx. \end{aligned} \tag{3.7}$$

Finally, because of the continuity of f and of g we may write (3.7) in the form

$$\begin{aligned} y(x) &= y_0 + \int_{x_0}^{x} f[x, y(x), z(x)]\, dx, \\ z(x) &= z_0 + \int_{x_0}^{x} g[x, y(x), z(x)]\, dx. \end{aligned} \tag{3.8}$$

The right-hand members of (3.8) possess continuous derivatives with respect to x on $x_0 \leq x \leq x_0 + h$, and, consequently, so do the left-hand members. Accordingly,

$$\begin{aligned} y'(x) &= f[x, y(x), z(x)], \\ z'(x) &= g[x, y(x), z(x)], \end{aligned}$$

for each x on $x_0 \leq x \leq x_0 + h$. That is to say, the functions $y(x)$ and $z(x)$ satisfy (3.1) and are of class C^1 on this interval. Together, they provide a solution. We note that

$$\begin{aligned} y(x_0) &= y_0, \\ z(x_0) &= z_0. \end{aligned} \tag{3.9}$$

It remains, finally, to show that the pair of functions $y(x)$ and

$z(x)$ so determined provides the *only* solution of (3.1) on the interval $x_0 \leq x \leq x_0 + h$ satisfying (3.9).

To this end let the columns

$$\begin{matrix} y(x) & y_1(x) \\ z(x), & z_1(x) \end{matrix}$$

be two solutions of (3.1) on $x_0 \leq x \leq x_0 + h$ satisfying conditions (3.9). We shall show that these solutions are identical. We have

$$\begin{aligned} |y(x) - y_1(x)| &\leq \int_{x_0}^{x} |f[x,y(x),z(x)] - f[x,y_1(x),z_1(x)]|\, dx, \\ |z(x) - z_1(x)| &\leq \int_{x_0}^{x} |g[x,y(x),z(x)] - g[x,y_1(x),z_1(x)]|\, dx. \end{aligned} \tag{3.10}$$

We shall show that the left-hand members of (3.10) are not greater than

$$2M(A + B)^{n-1} \frac{(x - x_0)^n}{n!} = t_n(x)$$

for each value of $n = 1, 2, \ldots$. Again we shall confine our attention to the difference $d = |y(x) - y_1(x)|$. First, we verify the inequality for $n = 1$:

$$d \leq 2M \int_{x_0}^{x} dx = 2M(x - x_0).$$

Suppose the inequality is valid for $n = r - 1$. We apply the Lipschitz condition to the first inequality (3.10), obtaining

$$d \leq \int_{x_0}^{x} [A|y(x) - y_1(x)| + B|z(x) - z_1(x)|]\, dx. \tag{3.11}$$

The induction may now be readily completed by applying the induction hypothesis to the differences in the right-hand member of (3.11).

We have then

$$\begin{aligned} |y(x) - y_1(x)| &\leq t_n(x), \\ |z(x) - z_1(x)| &\leq t_n(x) \end{aligned} \tag{3.12}$$

for each value of x on the interval $x_0 \leq x \leq x_0 + h$ and for each value of $n = 1, 2, \ldots$.

For any fixed value of x, the left-hand members of (3.12) are definite fixed numbers greater than or equal to zero. These numbers are, however, less successively than each term in a convergent positive term series; accordingly, they are the number zero, and

$$y(x) \equiv y_1(x),$$

$$z(x) \equiv z_1(x).$$

The proof of the theorem is complete.

EXERCISE

Modify the proof of Theorem 3.1 to show that if $a(x)$, $b(x)$, $c(x)$, and $d(x)$ are continuous on the interval $x_0 \leq x \leq x_1$ and if y_0, z_0 are arbitrary constants, the differential system

$$\frac{dy}{dx} = a(x)y + b(x)z,$$

$$\frac{dz}{dx} = c(x)y + d(x)z,$$

$$y(x_0) = y_0, \qquad z(x_0) = z_0,$$

has a unique solution

$$y(x)$$

$$z(x)$$

valid on the entire interval $x_0 \leq x \leq x_1$.

Example. Consider the differential system

$$[r(x)y']' + p(x)y = 0,$$

$$\text{(3.13)} \qquad y(a) = a_0,$$

$$y'(a) = b_0,$$

where $r(x) > 0$ and $r(x)$ and $p(x)$ are continuous on the interval

$a \leq x \leq b$. We may set $z = r(x)y'$, and replace (3.13) by the system

$$\begin{aligned} y' &= \frac{1}{r(x)} z, \\ z' &= -p(x)y, \\ y(a) = a_0, &\qquad z(a) = r(a)b_0 \end{aligned} \tag{3.14}$$

to which the fundamental existence theorem is applicable.

By the result of the preceding exercise, there exists a unique solution

$$\begin{gathered} y(x) \\ z(x) \end{gathered}$$

of the system (3.14) on the interval $a \leq x \leq b$. Further, it follows from (3.14) that

$$\begin{aligned} [r(x)y'(x)]' &\equiv -p(x)y(x) \qquad (a \leq x \leq b), \\ y(a) &= a_0, \\ y'(a) &= b_0; \end{aligned}$$

that is, there exists a unique solution of (3.13) on the interval $a \leq x \leq b$.

For completeness we note that the differential system

$$\begin{gathered} [r(x)y'] + [p(x) + \lambda q(x)]y = 0, \\ y(a) = a_0, \qquad y'(a) = b_0, \end{gathered} \tag{3.15}$$

where $q(x)$ is positive and continuous on the interval $a \leq x \leq b$, and $r(x)$ and $p(x)$ are as previously described, is of the same type as the preceding. The coefficient of y contains, however, a parameter λ. If λ is limited to any bounded interval Λ, the functions $y_n(x,\lambda)$ provided by successive approximations converge uniformly for x on $[a,b]$ and λ on Λ to a unique (for each fixed λ) solution $y(x,\lambda)$ of (3.15) which is of class C^1 in x and is continuous* in λ.

* Actually, $y(x,\lambda)$ can be shown by methods of the theory of functions to be an *analytic* function of λ, a consequence of which is that it possesses a continuous partial derivative of every order with respect to λ. But continuity in λ of the function is all that we shall require here.

We shall conclude this chapter by noting that if $f(x,y,z)$ and $g(x,y,z)$ possess in R continuous first partial derivatives with respect to both y and z, the Lipschitz condition is satisfied in every closed rectangular region $\bar{R}$ interior to R. This follows from the law of the mean:

$$f(x,y_1,z_1) - f(x,y_2,z_2) = (y_1 - y_2)f_y^* + (z_1 - z_2)f_z^*,$$

$$g(x,y_1,z_1) - g(x,y_2,z_2) = (y_1 - y_2)g_y^{**} + (z_1 - z_2)g_z^{**},$$

where the asterisks indicate evaluation of the partial derivatives at suitable mean-value points. Since there exist constants A and B such that

$$|f_y(x,y,z)| \leq A, \qquad |g_y(x,y,z)| \leq A,$$

$$|f_z(x,y,z)| \leq B, \qquad |g_z(x,y,z)| \leq B,$$

for all points (x,y,z) in $\bar{R}$, it follows at once that

$$|f(x,y_1,z_1) - f(x,y_2,z_2)| \leq A|y_1 - y_2| + B|z_1 - z_2|,$$

$$|g(x,y_1,z_1) - g(x,y_2,z_2)| \leq A|y_1 - y_2| + B|z_1 - z_2|,$$

in $\bar{R}$.

10

Oscillation Theory

1 Self-adjoint Linear Differential Equations of Second Order

The importance of the self-adjoint form in the study of linear differential equations of second order can hardly be overemphasized. It arises naturally in mechanics; it has a central role in the calculus of variations. The student will observe its use throughout the present chapter as we study the behavior of solutions of the linear differential equation of second order.

A self-adjoint linear differential equation of second order, it will be recalled, is a differential equation of the form

$$[r(x)y']' + p(x)y = 0, \tag{1.1}$$

where $r(x)$ and $p(x)$ are continuous and $r(x) > 0$ on an interval $x_0 \le x \le x_1$. The results will apply to the differential equation

$$a(x)y'' + b(x)y' + c(x)y = 0, \tag{1.2}$$

where $a(x) > 0$ and $a(x)$, $b(x)$, and $c(x)$ are continuous on the interval $[x_0,x_1]$ because, as we have seen, equation (1.2) can be put in self-adjoint form by multiplying both members of the equation by the function

$$\frac{1}{a(x)} e^{\int_{x_0}^{x} [b(x)/a(x)]\,dx}.$$

Then

$$r(x) = e^{\int_{x_0}^{x} [b(x)/a(x)]}, \qquad p(x) = \frac{c(x)}{a(x)}\, r(x).$$

The results will not require the existence of the derivative of $r(x)$, but for simplicity we shall suppose that $r'(x)$ exists and is continuous on $[x_0,x_1]$—that is, we shall suppose that $r(x)$ is of class C' on this interval.

2 Abel's Formula

Let $u(x)$ and $v(x)$ be any two solutions of (1.1). We shall show that

$$r(x)[u(x)v'(x) - u'(x)v(x)] \equiv k, \tag{2.1}$$

a constant. Since $u(x)$ and $v(x)$ are solutions of (1.1), we have

$$[r(x)u'(x)]' + p(x)u(x) \equiv 0,$$

$$[r(x)v'(x)]' + p(x)v(x) \equiv 0.$$

If we multiply both sides of the first identity by $-v(x)$, both members of the second identity by $u(x)$, and add, we obtain

$$u(x)[r(x)v'(x)]' - v(x)[r(x)u'(x)]' \equiv 0.$$

We integrate both members of the last identity from a to x, and integration by parts yields

$$r(x)[u(x)v'(x) - u'(x)v(x)] \equiv r(a)[u(a)v'(a) - u'(a)v(a)];$$

that is to say, the left-hand member is constant. As we saw in an earlier chapter, the quantity in brackets $u(x)v'(x) - u'(x)v(x)$ is the wronskian of the two solutions $u(x)$ and $v(x)$. Thus the constant k is zero if and only if $u(x)$ and $v(x)$ are linearly dependent. The identity (2.1) is known as *Abel's formula.*

3 The Sturm Separation Theorem

We are now prepared to prove a fundamental result due to

Sturm. It will be helpful in that proof to have available the following lemma.

Lemma. If two solutions $u(x)$ and $v(x)$ have a common zero, they are linearly dependent. Conversely, if $u(x)$ and $v(x)$ are linearly dependent solutions, neither identically zero, then if one of them vanishes at $x = x_0$, so does the other.

To prove the first statement of the lemma, we employ Abel's formula

$$r(x)[u(x)v'(x) - u'(x)v(x)] \equiv k. \tag{3.1}$$

Let the common zero of $u(x)$ and $v(x)$ be $x = x_0$, and replace x by x_0 in (3.1). It follows that the constant k is zero, and hence that $u(x)$ and $v(x)$ are linearly dependent.

We could also employ (3.1) to prove the second statement of the lemma. It will be somewhat simpler, however, to use the definition of linear dependence which states that there exist constants c_1 and c_2 not both zero such that

$$c_1u(x) + c_2v(x) \equiv 0.$$

Since we have assumed that neither $u(x)$ nor $v(x)$ is identically zero, we see that both c_1 and c_2 are different from zero. Thus, if $u(x_0) = 0$, then $v(x_0) = 0$ also.

The proof of the lemma is complete.

Theorem 3.1. THE STURM SEPARATION THEOREM. *If $u(x)$ and $v(x)$ are linearly independent solutions of* (1.1), *between two consecutive zeros of $u(x)$ there will be precisely one zero of $v(x)$.*

Let $x = x_0$ and $x = x_1$ be the two consecutive zeros of $u(x)$ whose existence is supposed by the theorem (see Fig. 10.1). Let x_0 be the smaller of the two. We may without loss in generality assume that $u(x) > 0$ for $x_0 < x < x_1$. This follows from the fact that $-u(x)$ is also a solution having the same zeros as $u(x)$. It follows that $u'(x_0) > 0$ and $u'(x_1) < 0$. Similarly, we may suppose without loss in generality that $v(x_0) > 0$, since $v(x_0) \neq 0$ by the lemma.

To prove the theorem, we set $x = x_0$ in equation (3.1), and note that therefore $k < 0$. It follows that

$$r(x_1)[u(x_1)v'(x_1) - u'(x_1)v(x_1)] < 0.$$

But $u(x_1) = 0$, $u'(x_1) < 0$; hence $v(x_1) < 0$. Since $v(x)$ is a continuous function, it must have at least one zero between x_0, where

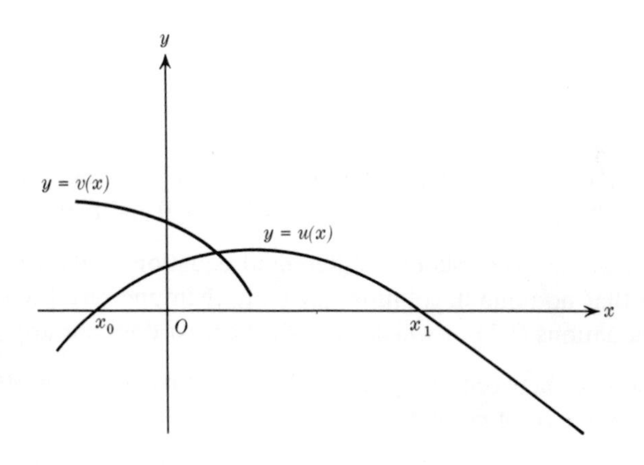

FIG. 10.1

it is positive, and x_1, where it is negative. There cannot be more than one because the argument above, with the roles of $u(x)$ and $v(x)$ reversed, shows that between two consecutive zeros of $v(x)$ there must be at least one zero of $u(x)$.

The proof of the Sturm separation theorem is complete.

EXERCISES

1. Put the following differential equations in self-adjoint form:

(a) $x^2y'' + xy' + (x^2 - n^2)y = 0$ (n constant);
(b) $(1 - x^2)y'' - 2xy' + n(n + 1)y = 0$ (n constant);
(c) $(1 - x^2)y'' - xy' + n^2y = 0$ (n constant);
(d) $xy'' + (1 - x)y' + ny = 0$ (n constant);
(e) $y'' - 2xy' + 2ny = 0$ (n constant).

(f) $(1 - x^2)y'' - [(\alpha - \beta) + (\alpha + \beta)x]y' + n(n + \alpha + \beta + 1)y = 0$ $(\alpha > -1, \beta > -1)$.

2. Prove that between every pair of consecutive zeros of $\sin x$ there is one zero of $\sin x + \cos x$. (*Hint.* Use Sturm's theorem.)

3. Prove that between every pair of consecutive zeros of

$$\sin x + \sqrt{2} \cos x$$

there is a zero of $\sin x - \cos x$.

4. Sketch the curves $y = \sin x$ and $y = \sin x - \cos x$ on the interval $-2\pi \leq x \leq 2\pi$.

5. If $u(x)$ is a solution of (1.1) such that $u(x_0) = u(x_1) = 0$ and $u(x) > 0$ $(x_0 < x < x_1)$, prove that $u'(x_0) > 0$ and that $u'(x_1) < 0$.

6. Construct an example of a differential equation in the form (1.1) such that no nonnull solution has more than one zero [thus, there are equations (1.1) to which Sturm's theorem does not apply].

7. Show that between every pair of consecutive zeros of $\sin \log x$ there is a zero of $\cos \log x$.

8. Find a self-adjoint differential equation which has the solution $r(x)y'(x)$, where $y(x)$ is any solution of (1.1).

9. Prove that a necessary and sufficient condition that equation (1.1) have linearly independent solutions of the form $\sin v(x)$ and $\cos v(x)$ is that $r(x)p(x) \equiv k^2$, a positive constant. Show that $v(x)$ may be taken as any of the functions

$$\int p(x)\, dx.$$

10. Let $m(x)$ be a function of class C' on the interval $a \leq x \leq b$, and suppose that $m(x) \not\equiv 0$ on any subinterval of $[a,b]$. The differential equation

$$\left[\frac{1}{m(x)} y'\right]' + km(x)y = 0 \qquad (k \text{ constant}, \neq 0)$$

will then have a singular point whenever $m(x) = 0$. Prove, however, that all solutions of this equation are of class C'' on $[a,b]$.

11. Given equation (1.1) with the usual conditions on the coefficients

$r(x)$ and $p(x)$, discuss the possibility of solutions $u(x)$ and $v(x)$ having the configuration in Fig. 10.2.

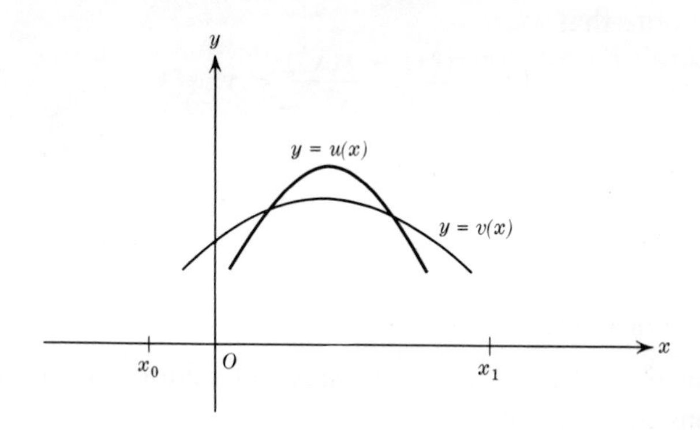

FIG. 10.2

ANSWER

8. $[(1/p)z']' + (1/r)z = 0$.

4 The Number of Zeros on a Finite Interval

In this section we shall prove the following result.

Theorem 4.1. *If* $r(x) > 0$ *and* $r(x)$ *and* $p(x)$ *are continuous on the interval* $a \leq x \leq b$, *the only solution of equation* (1.1) *which vanishes infinitely often on this interval is the null solution.*

This theorem may be proved as follows. Suppose the solution $y(x)$ has an infinity of zeros on this interval. The set of zeros will then have a limit point x^* on the interval, and there will exist a sequence $\{x_n\}_0^\infty$ of the zeros converging to x^* with

$$x_n \neq x^* \qquad (n = 0, 1, 2, \ldots).$$

We shall show that $y(x^*) = y'(x^*) = 0$. It will follow from the corollary to Theorem 1.1, Chapter 5, that $y(x) \equiv 0$. To that end note that $y(x)$ is a continuous function of x. Thus

$$\lim_{x \to x^*} y(x) = y(x^*)$$

as x tends to x^* through any sequence of numbers on $[a,b]$.

Choosing as this sequence the numbers $x_0, x_1, x_2, \ldots$, we see that $y(x^*) = 0$.

Next, note that

$$\lim_{x \to x^*} \frac{y(x) - y(x^*)}{x - x^*} = y'(x^*).$$

Since $y'(x^*)$ is known to exist, we may evaluate the limit by letting x tend to x^* through members of the sequence $x_0, x_1, x_2, \ldots$. Thus $y'(x^*) = 0$, and the proof is complete.

5 The Sturm Comparison Theorem

In this section we continue the study of solutions of differential equations of the form

$$[r(x)y']' + p(x)y = 0, \tag{5.1}$$

where $r(x) > 0$, and $r(x)$, $r'(x)$, and $p(x)$ are continuous on the closed interval $a \le x \le b$. The student will recall that the Sturm separation theorem asserts that between two consecutive zeros of a solution of (5.1) there appears one zero of every linearly independent solution. Thus, speaking roughly, the number of zeros on an interval of any solution of (5.1) is about the same as the number any other solution possesses.

On the other hand, it is easy to see that solutions (for example, $\sin 2x$) of

$$y'' + 4y = 0$$

oscillate more frequently (that is, have more zeros) on the interval $0 \le x \le 2\pi$ than do the solutions of

$$y'' + y = 0$$

on that interval. A typical solution of the last equation is, of course, $\sin x$. The Sturm comparison theorem compares the rates of oscillation of solutions of two equations,

$$[r(x)y']' + p(x)y = 0, \tag{5.2}$$

$$[r(x)z']' + p_1(x)z = 0, \tag{5.3}$$

where $r(x) > 0$, $r(x)$, $p(x)$, $p_1(x)$ are continuous on $a \le x \le b$.

Theorem 5.1. THE STURM COMPARISON THEOREM. *If a solution $y(x)$ of (5.2) has consecutive zeros at $x = x_0$ and $x = x_1$ ($x_0 < x_1$), and if $p_1(x) \geq p(x)$ with strict inequality holding for at least one point of the interval $[x_0 x_1]$, a solution $z(x)$ of (5.3) which vanishes at $x = x_0$ will vanish again on the interval $x_0 < x < x_1$.*

That is to say, speaking roughly, the larger is $p(x)$, the more rapidly the solutions of (5.1) oscillate (see Fig. 10.3).

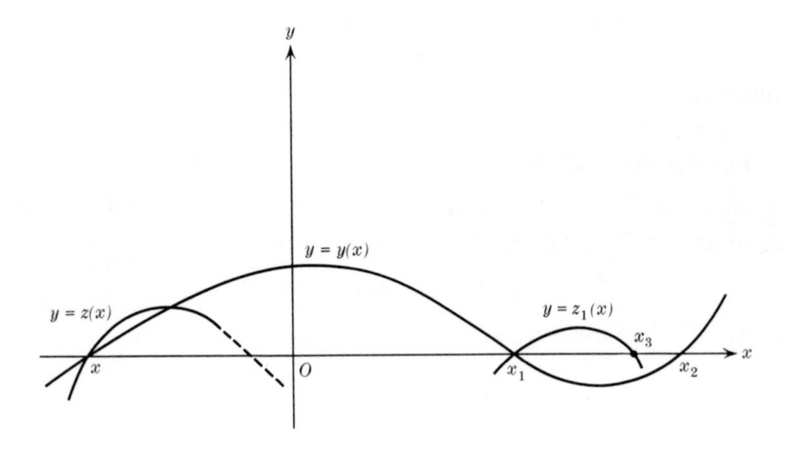

FIG. 10.3

To prove the theorem, we may suppose without loss in generality that $y(x) > 0$ on the interval $x_0 < x < x_1$, and that $y'(x_0) > 0$, $y'(x_1) < 0$, and $z'(x_0) > 0$. Since $y(x)$ and $z(x)$ are solutions, respectively, of equations (5.2) and (5.3), we have the identities

$$[r(x)y'(x)]' + p(x)y(x) \equiv 0,$$

$$[r(x)z'(x)]' + p_1(x)z(x) \equiv 0.$$

If we multiply the first of these by $-z(x)$ and the second by $y(x)$ and add, we may integrate both members of the resulting identity over the interval $x_0 \leq x \leq x_1$, obtaining easily

$$r(x)[y(x)z'(x) - y'(x)z(x)]\Big|_{x_0}^{x_1} + \int_{x_0}^{x_1} [p_1(x) - p(x)]y(x)z(x)\,dx = 0,$$

or

$$(5.4) \qquad r(x_1)y'(x_1)z(x_1) = \int_{x_0}^{x_1} [p_1(x) - p(x)]y(x)z(x)\,dx.$$

Now suppose $z(x) > 0$ on $x_0 < x < x_1$. Then the integral in (5.4) is positive while the left-hand member is negative. From this contradiction we infer the truth of the theorem.

We may note further that if $y(x)$ vanishes again at $x = x_2 > x_1$, $z(x)$ will also vanish on the interval $x_1 < x < x_2$. For consider a second solution $z_1(x)$ of (5.3), defined by the conditions $z_1(x_1) = 0$, $z_1'(x_1) = 1$. By the foregoing, $z_1(x)$ has a zero x_3 on the interval $x_1 < x < x_2$, and applying the Sturm separation theorem, we conclude that $z(x)$ has a zero on the interval $x_1 < x < x_3$.

For completeness we add the following theorem.

Theorem 5.2. *The conclusions of Theorem* 5.1 *are valid when equations* (5.2) *and* (5.3) *are replaced, respectively, by*

$$(5.2)' \qquad [r(x)y']' + p(x)y = 0,$$

$$(5.3)' \qquad [r_1(x)z']' + p_1(x)z = 0,$$

$$r_1(x) \le r(x),$$

$$p_1(x) \ge p(x),$$

with strict inequality holding in at least one of these conditions at at least one point of the interval.

The proof of this theorem is omitted. It is known as the *Sturm-Picone theorem.*

EXERCISE

Show that if $p(x) \le 0$ on $[a,b]$, no nonnull solution of (5.1) can have more than one zero on $[a,b]$. (*Hint.* Compare with solutions of $[r(x)y']' = 0$.)

6 A Canonical Form

Let $y_1(x)$ and $y_2(x)$ be any two linearly independent solutions of (5.1). Then

$$(6.1) \qquad r(x)[y_1'(x)y_2(x) - y_1(x)y_2'(x)] \equiv c,$$

where c is a fixed constant not equal to zero. Since $y_1(x)$ and $y_2(x)$ have no zeros in common, these solutions may be written in the form

$$y_1(x) = u(x)\sin v(x), \qquad y_2(x) = u(x)\cos v(x), \tag{6.2}$$

where

$$u(x) = \sqrt{y_1^2(x) + y_2^2(x)},$$

$$\sin v(x) = \frac{y_1(x)}{u(x)}, \tag{6.3}$$

$$\cos v(x) = \frac{y_2(x)}{u(x)}.$$

It is clear that $u(x) > 0$ on $a \le x \le b$. Upon substituting the solutions (6.2) in (5.1), we can readily verify that

$$ru^2v' = c, \tag{6.4}$$

$$ru^3[(ru')' + pu] = c^2. \tag{6.5}$$

Since the argument is reversible, we observe that if $c \neq 0$, and if $u(x)$ is any solution of (6.5) and $v(x)$ is then obtained from (6.4), the functions $u \sin v$ and $u \cos v$ are linearly independent solutions of (5.1) and $u \neq 0$. Solutions written in the form (6.2) are said to be in *canonical* form.

7 Oscillation on a Half Axis

In this section we shall develop a fundamental theorem which will provide a sufficient condition that solutions of an equation

$$[r(x)y']' + p(x)y = 0 \tag{7.1}$$

vanish infinitely often on the interval $0 < x < \infty$.

Theorem 7.1. *Let $r(x)$ be positive, and suppose that $r(x)$ and $p(x)$ are continuous on the interval $0 < x < \infty$. If the two improper integrals*

$$\int_1^\infty \frac{dx}{r(x)} = +\infty, \qquad \int_1^\infty p(x)\,dx = +\infty, \tag{7.2}$$

then every solution $y(x)$ of (7.1) *vanishes infinitely often on the interval* $1 < x < \infty$. *Similarly if the integrals*

$$\int_0^1 \frac{dx}{r(x)} = +\infty, \qquad \int_0^1 p(x)\,dx = +\infty, \tag{7.3}$$

every solution of (7.1) *vanishes infinitely often on the interval* $0 < x < 1$.

We shall prove the first statement of the theorem. The second will be left to the student as an exercise.

Note first that if any solution not identically equal to zero possesses an infinity of zeros on the interval $1 < x < \infty$, every solution has this property. Suppose then that the theorem is false. Some solution $y(x)$ will vanish at most a finite number of times on $1 < x < \infty$. That is to say, there exists a number $x_0 > 1$ such that $y(x) \neq 0$ when $x \geq x_0$. In (7.1) we make the substitution

$$z(x) = -\frac{r(x)y'(x)}{y(x)} \qquad (x \geq x_0),$$

and obtain

$$z'(x) = p(x) + \frac{1}{r(x)}\,z^2(x). \tag{7.4}$$

If both members of (7.4) are integrated from x_0 to x ($x_0 < x$), it is clear that conditions (7.2) imply that $z(x) \to +\infty$, as $x \to +\infty$. Thus, $y'(x)$ and $y(x)$ are, for x sufficiently large, of opposite sign. It follows that $y(x)$ tends to a finite limit as x becomes infinite. But if one solution has at most a finite number of zeros on $(1,\infty)$, all solutions not identically equal to zero have that property. Accordingly, all solutions approach finite limits. Therefore, $u(x)$ and $v(x)$ of (6.3) have finite limits. But from equation (6.4) we have

$$v(x) = c\int_{x_0}^{x} \frac{dx}{r(x)u^2(x)} \qquad (c \neq 0),$$

and $v(x)$ becomes infinite as x becomes infinite because of condition (7.2).

From this contradiction we may then infer the truth of the first statement of the theorem.

Example. In the equation $y'' + a^2y = 0$ $(a \neq 0)$, $r(x) = 1$, $p(x) = a^2$. Conditions (7.2) are satisfied, and all solutions vanish infinitely often on the interval $1 < x < \infty$. This was already known to us, since a solution of the differential equation is $\sin ax$.

Example. In the differential equation

$$(xy')' + \frac{1}{x}y = 0,$$

we note that $r(x) = x$, $p(x) = \frac{1}{x}$. Both conditions (7.2) and (7.3) are satisfied. Accordingly, all solutions vanish infinitely often on $(1,\infty)$ and also on $(0,1)$. It is easy to verify that $\sin \log x$ is a solution of this differential equation on the interval $(0,\infty)$.

If we were to consider the differential equation

$$y'' + \frac{a^2}{x^2}y = 0, \tag{7.5}$$

we would note that

$$\int_1^\infty \frac{dx}{r(x)} = +\infty, \qquad \int_1^\infty p(x)\,dx < +\infty.$$

The test would fail. Since the differential equation is of Euler type we may solve it. It will be seen that solutions are *oscillatory* (that is, have an infinity of zeros) on $(1,\infty)$ when $a^2 > \frac{1}{4}$, and are *nonoscillatory* when $a^2 \leq \frac{1}{4}$.

The reason the test fails is that for this equation $[r(x) = 1]$ the integral $\int_1^x \frac{dx}{r(x)}$ becomes infinite too rapidly. To overcome this difficulty, we may transform (7.5) by means of the substitution

$$y = x^{1/2}z$$

obtaining

$$(xz')' + \frac{a^2 - \frac{1}{4}}{x}z = 0. \tag{7.6}$$

Solutions z of (7.6) will be oscillatory if and only if solutions y of (7.5) are oscillatory. Theorem 7.1 applied to (7.6) yields the result that the solutions of (7.6) and hence those of (7.5) are oscillatory if $a^2 > \frac{1}{4}$.

It is frequently helpful, if the test of Theorem 7.1 fails to apply to an equation in the form (7.1), to try the substitution

$$y = \left(\frac{x}{r}\right)^{1/2} z,$$

and to attempt to apply the test given by the theorem to the resulting differential equation in z.

For completeness we add the following result.

Theorem 7.2. *Every nonnull solution of equation* (7.1) *has at most a finite number of zeros on the interval* $a \leq x < \infty$, *if*

$$\int_a^\infty \frac{dx}{r(x)} < +\infty \quad \text{and} \quad \left|\int_a^x p(x)\,dx\right| < M \qquad (a \leq x < \infty),$$

where M *is any positive constant.*

The proof is omitted.*

EXERCISES

1. Solve the differential equation $x^2y'' + a^2y = 0$. (Separate cases according as $a^2 > \frac{1}{4}$ or $\leq \frac{1}{4}$.)

2. Prove the final statement in Theorem 7.1.

3. Use Theorem 7.1 to test Bessel's equation,

$$x^2y'' + xy' + (x^2 - n^2)y = 0.$$

4. Prove that if

$$\int_1^\infty \left[xp(x) - \frac{1}{4x}\right] dx = +\infty,$$

the solutions of $y'' + p(x)y = 0$ are oscillatory on $(1,\infty)$.

* R. A. Moore, "The Behavior of Solutions of a Linear Differential Equation of Second Order," *Pac. Jour. Math.*, **5**, p. 135 (1955).

5. Prove that if

$$\int_0^1 \left[xp(x) - \frac{1}{4x}\right] dx = +\infty,$$

the solutions of $y'' + p(x)y = 0$ are oscillatory on $(0,1)$.

8 The Riccati Equation

If the substitution $z = \dfrac{r(x)y'}{y}$ is made in the self-adjoint differential equation

$$[r(x)y']' + p(x)y = 0, \tag{8.1}$$

where $r(x)$ and $p(x)$ are continuous on an interval $a \le x \le b$, we obtain

$$(yz)' + p(x)y = 0,$$

or

$$z' + \frac{1}{r(x)} z^2 + p(x) = 0. \tag{8.2}$$

Equation (8.2) is a Riccati equation (compare with Section 7). The general Riccati equation is usually written as

$$z' + a(x)z + b(x)z^2 + c(x) = 0, \tag{8.3}$$

where we shall suppose $a(x)$, $b(x)$, and $c(x)$ are continuous on the interval $a \le x \le b$. Equation (8.3) is only apparently more general than equation (8.2), since the substitution in (8.3) of

$$w = e^{\int_a^x a(x)\,dx} z \tag{8.4}$$

reduces this equation to

$$w' + q(x)w^2 + p(x) = 0, \tag{8.5}$$

where

$$q(x) = b(x)e^{-\int_a^x a(x)\,dx},$$

$$p(x) = c(x)e^{\int_a^x a(x)\,dx}.$$

If $b(x) \equiv 0$, equation (8.3) is, of course, linear and it is immediately integrable. If $b(x) \not\equiv 0$ on any subinterval of $[a,b]$, to study the solutions of (8.3) we may employ the substitution (8.4) to reduce (8.3) to the form (8.5). The substitution $qw = \frac{y'}{y}$ then reduces (8.5) to the form (8.1), where $r(x) = \frac{1}{q(x)}$. The zeros of $q(x)$ are then singular points of the differential equation (8.1). It will be observed that these successive substitutions may be replaced by the substitution $bz = \frac{y'}{y}$.

Example. Study the solutions of the Riccati equation

$$w' - w^2 - 1 = 0. \tag{8.6}$$

This equation is already in the form (8.5), where $q(x) = -1$ and $p(x) = -1$. The substitution $-w = \frac{y'}{y}$ leads then to the linear self-adjoint differential equation

$$y'' + y = 0,$$

the general solution of which is $c_1 \sin x + c_2 \cos x$. The null solution ($c_1 = c_2 = 0$) leads to no solution w. All other solutions y provide solutions

$$w = -\frac{c_1 \cos x - c_2 \sin x}{c_1 \sin x + c_2 \cos x} \qquad (c_1 \text{ and } c_2 \text{ not both zero}) \tag{8.7}$$

of (8.6). The choice $c_1 = 0$ leads to the particular solution $w = \tan x$.

Example. Study the solutions of the Riccati equation

$$z' + z - e^x z^2 - e^{-x} = 0. \tag{8.8}$$

The substitution $w = e^x z$ reduces this equation to (8.6). Thus solutions z of (8.8) are

$$z = -e^{-x}\frac{c_1 \cos x - c_2 \sin x}{c_1 \sin x + c_2 \cos x} \qquad (c_1 \text{ and } c_2 \text{ not both zero}). \tag{8.9}$$

The student will have observed that the method of the text enables us to find an infinity of solutions of a Riccati equation. Two observations come to mind. First, may there not be solutions of the Riccati equation other than those obtained in this way? And second, we note that the solutions so obtained [see (8.7) and (8.9)] contain *two* arbitrary constants c_1 and c_2. The Riccati equation is a first-order differential equation, and our experience suggests that *one* arbitrary constant might be expected.

Let us deal with the latter question first. In general, following the method of the text, we shall be led to solutions z of (8.3) of the form

$$z = -f(x)\,\frac{c_1u'(x) + c_2v'(x)}{c_1u(x) + c_2v(x)}, \tag{8.10}$$

where $f(x) \neq 0$, c_1 and c_2 are not both zero, and $u(x)$ and $v(x)$ are linearly independent solutions of the related linear differential equation (8.1). The solution $z = \dfrac{-f(x)v'(x)}{v(x)}$ is obtained by setting $c_1 = 0$ (hence $c_2 \neq 0$). For all other solutions given by (8.10), $c_1 \neq 0$, and (8.10) may accordingly be written in the form

$$z = -f(x)\,\frac{u'(x) + kv'(x)}{u(x) + kv(x)}, \tag{8.11}$$

where $k = \dfrac{c_2}{c_1}$ is an arbitrary constant. Thus the solutions which we have depend essentially on one arbitrary constant. The exceptional solution $\dfrac{-f(x)v'(x)}{v(x)}$ may be regarded (and commonly is) as being obtained from (8.11) when k is set equal to infinity. The student will no doubt prefer the form (8.10) which, as we shall see, yields *all* solutions.

To prove the last remark, note first that if $z(x)$ is a solution of (8.3), $w(x)$, defined by (8.4), is a solution of (8.5), and conversely. We have then the following result.

Theorem 8.1. *If $q(x) \neq 0$, and $p(x)$ and $q(x)$ are continuous on* *the interval* $a \leq x \leq b$, *every solution* $w(x)$ *of* (8.5) *may be written in the form*

$$\frac{1}{q(x)} \frac{c_1 u'(x) + c_2 v'(x)}{c_1 u(x) + c_2 v(x)}, \tag{8.12}$$

where c_1 *and* c_2 *are constants, not both zero, and where* $u(x)$ *and* $v(x)$ *are linearly independent solutions of the differential equation*

$$\left[\frac{1}{q(x)} y'\right]' + p(x)y = 0. \tag{8.13}$$

Conversely, if $u(x)$ *and* $v(x)$ *are linearly independent solutions of* (8.13) *and if* c_1 *and* c_2 *are any constants, not both zero, the function* (8.12) *is a solution of* (8.5) *on any interval in which* $c_1 u(x) + c_2 v(x) \neq 0$.

To prove the theorem, let $w(x)$ be an arbitrary solution of (8.5). We may then readily verify that the function

$$e^{\int_a^x q(x)w(x)\,dx}$$

is a solution not equal to zero of (8.13). Thus there exist constants not both zero such that

$$e^{\int_a^x q(x)w(x)\,dx} \equiv c_1 u(x) + c_2 v(x).$$

Upon differentiating both members of this identity the first statement of the theorem follows at once.

Conversely, we assume $u(x)$ and $v(x)$ are linearly independent solutions of (8.13), and $L(x) \equiv c_1 u(x) + c_2 v(x) \neq 0$ on $\alpha \leq x \leq \beta$. It is then easily seen that $\dfrac{L'(x)}{q(x)L(x)}$ is a solution of (8.5). For,

$$\begin{aligned} &\left[\frac{L'(x)}{q(x)L(x)}\right]' + q(x)\left[\frac{L'(x)}{q(x)L(x)}\right]^2 + p(x) \\ &\quad \equiv \left[\frac{L'(x)}{q(x)}\right]' \frac{1}{L(x)} - \frac{[L'(x)]^2}{q(x)L^2(x)} + q(x)\left[\frac{L'(x)}{q(x)L(x)}\right]^2 + p(x) \equiv 0. \end{aligned}$$

The proof of the theorem is complete.

EXERCISES

1. Show that if z, z_1, z_2, z_3 are any four different solutions of the Riccati equation (8.3), then

$$\frac{z - z_2}{z - z_1}\frac{z_3 - z_1}{z_3 - z_2} \equiv \text{constant}.$$

[*Hint*. First show that $u = \dfrac{1}{z - z_1}$ is a solution of the linear differential equation $u' - (a + 2bz_1)u = b$. Similarly, $u_1 = \dfrac{1}{z_2 - z_1}$ and $u_2 = \dfrac{1}{z_3 - z_1}$ are solutions of this differential equation. Consider the differences $u - u_1$ and $u_2 - u_1$.]

2. Find all solutions of the following Riccati equations:

(a) $z' + z^2 - 1 = 0$;
(b) $z' + z^2 - z - 2 = 0$;
(c) $z' + z^2 - 2z + 2 = 0$;
(d) $x^2z' - 2xz + x^2z^2 + 2 = 0$;
(e) $x^2z' - 3xz + z^2 + 2x^2 = 0$;
(f) $z' + z^2 + a^2x^{-2} = 0$ (a constant);
(g) $xz' - z + xz^2 + x^3 = 0$.

3. Find four distinct solutions for each of the differential equations in Exercise 2, and verify the conclusion of Exercise 1.

ANSWERS

2. (a) $\dfrac{c_1e^x - c_2e^{-x}}{c_1e^x + c_2e^{-x}}$;

(b) $\dfrac{2c_1e^{2x} - c_2e^{-x}}{c_1e^{2x} + c_2e^{-x}}$;

(c) $\dfrac{(c_1 - c_2)\sin x + (c_1 + c_2)\cos x}{c_1 \sin x + c_2 \cos x}$;

(d) $\dfrac{c_1 + 2c_2x}{c_1x + c_2x^2}$;

(e) $\dfrac{(c_1 - c_2)x \sin\log|x| + (c_1 + c_2)x\cos\log|x|}{c_1 \sin\log|x| + c_2\cos\log|x|}$;

(g) $\dfrac{x[c_1\cos(x^2/2) - c_2\sin(x^2/2)]}{c_1\sin(x^2/2) + c_2\cos(x^2/2)}$.

11

Characteristic Functions; Orthogonal Polynomials

1 Introduction

In this chapter we shall develop some of the simpler aspects of the theory of *characteristic functions* (also known as *eigenfunctions*) and their associated *characteristic numbers* (also known as *eigenvalues* and as *eigennumbers*).

Consider the differential system

$$y'' + \lambda y = 0,$$
$$(1.1) \qquad y(0) = 0, \qquad y(\pi) = 0,$$

where λ is a parameter independent of x. We seek solutions $y(x) \not\equiv 0$ of this system. It is clear at the outset that such a solution will exist only for certain values of λ. Indeed, the general solution of the differential equation is

$$c_1 \sin \sqrt{\lambda}\, x + c_2 \cos \sqrt{\lambda}\, x.$$

Since $y(0) = 0$, $c_2 = 0$. Thus, if there is a solution $y(x) \not\equiv 0$ of (1.1), it must be of the form

$$(1.2) \qquad y(x) = c_1 \sin \sqrt{\lambda}\, x \qquad (c_1 \neq 0).$$

Applying the condition $y(\pi) = 0$ to (1.2), we note that $\sqrt{\lambda}\,\pi$ must be an integral multiple of π. That is,

$$\lambda = n^2,$$

where n is an integer $\neq 0$. In other words, λ must be one of the numbers

$$1, 4, 9, \ldots. \tag{1.3}$$

Corresponding solutions $y(x)$ are, respectively,

$$\sin x, \ \sin 2x, \ \sin 3x, \ \ldots. \tag{1.4}$$

The numbers (1.3) are the *characteristic numbers*, and the set of functions (1.4) is a corresponding set of *characteristic functions*. Clearly, we might replace the set (1.4) by any set

$$a_1 \sin x, \ a_2 \sin 2x, \ a_3 \sin 3x, \ \ldots,$$

where each of the constants $a_1, a_2, a_3, \ldots$ may be given any value different from zero.

It will be observed that for this problem there is a smallest characteristic number ($\lambda = 1$), that there is an infinite sequence of characteristic numbers, and that the limit of this sequence is $+\infty$.

More generally, we consider the differential system

$$\begin{aligned} &[r(x)y']' + p(x)y + \lambda q(x)y = 0, \\ &y(a) = 0, \qquad y(b) = 0, \end{aligned} \tag{1.5}$$

where $r(x)$ and $q(x)$ are positive and $r(x)$, $q(x)$, and $p(x)$ are continuous real functions of x on the closed interval $a \leq x \leq b$. The constant λ is again a parameter independent of x. We seek solutions $y(x) \not\equiv 0$ of (1.5). The system (1.5) is an example of a *Sturm-Liouville* system.

Theorem 1.1. *There exists an infinite sequence of characteristic numbers* $\lambda_1, \lambda_2, \ldots$ *of* (1.5) *with the properties*

$$\lambda_1 < \lambda_2 < \cdots,$$

$$\lambda_n \to +\infty,$$

and a corresponding sequence of characteristic functions

$$y_1(x), y_2(x), \ldots$$

defined on the interval $a \leq x \leq b$. *The function* $y_n(x)$ *has precisely* n *zeros on the interval* $a < x \leq b$.

In the course of proving this theorem we shall need to have recourse to a number of fundamental theorems in differential equation theory and in analysis. We shall denote the interval $a < x \leq b$ by the symbol $(a,b]$.

The plan is to take a nonnull solution $y(x,\lambda)$ of the differential equation in (1.5) with the property that $y(a,\lambda) = 0$ and watch its behavior as λ increases. It will be shown that there is a number λ_1 with the property that $y(x, \lambda_1) > 0$ for $a < x < b$ and such that $y(b,\lambda_1) = 0$. As λ increases from λ_1, a second number λ_2 will appear. The solution $y(x,\lambda_2)$ will vanish once on the open interval (a,b), and $y(b,\lambda_2) = 0$. And so on. The numbers λ_n will then be shown to increase without bound as n increases.

First, we employ the result concerning the differential system (3.15) of Chapter 9; that is, there exists a solution $y(x,\lambda)$ of the system

$$\begin{aligned} &[r(x)y']' + [p(x) + \lambda q(x)]y = 0, \\ &y(a) = 0, \qquad y'(a) = 1, \end{aligned} \tag{1.6}$$

which for each fixed λ is unique. Further, $y(x,\lambda)$ is of class C^1 in x on $[a,b]$ and continuous in λ, for every value of λ. Finally, $y(x,\lambda) \not\equiv 0$.

We observe that since $r(x)$, $p(x)$, and $q(x)$ are continuous on the closed interval $[a,b]$, there exist constants r, R, p, P, q, Q such that

$$0 < r \leq r(x) \leq R, \qquad p \leq p(x) \leq P, \qquad 0 < q \leq q(x) \leq Q.$$

Roughly speaking, by the Sturm-Picone theorem, the solution $y(x,\lambda)$ oscillates more rapidly than the solution $y_0(x,\lambda)$ of the system

$$\begin{aligned} &[Ry']' + [p + \lambda q]y = 0, \\ &y(a) = 0, \qquad y'(a) = 1, \end{aligned} \tag{1.7}$$

and less rapidly than the solution $y_1(x,\lambda)$ of the system

$$\begin{aligned} &[ry']' + [P + \lambda Q]y = 0, \\ &y(a) = 0, \qquad y'(a) = 1. \end{aligned} \tag{1.8}$$

Because the coefficients in both (1.7) and (1.8) are constants we can readily determine solutions of these systems.

Note that if λ is any number such that

$$\frac{p + \lambda q}{R} > \frac{\pi^2}{(b - a)^2},$$

by the Sturm comparison theorem, the solution $y_0(x,\lambda)$ of (1.7) has at least one zero on the interval $a < x < b$. Indeed,

$$y_0(x,\lambda) = k \sin \left[\sqrt{\frac{p + \lambda q}{R}}\,(x - a)\right],$$

where k is a constant $\neq 0$. For such a choice of λ, the solution $y(x,\lambda)$ of (1.6) must then also have a zero on the interval $a < x < b$.

In a similar fashion, λ can be chosen small enough that $P + \lambda Q < 0$ in (1.8). For such a choice of λ, the solution $y_1(x,\lambda)$ of (1.8) has no zero on the interval $(a,b]$; hence, neither does the solution $y(x,\lambda)$. Accordingly, there are values of λ for which $y(x,\lambda)$ has zeros on (a,b) and there are values of λ for which $y(x,\lambda)$ has no zeros on (a,b). Further, if $y(x,\lambda)$ has a zero on (a,b) for a given value of λ, say λ', it will have a zero on (a,b) for every $\lambda > \lambda'$. If $y(x,\lambda)$ has no zero on (a,b) for $\lambda = \lambda''$, it will not vanish on (a,b) for any $\lambda < \lambda''$. There is then a greatest lower bound λ_1 of the values of λ for which $y(x,\lambda)$ has a zero on (a,b).

Suppose that $\lambda = \lambda^*$ is taken such that $y(x,\lambda^*)$ has a zero at $x = x_0$ on (a,b) (see Fig. 11.1).

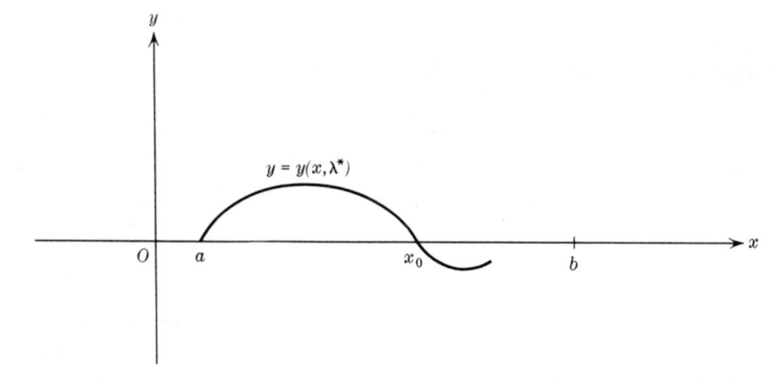

FIG. 11.1

The equation

$$y(x,\lambda) = 0 \tag{1.9}$$

can be solved for x as a function of λ by the implicit-function theorem* since

$$y(x_0,\lambda^*) = 0, \qquad y_x(x_0,\lambda^*) \neq 0.$$

The last inequality is valid for otherwise $y(x,\lambda^*)$ would be $\equiv 0$. We have then,

$$x = x(\lambda),$$

where $x(\lambda)$ is continuous. Further $x(\lambda)$ decreases, as λ increases, by the Sturm comparison theorem. That is to say that x_0 moves steadily toward a as λ increases and moves steadily toward b as λ decreases.

Consider the solution $y(x,\lambda_1)$ on $(a,b]$. Does this solution have a zero on (a,b)? No, for if it did, so would a solution $y(x,\lambda)$ where λ is slightly smaller than λ_1, contrary to the definition of λ_1. Thus, $y(x,\lambda_1) > 0$ for x on (a,b). Next, we take $\lambda > \lambda_1$ but sufficiently near λ_1 that $y(x,\lambda)$ has only one zero on (a,b). For each such λ, $x(\lambda) < b$, and, as $\lambda \to \lambda_1$, $x(\lambda) \to L \leq b$. If L were less than b, we could argue as before that there would be a contradiction of the definition of λ_1. Accordingly,

$$\lim_{\lambda \to \lambda_1} x(\lambda) = x(\lambda_1) = b.$$

Since $x(\lambda)$ is a solution of (1.9), we have

$$y(x(\lambda),\lambda) \equiv 0,$$

and

$$\lim_{\lambda \to \lambda_1} y(x(\lambda),\lambda) = y(x(\lambda_1),\lambda_1) = y(b,\lambda_1) = 0,$$

because of the continuity of $y(x,\lambda)$ and of $x(\lambda)$.

* See, for example, D. V. Widder, Advanced Calculus (2nd ed.), Prentice-Hall, Englewood Cliffs, N.J. (1961), p. 55. It will be observed that the proof of the implicit-function theorem is readily modified to extend to the case when $y(x,\lambda)$ is of class C^1 in x and continuous in λ.

We have shown that there exists a smallest characteristic number λ_1 of the system (1.6), and $y(x,\lambda_1)$ is the corresponding characteristic solution.

By allowing λ to increase from the value λ_1 and using arguments similar to the above one argues that there is a number $\lambda_2 > \lambda_1$ such that

$$y(b,\lambda_2) = 0,$$

and the solution $y(x,\lambda_2)$ will have precisely one zero between a and b. Indeed, it is sufficient to define λ_2 as the greatest lower bound of values of λ for which $y(x,\lambda)$ vanishes exactly twice on the interval (a,b).

The process can be continued, and there results a sequence of characteristic numbers

$$\lambda_1 < \lambda_2 < \lambda_3 < \cdots\cdot$$

and a corresponding sequence of characteristic functions

$$y(x,\lambda_1), \qquad y(x,\lambda_2), \qquad y(x,\lambda_3), \ldots.$$

Further, $y(x,\lambda_n)$ will have precisely n zeros on the interval $(a,b]$.

It remains to prove that

$$\lim_{n \to \infty} \lambda_n = \infty. \tag{1.10}$$

First, observe that $\lim \lambda_n$ exists, finite or infinite, since λ_n is an increasing sequence. Suppose $\lim \lambda_n = L$, finite. Then every characteristic number is less than L. The solution $y(x,L)$ cannot have more zeros on (a,b) than the solution of the system (1.8) with $\lambda = L$. But this solution can be written

$$y_1(x,L) = k \sin \left[\sqrt{\frac{P + LQ}{r}}\,(x - a)\right] \qquad (k \neq 0), \tag{1.11}$$

and the number of zeros of $y_1(x,L)$ on $(a,b]$ is not greater than

$$\frac{b - a}{\pi}\sqrt{\frac{P + LQ}{r}}. \tag{1.12}$$

Since $y(x,L)$ has no fewer zeros on $(a,b]$ than $y(x,\lambda)$ when $\lambda < L$, it would follow that the number of zeros of $y(x,\lambda_n)$ on $(a,b]$ is less than the quantity in (1.12), for all n. From this contradiction we infer the truth of (1.10); and the theorem is proved.

Schematic graphs of the first three characteristic functions will be found in Fig. 11.2.

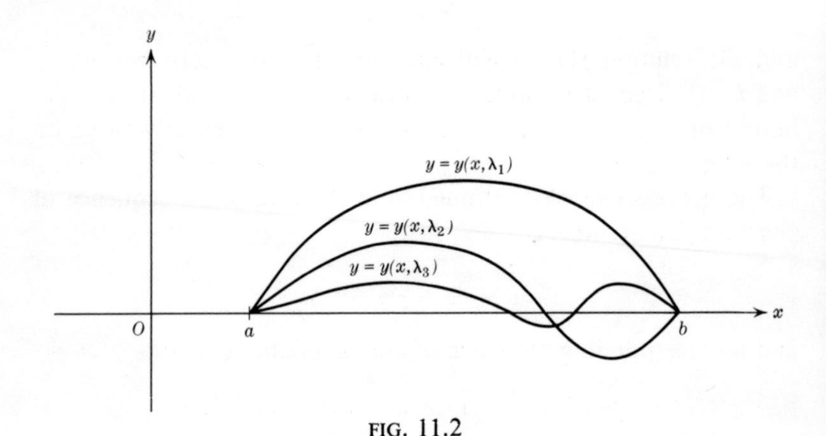

FIG. 11.2

EXERCISES

Determine the sequences of characteristic numbers and functions for the following Sturm-Liouville systems.

1. $y'' + \lambda y = 0,$
$y(0) = 0,$
$y\left(\frac{\pi}{2}\right) = 0.$

2. $y'' + \lambda y = 0,$
$y(-\pi/2) = 0,$
$y\left(\frac{\pi}{2}\right) = 0.$

3. $y'' + y + \lambda y = 0,$
$y(0) = 0,$
$y(\pi) = 0.$

4. $y'' + \lambda y = 0,$
$y(0) = 0,$
$y(1) = 0.$

5. $(xy')' + \lambda \dfrac{1}{x} y = 0,$
$y(1) = y(e^{\pi}) = 0.$

6. $(x^2y')' + \lambda \dfrac{1}{x^2} y = 0,$
$y(1) = y(2) = 0.$

ANSWERS

1. $\lambda = 4n^2,\ y_n(x) = \sin 2nx \qquad (n = 1, 2, 3, \ldots).$

2. $\lambda = n^2,\ y_n(x) = \sin n\left(x + \dfrac{\pi}{2}\right) \qquad (n = 1, 2, 3, \ldots).$

3. $\lambda = n^2 - 1,\ y_n(x) = \sin nx \qquad (n = 1, 2, 3, \ldots).$

4. $\lambda = n^2\pi^2,\ y_n(x) = \sin n\pi x \qquad (n = 1, 2, 3, \ldots).$

5. $\lambda = n^2,\ y_n(x) = \sin (n \log x) \qquad (n = 1, 2, 3, \ldots).$

6. $\lambda = 4n^2\pi^2,\ y_n(x) = \sin 2n\pi[1 - (1/x)] \qquad (n = 1, 2, 3, \ldots).$

2 Orthogonality

Two functions $f(x)$ and $g(x)$ are said to be *orthogonal* on the interval (a,b) with respect to the *weight* function $q(x)$ if

$$\int_a^b q(x)f(x)g(x)\,dx = 0.$$

Theorem 2.1. *Each characteristic function associated with the Sturm-Liouville system* (1.5) *is orthogonal to every other characteristic function on the interval* (a,b) *with respect to the weight function* $q(x)$.

Let $y_n(x)$ and $y_m(x)$ be arbitrary characteristic functions, and let λ_n and λ_m be, respectively, their associated characteristic numbers. We have to show that

$$\int_a^b q(x)y_n(x)y_m(x)\,dx = 0 \qquad (n \neq m). \tag{2.1}$$

To prove (2.1), we observe that

$$
\begin{aligned}
&[r(x)y_n'(x)]' + [p(x) + \lambda_n q(x)]y_n(x) \equiv 0, \\
&[r(x)y_m'(x)]' + [p(x) + \lambda_m q(x)]y_m(x) \equiv 0,
\end{aligned} \tag{2.2}
$$

since $y_n(x)$ and $y_m(x)$ are solutions of the system (1.5) when $\lambda = \lambda_n$ and $\lambda = \lambda_m$, respectively. Let us multiply both members of the first identity by $y_m(x)$, those of the second by $-y_n(x)$, and add. We obtain

(2.3)
$$
y_m(x)[r(x)y_n'(x)]' - y_n(x)[r(x)y_m'(x)]' \equiv (\lambda_m - \lambda_n)q(x)y_n(x)y_m(x).
$$

If both members of the identity (2.3) are integrated from a to b, and if integration by parts is applied to the left-hand member, there results

(2.4)
$$
r(x)[y_m(x)y_n'(x) - y_n(x)y_m'(x)]_a^b = (\lambda_m - \lambda_n)\int_a^b q(x)y_n(x)y_m(x)\,dx.
$$

The left-hand member of (2.4) is clearly zero, and since $\lambda_m \neq \lambda_n$ when $m \neq n$, equation (2.1) follows at once.

The sequence of characteristic functions is said to be an *orthogonal sequence*. If, in addition,

$$
\int_a^b q(x)y_n^2(x)\,dx = 1 \qquad (n = 1, 2, \ldots),
$$

the sequence $y_1(x), y_2(x), \ldots$ is said to be *normal*. Recall that if $y_n(x)$ is a characteristic function, so is $a_n y_n(x)$, where a_n is any constant different from zero. Accordingly, we can normalize the sequence of characteristic functions by means of the following device. Let

$$
\int_a^b q(x)y_n^2(x)\,dx = c_n^2 \qquad (n = 1, 2, 3, \ldots).
$$

Since $c_n^2 > 0$, the sequence

$$
\frac{y_1(x)}{c_1}, \frac{y_2(x)}{c_2}, \ldots
$$

is immediately seen to be both normal and orthogonal with respect to the weight function $q(x)$ on the interval (a,b).

EXERCISE

Using the first three computed characteristic functions for the various exercises at the end of Section 1, verify directly that these three functions are orthogonal in pairs. Find also the associated normal characteristic functions.

3 The Expansion of a Function in a Series of Orthogonal Functions

Thousands of pages have been written on this subject and its ramifications. We shall have to be content here with an indication as to how the formal expansion of a given function may be achieved.

Let $y_1(x), y_2(x), \ldots$ be a sequence of normal characteristic functions of (1.5), and suppose that $f(x)$ is a given function continuous on the interval $a \le x \le b$ which may be represented there by a series $\sum_1^\infty b_n y_n(x)$, where the b_n are constants. Proceeding formally, we have*

$$f(x) = b_1y_1(x) + b_2y_2(x) + \cdots = \sum_{n=1}^{\infty} b_n y_n(x),$$

$$q(x)f(x)y_m(x) = b_1q(x)y_1(x)y_m(x) + b_2q(x)y_2(x)y_m(x) + \cdots$$

$$= \sum_{n=1}^{\infty} b_n q(x) y_n(x) y_m(x),$$

$$\begin{aligned}(3.1)\quad \int_a^b q(x)f(x)y_m(x)\,dx &= \int_a^b b_1q(x)y_1(x)y_m(x)\,dx \\ &\quad + \int_a^b b_2q(x)y_2(x)y_m(x)\,dx + \cdots \\ &= \int_a^b \left[\sum_{n=1}^{\infty} b_n q(x)y_n(x)y_m(x)\right] dx \\ &= \sum_{n=1}^{\infty} b_n \int_a^b q(x)y_n(x)y_m(x)\,dx.\end{aligned}$$

* The manipulations which follow would be valid if we assumed, for example, that the series converged uniformly to $f(x)$ on the interval.

From (3.1) we have

$$\int_a^b q(x)f(x)y_m(x)\,dx = b_m \qquad (m = 1, 2, \ldots). \tag{3.2}$$

Thus, if there is a series expansion of the type assumed, then

$$f(x) = b_1y_1(x) + b_2y_2(x) + \cdots,$$

where the numbers b_m are determined by (3.2). Having determined the form of the coefficients b_m, we may now present the basic problem of expanding a given function in a series of normal characteristic functions. Let $f(x)$ be the given function, which we suppose for simplicity to be continuous on the interval $a \leq x \leq b$, and define numbers b_m by the equations

$$b_m = \int_a^b q(x)f(x)y_m(x)\,dx \qquad (m = 1, 2, \ldots).$$

Then the formal expansion of $f(x)$ is given by

$$f(x) \sim b_1y_1(x) + b_2y_2(x) + \cdots. \tag{3.3}$$

The symbol " $\sim$ " is used rather than " $=$ " since we have no *a priori* assurance that the series will converge or, if it is convergent, that it will converge to the function $f(x)$. Indeed, it may not converge, and if it is convergent, it need not converge to $f(x)$. We may then ask what conditions (in addition to continuity) must be imposed upon $f(x)$ to ensure that the series actually converges to $f(x)$ on $[a,b]$; when will the convergence be uniform; when will it be absolute; and so on. New concepts of convergence arise in which the theory of the Lebesgue integral plays a fundamental role. For completeness we state without proof the following theorem.*

Theorem 3.1. *If $f(x)$ is continuous and if $f'(x)$ exists and is piecewise continuous*† *on the interval $a \leq x \leq b$, the series* (3.3)

* See E. L. Ince, *Ordinary Differential Equations*, p. 273, Longmans, Roberts and Green, London (1927).

† A function is *piecewise continuous* on an interval $(a.b)$ if the interval can be divided into a finite number of subintervals on the closure of each of which the function is continuous.

converges uniformly and absolutely to $f(x)$ on every closed interval interior to the open interval $a < x < b$.

EXERCISES

1. Expand the following functions defined on $(0,\pi)$ in a series of characteristic functions of the system

$$y'' + \lambda y = 0,$$
$$y(0) = y(\pi) = 0.$$

(a) x;
(b) x^2;
(c) e^x.

2. Let the system be

$$(xy')' + \lambda \frac{1}{x} y = 0,$$
$$y(1) = y(e^\pi) = 0,$$

and expand formally the function x^{-2} in a series of characteristic functions on the interval $(1,e^\pi)$.

3. The Legendre differential equation

$$[(1 - x^2)y']' + n(n + 1)y = 0 \qquad (n = 0, 1, 2,\ldots)$$

is known to have polynomial solutions $P_n(x)$ of degree n. Compute $P_n(x)$ when $n = 0, 1, 2, 3, 4$, subject to the condition that $P_n(1) = 1$. Show that the sequence $P_1(x), P_2(x),\ldots$ is an orthogonal sequence of functions on $(-1,1)$ with weight function unity.

4. Obtain the first few terms in the expansion of e^x in a series of Legendre polynomials on the interval $(-1,1)$.

ANSWERS

1. (a) $2(\sin x - \frac{1}{2}\sin 2x + \frac{1}{3}\sin 3x - \cdots)$;

(b) $$2\left[\left(\pi - \frac{4}{\pi}\right)\sin x - \frac{\pi}{2}\sin 2x + \left(\frac{\pi}{3} - \frac{4}{3^3\pi}\right)\sin 3x - \frac{\pi}{4}\sin 4x + \cdots\right];$$

(c) $$\sum_1^\infty a_n \sin nx,\ a_n = \frac{2n}{1 + n^2}\frac{1}{\pi}[1 - (-1)^n e^\pi].$$

2. $\sum_{1}^{n} a_n \sin (n \log x)$, $a_n = \dfrac{1 + 4n^2}{2n(1 + n^2)} \dfrac{1 - (-1)^n e^{-\pi}}{e^{\pi} - 1}$.

3. $P_0(x) = 1$, $P_1(x) = x$, $P_2(x) = \frac{1}{2}(3x^2 - 1)$, $P_3(x) = \frac{1}{2}(5x^3 - 3x)$, $P_4(x) = \frac{1}{8}(35x^4 - 30x^2 + 3)$.

4. $\frac{1}{2}(e - e^{-1}) + 3e^{-1}x + \frac{5}{4}(e - 7e^{-1})(3x^2 - 1) + \cdots$.

4 The Bessel Equation

The differential equation

$$x^2y'' + xy' + (x^2 - n^2)y = 0 \qquad (n \geq 0) \tag{4.1}$$

is known as *Bessel's equation*. It is of considerable importance in mathematical physics. It is also of interest in its own right to mathematicians. We shall examine some of the simpler properties of solutions of this equation.

First, we note that Bessel's equation has a regular singular point at $x = 0$. The indicial equation associated with this point is

$$\rho^2 - n^2 = 0.$$

The indicial roots are $\rho = n, -n$. Thus, there exists a solution of (4.1) of the form $x^nP(x)$, where $P(x)$ is a convergent power series in powers of x, and $P(0) \neq 0$. If the substitution

$$y = x^n \sum_{0}^{\infty} a_m x^m \tag{4.2}$$

is made in equation (4.1), we find after the usual computation that

$$(2n + 1)a_1 = 0,$$

$$a_m = -\frac{a_{m-2}}{m(2n + m)} \qquad (m = 2, 3, \ldots).$$

Accordingly,

$$a_1 = a_3 = a_5 = \cdots = 0.$$

If a_0 is set equal to 1, we have

$$a_{2m} = \frac{(-1)^m}{2^{2m}m!(n + 1)(n + 2)\cdots(n + m)} \qquad (m = 1, 2, \ldots).$$

The solution (4.2) may then be written ($n \geq 0$)

$$(4.3)\quad y = x^n\left[1 - \frac{x^2}{2^2 1!(n+1)} + \frac{x^4}{2^4 2!(n+1)(n+2)} - \frac{x^6}{2^6 3!(n+1)(n+2)(n+3)} + \cdots\right].$$

This series has the test-ratio

$$\left|\frac{x^{2m}}{4(m+1)(n+m+1)}\right|,$$

which approaches zero as m becomes infinite. Thus the series in brackets in (4.3) converges for all values of x.

When n is an integer it is customary to multiply this solution by

$$c_n = \frac{1}{2^n n!}.$$

The resulting solution is called a Bessel function of order n and is designated by the symbol $J_n(x)$. It follows from the form of (4.1) that if n is not an integer, $J_{-n}(x)$ is also a solution of (4.1). Further, in this case $J_n(x)$ and $J_{-n}(x)$ are linearly independent, for $J_{-n}(x) \not\equiv cJ_n(x)$ (c constant).

When n is an integer, the "second" solution may be obtained by the usual device of setting

$$y = J_n(x)v.$$

The second solution will be found to involve $\log x$, as we might expect from Theorem 3.1 of Chapter 8.

We observe from (4.4) and Theorem 7.1 of Chapter 10 that $J_n(x)$ has an infinity of zeros on the interval $(0,\infty)$. Further, if the substitution

$$y = x^{-1/2}z$$

is made in (4.4), this equation becomes

$$(4.5)\qquad z'' + \left[1 - \frac{n^2 - \frac{1}{4}}{x^2}\right]z = 0.$$

When x is large this equation is approximately $z'' + z = 0$. This suggests comparing the oscillation of solutions $z(x)$ of (4.5) with solutions $\sin(x - a)$ of the differential equation

$$v'' + v = 0. \tag{4.6}$$

Inasmuch as the coefficient of z in (4.5) is smaller than that of v in (4.6) when $n^2 > \frac{1}{4}$, it follows that consecutive zeros of a solution of (4.1) differ by more than π when $n^2 > \frac{1}{4}$. Similarly, the distance between consecutive zeros of a solution of (4.1) is less than π when $n^2 < \frac{1}{4}$.

Clearly, when $n^2 = \frac{1}{4}$, equation (4.5) becomes

$$z'' + z = 0,$$

and [from (4.3), for example]

$$J_{1/2}(x) = c_1 \frac{\sin x}{\sqrt{x}},$$

$$J_{-1/2}(x) = c_2 \frac{\cos x}{\sqrt{x}}.$$

$$J_0(x) = 1 - \frac{x^2}{2^2} + \frac{x^4}{2^2 4^2} - \frac{x^6}{2^2 4^2 6^2} + \cdots.$$

The general solution for $n = 0$ appears in the answer to Exercise 12 of Section 3, Chapter 8. A graph of the functions $J_0(x)$ and $J_1(x)$ is given in Fig. 11.3.

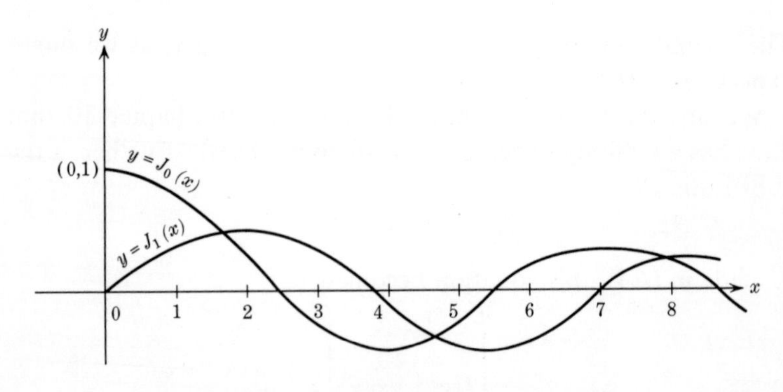

FIG. 11.3

The graphs in Fig. 11.3 suggest that the zeros of $J_1(x)$ separate those of $J_0(x)$, and vice-versa. By the Sturm comparison theorem we note that between every two consecutive positive zeros of $J_m(x)$ there is a zero of $J_n(x)$, if $n < m$. The same will be true of two consecutive negative zeros of $J_m(x)$, since $x^{-k}J_k(x)$ is an even function of x for all values of k—that is to say, its graph is symmetric in the y-axis.

Thus, we know, in particular, that between every two consecutive positive zeros of $J_n(x)$ there is a zero of $J_{n-1}(x)$. We shall show that between every two consecutive positive zeros of $J_n(x)$ there is also a zero of $J_{n+1}(x)$. Let

$$J_n(x) = c_n x^n W_n(x);$$

that is,

$$(4.7) \quad W_n(x) = 1 - \frac{x^2}{2^2 1!(n+1)} + \frac{x^4}{2^4 2!(n+1)(n+2)} - \frac{x^6}{2^6 3!(n+1)(n+2)(n+3)} + \cdots.$$

It is clear that the positive zeros of $J_n(x)$ and of $W_n(x)$ are identical. Further,

$$W_n'(x) = \frac{-2x}{2^2 1!(n+1)} + \frac{4x^3}{2^4 2!(n+1)(n+2)} - \frac{6x^5}{2^6 3!(n+1)(n+2)(n+3)} + \cdots$$

$$= -\frac{x}{2(n+1)}\left[1 - \frac{x^2}{2^2 1!(n+2)} + \frac{x^4}{2^4 2!(n+2)(n+3)} - \cdots\right];$$

or

$$(4.8) \qquad W_n'(x) = -\frac{x}{2(n+1)} W_{n+1}(x).$$

We are now prepared to complete the argument. Between two positive zeros of $W_n(x)$ there is a zero of $W_n'(x)$, by Rolle's theorem. But each positive zero of $W_n'(x)$ is a zero of $W_{n+1}(x)$, according to (4.8).

We have proved the following result.

Theorem 4.1. *Between every two consecutive positive zeros of $J_n(x)$ there is a zero of $J_{n-1}(x)$ and also of $J_{n+1}(x)$. The same conclusion is valid for each pair of consecutive negative zeros of $J_n(x)$.*

Two more observations should be made in connection with the last demonstration. We have assumed that $W_n'(x)$ may be computed by differentiating the series for $W_n(x)$ term by term, and this is known to be valid. Also, we should show that the differentiation of the "general" term in the series for $W_n(x)$ does lead to the "general" term in the series for $W_{n+1}(x)$. More precisely, it will be sufficient to show that

$$\left[\frac{x^{2m}}{2^{2m}m!(n+1)(n+2)\dots(n+m)}\right]' = \frac{x}{2(n+1)}\left[\frac{x^{2m-2}}{2^{2m-2}(m-1)!(n+2)(n+3)\dots(n+m-1)}\right]. \tag{4.9}$$

This is immediate, and the proof is left to the student.

EXERCISES

1. Show that $W_n(x)$ is a solution of the differential equation

$$(x^{2n+1}W_n')' + x^{2n+1}W_n = 0.$$

2. It is customary to write

$$J_{1/2}(x) = \sqrt{\frac{2}{\pi}}\frac{\sin x}{\sqrt{x}},$$

$$J_{-1/2}(x) = \sqrt{\frac{2}{\pi}}\frac{\cos x}{\sqrt{x}}.$$

Show that

$$J_{3/2}(x) = \frac{c}{\sqrt{x}}\left(\frac{\sin x}{x} - \cos x\right).$$

The constant c is traditionally taken to be $\sqrt{2/\pi}$.

3. Find $J_{5/2}(x)$ to within a multiplicative constant.

4. Verify that

$$J_{n+1}(x) = -\frac{2n}{x} J_n(x) - J_{n-1}(x),$$

when n is a positive integer.

5. The formula in Exercise 4 is valid for all $n \geq 0$. Use it to determine the answer to Exercise 3.

6. Show that the general solution of $y'' + 9x^2y = 0$ is given by

$$y = \sqrt{x}[c_1 J_{1/4}(\tfrac{3}{2}x^2) + c_2 J_{-1/4}(\tfrac{3}{2}x^2)].$$

5 Orthogonal Polynomials

Earlier in this chapter we met several systems of orthogonal functions. In Exercise 3 of Section 3 we obtained the Legendre polynomials of degree 0, 1, 2, 3, 4 and observed that the Legendre polynomials form a sequence of functions orthogonal in the interval $(-1,1)$ with respect to the weight function 1.

There are four other classical sequences of orthogonal polynomials given below, but, as we shall see, we may assume any positive continuous weight function $p(x)$ on an arbitrary interval (a,b) and construct a corresponding sequence of orthogonal polynomials.

CLASSICAL ORTHOGONAL POLYNOMIALS

SYSTEM	DIFFERENTIAL EQUATION	WEIGHT FUNCTION	INTERVAL
Legendre	$[(1 - x^2)y']' + n(n + 1)y = 0$	1	$(-1,1)$
Chebyshev	$[(1 - x^2)^{1/2}y']' + n^2(1 - x^2)^{-1/2}y = 0$	$(1 - x^2)^{-1/2}$	$(-1,1)$
Laguerre	$(xe^{-x}y')' + ne^{-x}y = 0$	e^{-x}	$(0,\infty)$
Hermite	$(e^{-x^2}y')' + 2ne^{-x^2}y = 0$	e^{-x^2}	$(-\infty,\infty)$
Jacobi	$[(1 - x)^{1+\alpha}(1 + x)^{1+\beta}y']' + n(n + \alpha + \beta + 1) \times (1 - x)^{\alpha}(1 + x)^{\beta}y = 0$	$(1 - x)^{\alpha} \times (1 + x)^{\beta}$	$(-1,1)$ $(\alpha > -1,$ $\beta > -1)$

We have chosen to write the above differential equations in self-adjoint form, for the weight function can be seen immediately. In addition, this form is the natural one to use in proving the polynomials orthogonal. (These equations will be found in expanded form in Exercise 1, Section 3, Chapter 10.)

For example, suppose $y_n(x)$ and $y_m(x)$ are polynomial solutions of Hermite's equation, where $n \neq m$. Since the coefficient of y, except for a constant factor, is e^{-x^2}, we anticipate that e^{-x^2} is the weight function. We have

$$[e^{-x^2}y_n'(x)]' + 2ne^{-x^2}y_n(x) \equiv 0,$$

$$[e^{-x^2}y_m'(x)]' + 2me^{-x^2}y_m(x) \equiv 0 \qquad (n \neq m).$$

Multiply both members of the first equation by $y_m(x)$ and both members of the second equation by $-y_n(x)$ and add. Then

$$y_m(x)[e^{-x^2}y_n'(x)]' - y_n(x)[e^{-x^2}y_m'(x)]' \equiv 2e^{-x^2}(m - n)y_n(x)y_m(x). \tag{5.1}$$

Next, integrate both members of (5.1) on the interval $(-\infty,\infty)$. We have, after an integration by parts,

$$e^{-x^2}[y_m(x)y_n'(x) - y_n(x)y_m'(x)]_{-\infty}^{\infty} = 2(m - n)\int_{-\infty}^{\infty} e^{-x^2}y_n(x)y_m(x)\,dx,$$

or,

$$0 = 2(m - n)\int_{-\infty}^{\infty} e^{-x^2}y_n(x)y_m(x)\,dx. \tag{5.2}$$

Since $m - n \neq 0$, we see that the polynomials $y_n(x)$ and $y_m(x)$ are orthogonal on the interval $(-\infty,\infty)$ with respect to the weight function e^{-x^2}.

The Schmidt orthogonalization process. Suppose $p(x)$ is positive and continuous on the interval $[a,b]$. We shall construct a sequence of polynomials $P_0(x), P_1(x), P_2(x), \ldots$ orthogonal on this interval with respect to the weight function $p(x)$. The degree of $P_n(x)$ will be n.

We set

$$P_0(x) = 1,$$

and write $P_1(x) = a_1x + b_1$, where the constants a_1 and b_1 are to be determined. Since $P_0(x)$ and $P_1(x)$ are to be orthogonal we have

$$\int_a^b p(x)(1)(a_1x + b_1)\,dx = 0,$$

or

$$a_1k_1 + b_1k_0 = 0, \tag{5.3}$$

where

$$k_1 = \int_a^b xp(x)\,dx,$$

$$k_0 = \int_a^b p(x)\,dx.$$

We may then write

$$P_1(x) = a_1\left(x - \frac{k_1}{k_0}\right),$$

and note that a_1 may be chosen as any number not equal to zero. For simplicity, we write

$$P_1(x) = \alpha_1x + \beta_1 \qquad (\alpha_1 \neq 0).$$

Next, we write

$$P_2(x) = a_2x^2 + b_2x + c_2.$$

We wish to determine the constants $a_2 \neq 0$, b_2, c_2, such that P_2 is orthogonal to P_0 and to P_1. Then,

$$\int_a^b p(x)(1)(a_2x^2 + b_2x + c_2)\,dx = 0,$$

$$\int_a^b p(x)(\alpha_1x + \beta_1)(a_2x^2 + b_2x + c_2)\,dx = 0.$$

If we set

$$k_2 = \int_a^b x^2p(x)\,dx,$$

$$k_3 = \int_a^b x^3p(x)\,dx,$$

we have the equations

$$a_2 k_2 + b_2 k_1 + c_2 k_0 = 0, \tag{5.4}$$

$$a_2(\alpha_1 k_3 + \beta_1 k_2) + b_2(\alpha_1 k_2 + \beta_1 k_1) + c_2(\alpha_1 k_1 + \beta_1 k_0) = 0$$

for the determination of a_2, b_2, c_2.

Solutions of (5.4) may be verified to be

$$\begin{aligned} a_2 &= \alpha_1(k_1^2 - k_0 k_2), \\ b_2 &= \alpha_1(k_0 k_3 - k_1 k_2), \\ c_2 &= \alpha_1(k_2^2 - k_1 k_3). \end{aligned} \tag{5.5}$$

All other solutions of these equations are proportional to the set (5.5). Recall that $\alpha_1 \neq 0$. Because we wish to be sure that the degree of $P_2(x)$ is actually 2, it remains to be shown that $k_1^2 - k_0 k_2 \neq 0$; that is, that the determinant

$$\begin{vmatrix} \int_a^b p(x)\,dx & \int_a^b xp(x)\,dx \\ \int_a^b xp(x)\,dx & \int_a^b x^2 p(x)\,dx \end{vmatrix} \neq 0. \tag{5.6}$$

Suppose the determinant were zero. There would then exist constants c_1 and c_2, not both zero, such that

$$c_1 \int_a^b p(x)\,dx + c_2 \int_a^b xp(x)\,dx = 0,$$

$$c_1 \int_a^b xp(x)\,dx + c_2 \int_a^b x^2 p(x)\,dx = 0.$$

We multiply the first equation by c_1, the second by c_2, and add. The result may be written in the form

$$\int_a^b [c_1\sqrt{p(x)} + c_2 x\sqrt{p(x)}]^2\,dx = 0.$$

It would follow that

$$c_1\sqrt{p(x)} + c_2 x\sqrt{p(x)} \equiv 0,$$

and, hence, that

$$c_1 + c_2 x \equiv 0,$$

which contradicts the hypothesis that not both c_1 and c_2 are zero.

The process may be continued, and each polynomial will be determined in turn. In each case, we may argue as before that the leading coefficient of the polynomial is different from zero.

EXERCISES

1. Develop $P_0(x)$, $P_1(x)$, $P_2(x)$, $P_3(x)$ from the:

(a) Chebyshev differential equation;
(b) Laguerre differential equation;
(c) Hermite differential equation.

(*Suggestion.* Use the expanded forms of the differential equations.)

2. Prove that the Tchebycheff polynomials form an orthogonal sequence.

3. Prove that the Laguerre polynomials form an orthogonal sequence.

4. Prove that the Jacobi polynomials form an orthogonal sequence.

5. Let $p(x)$ be positive and continuous on the interval $[a,b]$. Prove that the determinant

$$\begin{vmatrix} \int_a^b p(x)\,dx & \int_a^b xp(x)\,dx & \int_a^b x^2p(x)\,dx \\ \int_a^b xp(x)\,dx & \int_a^b x^2p(x)\,dx & \int_a^b x^3p(x)\,dx \\ \int_a^b x^2p(x)\,dx & \int_a^b x^3p(x)\,dx & \int_a^b x^4p(x)\,dx \end{vmatrix} \neq 0.$$

6. Given the weight function 1 and the interval $(-1,1)$, use the Schmidt process of orthogonalization to derive $P_0(x)$, $P_1(x)$, $P_2(x)$, $P_3(x)$. (Your answers should be Legendre polynomials except for multiplicative constants.)

7. Discuss solutions of the Chebyshev differential equation in the light of Exercise 9 of Chapter 10, Section 3.

ANSWERS

1. (a) $T_0(x) = 1$, $T_1(x) = x$, $T_2(x) = x^2 - \frac{1}{4}$, $T_3(x) = x^3 - \frac{x}{2}$;

(b) $L_0(x) = 1$, $L_1(x) = -x + 1$, $L_2(x) = x^2 - 4x + 2$,
$L_3(x) = -x^3 + 9x^2 - 18x + 6$;

(c) $H_0(x) = 1$, $H_1(x) = 2x$, $H_2(x) = 4x^2 - 2$, $H_3(x) = 8x^3 - 12x$.

INDEX